D0971307

WITHDRAWN
UTSA LIBRARIES

As Others See Us

As Others See Us
by Goran Palm
Translated by
Verne Moberg

The Bobbs-Merrill Company
Indianapolis · New York

University of Texas

The Bobbs-Merrill Company, Inc.
A Subsidiary of Howard W. Sams & Co., Inc.
Publishers / Indianapolis • Kansas City • New York

Copyright © 1968 by The Bobbs-Merrill Company, Inc.
All rights reserved

The quotations from *The Wretched of the Earth* by
Frantz Fanon, translated by Constance Farrington,
are reproduced with the permission of Grove Press, Inc.
Copyright © 1963 by *Presence Africaine.*
This book was first published in Sweden in 1966 under
the title *En orättvis betraktelse (An Unfair Appraisal)*
by P. A. Norstedt & Söners Förlag.

First printing 1968
Library of Congress catalogue card number 68-29290
Designed by Martin Moskof and Associates Inc.
Printed in the United States of America

**Library
University of Texas**
at San Antonio

Blessed are the meek,
for they shall inherit the earth.

—The Sermon on the Mount

Contents

Foreword

This book is about two faces. One is the face of want, hunger, destitution. The other face is ours.

Today when the privileged people of the earth are confronted by the oppressed—for the first time in centuries or for the first time ever—their meeting is not face to face. In order for it to be a face-to-face meeting both parties must change their stance in relation to the other. The oppressed must rise to their full height, so that when they level their gaze directly forward they really see a face and not a dais, a boot, or a bulging paunch. At the same time the privileged people must step down from their platform so that when they look straight ahead, they too see a face and not a territory, a herd, or a demonstrating mass. It's also desirable for them to stand so close that the first thing they see is each other's eyes—not the skin or the nose but the eyes.

The latter objective is long-range. What is important for now is that the parties stand on the same level, yet this too seems extraordinarily difficult to bring about. The oppressed are still standing with their knees bent, and though the privileged people make constant gestures of leaving their platform, they do not leave their platform. Considering what is requested of the two—that the oppressed leave their degradation behind and that the privileged relinquish their privileged position—it's not hard to determine which of the two parties is offering resistance and will continue to offer resistance to the end. The oppressed seem to have everything to gain and little to lose by rising up. The privileged, on the other hand, have everything to lose and little to gain—at least in the short run.

The longer this meeting is put off, the greater grows the irritation among the oppressed; more and more often they are seen grabbing the privileged people by the legs to get them down off the platform, and the privileged reply by planting their heels in the outstretched hands of the oppressed. But when this happens, up on the platform the irritation spreads, and the ones standing up front start hearing from behind their backs, among their own, the same discontented murmuring they've heard for centuries from down on the ground. The murmuring from behind is a good deal weaker, for it comes not from desperate people seeking their rights, but from privileged people of tender conscience who generally lack power. When it gets right down to it, these people don't want to step off the platform either, at least not individually, yet the longer the meeting is delayed, the more strongly they sense that what's going on in front of them is madness. If they can do nothing else, at least they can use their eyes and imagination, still on the platform, to observe what is happening from the viewpoint of the oppressed.

In the West, unfair appraisals are called factual analyses when they do justice to the West and are unfair only to the Third World. Such appraisals are common among us rich. Appraisals that try to do justice to the Third World and are therefore unfair to the West might be every bit as factual and analytical, yet we consider them unfair because they are unfavorable to us. Such appraisals are less common among us rich. However, the destitution of our times demands them.

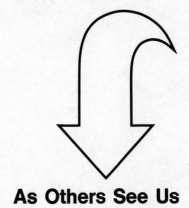

As Others See Us

Beggars

Beggar: Still, I have to live.
Talleyrand: I can't see that that should be necessary.

A Swedish writer reports from Calcutta:

> Not infrequently beggars offer up their own children or buy children from destitute parents. Without hesitation they maim these children, stick out their eyes or the like. Presumably it's considered to be for the children's own best: in this way they have greater chances as beggars. They are trained to cry and moan uninterruptedly, until they can keep it up mechanically for hours or days at a time. Then they're set out on the street to appeal to people's charity. . . . It is they who are the watershed of the crowd on Calcutta's large streets. They throw themselves in front of their victims' feet, cling tight to them, and drag along the

street. They are the city's daily torment, the screaming refuse of the streets. They seem so sure of their task in life, their place in society. They are the wheels beneath the forward-rolling cart of misery and they demand their tribute. . . . "I beg in God's name!" these beggars howl, scrutinizing the passersby with fierce or scornfully challenging looks. "Do you dare keep from giving something?" they seem to mean. "Do you curse the gods, defy fate?" Their beggary is undisguised extortion. The reward is promised in blessings. The punishment (if the tribute is not forthcoming) in threatening maledictions or malicious looks, long and sharp as knives.[1]

These days there's a conspicuous shortage of beggars in Northern Europe and much of the United States, but in reading this stormy description one is struck by what definite ideas we continue to harbor on how begging ought and ought not be conducted. The guided group tours that many people take annually to impoverished Mediterranean countries may well help us to preserve and reinforce them.

A beggar should be humble—that's the first thing we ask. He is not permitted to be aggressive, and he may not mock or threaten. To grant him the slightest fear of reprisal is uncalled for; the humanitarian nature of the giver would then be contaminated. A beggar should be congenial in his deprivation, humanly attractive in his destitution, so that just from his countenance people are moved to generous compassion. Sorrow—not rage—should be delineated on whatever facial features he still possesses. It's unpleasing for him to appear completely apathetic but sooner that than loud and demanding. A sad, lyrical smile is also desirable; this is one good reason why children are often successful as beggars. In certain cases a beggar may be permitted to demonstrate his particular type of affliction,

[1] Artur Lundkvist, *Indiabrand* (Stockholm: Albert Bonniers Förlag AB, 1950), p. 74.

2

though not so shamelessly that the viewer grows ill. At worst, he may also be a criminal, so long as it's not so conspicuous that the passerby's safety is threatened—even the criminal should be picturesque.

It's important for the beggar to be of a smaller size than his benefactor: if he is bigger he should avert the threat (which for some reason is always presented by someone or something larger) by sitting or lying down. For this reason, too, children are often successful beggars. Alms must be given from above: otherwise there's a real danger that the beggar may hold on to the giver's hand. Furthermore, the suffering should be rationed out at appropriate intervals so that it doesn't stick in the throat; beggars should not appear in groups. Nor should they make such an impression of physical strength or spiritual desperation that the passerby *himself* runs the risk of feeling weak, dispirited, or threatened. Beggars may not invite any such comparisons! Nor may they make a show of self-confidence or vocational competence; it's better if they are resigned, insecure, wretched, broken-down amateurs in the practice of their trade as well.

In his travel reportage Artur Lundkvist seldom touches upon personal reactions, but in Calcutta he is no better than other travelers in India at concealing his torment and irritation. The beggars never leave him in peace. They persecute him. They flatly ignore what he says. In vain—as the perceptive traveler in India soon finds—does he formulate those strong arguments for passing on by. Begging is a business in which profits seldom go to the most needy—usually they go to rich beggar kings instead; many beggars are bluffers (a weaker argument in those cases where the eyes are poked out or the legs cut off); the religious threats and blessings have no effect on a Western skeptic. "I'm excluded, since I don't believe in your gods," Lundkvist protests. "Your begging is not an appeal; it's blackmail by threat: stubborn, aggressive pursuit. That's why I'm giving you nothing." But even so, the beggars don't give up.

In Madras, Lundkvist encounters suffering that summons compassion in a completely different way. In the crowded street he sees a girl:

> In the midst of the traffic she staggers around as if drunk, seems neither to see nor hear, only gropes in confusion among the impatiently shrieking autos. Someone runs up and pulls her in onto the sidewalk, where she collapses with a rattling. Lies there, overcome as an animal, bent up in fetal position, trembling in her body. A girl of some ten years, perhaps, dressed only in a rag that doesn't conceal much of her body's misery. She is horribly emaciated, with thighs just as thin as her bones and fastened at the trunk as if on a doll. Her stomach swollen as if she were pregnant, her back scratched all over and full of purulent sores, with skinless streaks of lilac color. A starved child nobody cares about, perhaps without parents, wandering on the streets dazed by starvation. Without will or strength to beg, without sense to grub in the trash cans together with the dogs or stay lying in the shade. No, staggering around in the torments of hunger and hurt, in the burning sun.[2]

It's a clear portrait. Then he adds a comment in the way of comparison:

> One cares less then about the successful beggars who stick to strategic places and assail one with their entire tested arsenal of loud complaints and intimately demonstrated defects.[3]

It is not my intention to pass moral "judgment" on the person who wrote this. Presumably anybody at all who can see would choose his neighbor—someone deserving his concern and commitment—in the same way if he were in Artur Lundkvist's shoes. Destitution that capitalizes upon itself

[2] Lundkvist, *op. cit.*, pp. 57–58.
[3] Lundkvist, *op. cit.*, p. 58.

cannot be weighed, either statistically or ethically, against destitution that is powerless and helpless. Of these two, the girl is obviously "our neighbor."

But it's no accident, I think, that the affliction we generally deem greater and especially worthy of compassion also happens to be the affliction incapable of encroaching upon us. The girl in the street is powerless: she cannot threaten us, she cannot keep us from passing on by; thus we are free to feel supremely sorry for her. We might even venture to toss her a bit of bread. The risk of her throwing it in our faces—or doing something else unanticipated —seems small when she's so weak. The beggar, however, is not powerless: he can surprise us, he can come too close; in certain respects, perhaps, he is superior to us, too (in his hatred, for example). As opposed to the girl, who is wandering about homeless, cut off from all human contact, he is active and seeking contact; he addresses us brusquely, makes his plea, and hounds us. Can't we feel sorry for the beggar too? Sure. But to a lesser degree. A person who isn't congenial, a person who is troublesome, a person who for good cause may be suspected of cynicism and a lack of humility, can't count on as much of our compassion for the simple reason that other feelings within us vie successfully with this compassion: annoyance, escape wishes, distaste, and fear.

In order for us to feel really sorry for a stranger, he has to be harmless, it seems. He has to keep at a safe distance.

As long as the German shepherd is tied up and the gate is closed, he can bark at me as irately as he wants: I'm on the safe side, free to regret his situation profoundly and condemn the cruelty of people who keep their dogs tied up. But if the shepherd is running free and the gate is open and he comes close, growling, my essential choice is to take to my heels, panic-stricken.

In a certain pedestrian tunnel in Stockholm now and

then you still see a beggar sitting and playing music, with a cap out in front of him. Some people who pass by are of the opinion that individuals like this ought to be taken in hand by the social authorities—they shouldn't be allowed to clutter up public places in a welfare state. But no one who passes needs to feel threatened: everybody is free to go on by or stop, to give or not give, for the beggar remains in his sitting position, and his hands are occupied by the resonant instrument. For that matter, it makes it rather nice with music in a tunnel.

It would be worse if the beggar stood upright instead and were tall and strong. It would be worse if, instead of playing, he used his hands to beg and his legs to chase his potential benefactors. It would be worse if he forced everybody—with a stiletto or revolver—to stop and give.

It would be worse for us, but it would be better for the beggar: his income would rise in a hurry. Few people can fill their bellies on other people's tear-laden sympathy.

Indian beggars seem to have the same kind of insight as that acquired generally by people in Asia and Africa after the second world war, and that insight which people in Latin America in many instances had the military means to acquire as early as the nineteenth century.

Humility, despair, and passive appeals don't pay. Then the colonialists feel terribly sorry for the colonized people, lament over their helplessly low level of existence, build locations, found indoctrination schools, furnish medical care, ease the curfew law, or provide charity. But they don't give up the colonies and they don't stop oppressing the people, for they have nothing to fear.

Only unrelenting demands, resistance, demonstrations, threats of violence, and violence itself seem to bring results. Then, it's true, the colonialists stop feeling sorry for the colonized people: the tears dry up, social benefits and charity are withdrawn, and talk of the natives' laziness and low intelligence grows quieter and more hesitant. Instead, the colonialists grow alarmed, for they think they know just how savage savages can be—especially if they're in the majority—and the alarm is followed by uncertainty and discord among the powers-that-be, for colonial wars are often expensive and lately have fallen into moral disrepute besides. And judging from the history of colonialism, it is precisely these feelings—of fear and uncertainty—that by themselves can give the colonized people real hope of concessions: in the best examples, orderly de-colonization (Sudan and Tanzania); in more dismal cases, panic-stricken mass evacuation resulting in administrative chaos (the Congo); in the worst cases, bloodbath (Indonesia, Burma, and Algeria). But first the colonized people must wave their clenched fists.

If our vision is dimmed with tears for the world's destitute, it may be hard to detect this mechanism of social psychology properly; when destitution is pounding on our doors with the butt ends of rifles and the tears of sympathy freeze to fear, it instantly gets easier.

Perhaps this truth is sufficiently cruel as to have universal application: a person has to feel threatened by another person's or another people's suffering in order to take it seriously. In any case, to lament, to tyrannize with velvet gloves, or to give charity is not taking suffering seriously. When the Belgians realized that the Congolese didn't acknowledge the custom of chopping off resistors' hands as a royal European monopoly, they fled, head over heels. One might say that this was the first time they considered blacks as their equals.

Must want, hunger, destitution take to arms? Must the destitute abandon their plight and take up weapons in order for destitution to be recognized, admitted, and seen? It seems so. In way of comfort to the whites, it will be added immediately that a substantial share of the world's destitute are so completely devastated they simply aren't able to take up arms. By means of our tears, trust companies, and packages of powdered milk, we're free to keep them in our power indefinitely.

So long as the wounded guerrilla soldier is content to display his suffering within the frame of the TV screen, there are no bounds to the warmhearted, sobbing despair we occasionally manage to produce. If we vomit as a result or turn off the set or choke up with benevolence, it's all the same—for the guerrilla soldier at least. Not until he jumps out of the TV set, walks up to our table, tosses aside our plates and glasses, and threatens, with his bayonet, to show us how his pain feels, are we forced to realize that this suffering is taking place in *our* world.

Such dramatic scenes are seldom enacted in our living rooms. And it's entirely conceivable that we'll never learn to take the world's destitution seriously.

Some Reminders

The Java Man and the Peking Man lived at the same time as the Heidelberg Man.

Overpopulation in the world today is greatest in Central Europe; next comes South Asia, then Southern Europe, and after that Northern and Western Europe; last come Africa, South America, and Oceania, including Australia. In Holland there are 345 well-nourished people per square kilometer; in large parts of the Third World there are 2 undernourished people per square kilometer.

In the seventeenth century, upon discovering that many

Christian missionaries had connections with European merchants, the Chinese wanted to drive them away. When this happened, the Pope proclaimed China a Roman feudal state.

The underdeveloped countries' share in world commerce decreases annually.

According to legend, Moses was born in the thirteenth century before Christ. The Vedas first appeared around the year 1000 before Christ. Zarathustra was born between the years 1000 and 600 before Christ. The Upanishads first appeared between the years 800 and 500 before Christ. According to legend, Lao-tse was born in the year 604 before Christ. Buddha was born around the year 563 before Christ. Confucius was born in the year 551 before Christ. Muhammad was born around the year 570 after Christ. Nihongi, the original document of Shintoism, appeared in the year 720 after Christ. Sikhism's Nanak was born in the year 1469 after Christ. Ramakrishna was born in the year 1834 after Christ. The fourteenth Dalai Lama was born in the year 1935 after Christ.

Christ was born in the year 6 before Christ.

The two smallest continents on earth are Australia and Europe.

The European colonies that were first to win their national independence were those dominated by whites from the start and/or those with strong armies: the United States, Argentina, Brazil, Australia, and South Africa. It could not be expected that colonies dominated by natives—such as Egypt, India, Mesopotamia, and Syria—would be ready for good self-government as early; in addition, they lacked weapons. The Europeans made them wait until they had achieved a higher level of civilization, a stage Egypt reached in 1922, Mesopotamia in 1932 (Iraq), Syria in 1946, and India in 1947.

One out of every three people alive today is Chinese or Indian.

One of the favorite diversions of the Russians in the seventeenth century was making fun of dwarfs, cripples, and idiots in public.

In four hours it is possible to go on foot or by oxcart from Stockholm to its suburbs; ride a bicycle or horse from Stockholm to Uppsala; travel by train or car from Stockholm to Gothenburg; fly from Stockholm to Beirut; make a telephone call from Stockholm to Montevideo; send a cable from Stockholm to Sydney and back; or do three laps around the earth in a space capsule. However, the greater part of the world's population is restricted to going on foot or by oxcart. They never get farther than the suburbs.

Up to now, man has devoted 2 per cent of his time on earth to creating civilizations. By the time Egyptian civilization died out in the fifth century A.D., it had been in existence three times as long as Western civilization has existed to date.

Only a modest share of the Western world's private economic sector today may be ascribed to free competition.

In the days of Herodotus, for the first time in history, Hellas and the Hellenes were placed in the center of the known world and endowed with the qualities of moderation, love of freedom, and democracy. What remained for the people in the East and South were the qualities of arrogance (toward the Hellenes), servility (toward the Crown), and barbarianism. Through large parts of the known world, Alexander did away with the borders between East and West and replaced both these worlds with an affiliation of Hellenic cultures, an all-inclusive Hellas.

Beginning in this fashion with Alexander and Herod-

11

otus, the cultural-geographical deformation of Europe continued unimpeded until 1939. Hellas = the world, European knowledge = world knowledge. Western imperialism too seems to begin with Alexander: "Greek industry, which now found ready markets in all of Western Asia, developed rapidly. In Egypt, Syria, and Babylonia," writes Hartvig Frisch in *Europas kulturhistorie (A Cultural History of Europe)*, "there was a large and poor population that gave the Greek industrialists and businessmen precisely what they wanted most: cheap, plentiful labor."[1]

Then the Romans came up with the idea that they could clear out the land in their northern provinces by using slaves imported from the Orient.

Slave trading is estimated to have victimized 115 million people, mainly blacks.

The Hindus regard Jesus as a great yogi and a great *Paramahamsa sannyasin*.

On January 1, 1964, there were 243 states and territories on earth. A good half of these (125) were sovereign states, 11 were partially dependent states, and 107 completely dependent territories (colonies, protectorates, "overseas provinces," Antarctic territories, etc.). Most of the dependent states and territories were ruled by Great Britain, France, Portugal, and the United States.

During the Ice Age Europe and Africa comprised one continuous continent with three large lakes a bit above the middle: the Tyrrhenian Lake, the Adriatic Lake, and the Aegean Lake.

In 1960 every Swede purchased about $273 worth of food and provisions and gave $1.40 toward aid to underdeveloped countries. In 1964 every Swede spent $28 on packaging and $2.40 on aid to underdeveloped countries.

[1] Copenhagen: Henrik Koppels Forlag, 1928, Vol. I, p. 249 *ff*.

For years rumors of the terrible headhunters in New Guinea frightened Europeans from letting the roots of Western culture take hold in these rugged regions as well, but by the end of the nineteenth century, the British, Dutch, and Germans felt obliged to do their duty and civilize the area—the terrible headhunters notwithstanding. They began their missionary activity by dividing the island up among them. The Dutch took the western part, the Germans took the northeastern part, and the British took the southeastern part. The partitioning took place in a democratic spirit, but unfortunately there was nothing left over for the terrible headhunters.

The Eskimos have no word in their language for "war."

The Congo is richer in natural resources than Belgium; Indonesia is richer in natural resources than Holland; Angola is richer in natural resources than Portugal; Venezuela is richer in natural resources than Spain; India is richer in natural resources than England. In terms of land area, Belgium, Holland, Portugal, Spain, and Great Britain could all fit inside Angola. There would also be room for West Germany.

The electric chair was first used on August 6, 1890. Before the electrocution, the victim, murderer William Klemmer, was requested to express his pleasure at being able to contribute in this way to scientific progress.

Japan intends to become the fourth nation to succeed in sending a satellite into orbit around the earth and the sixth nation to explode an atom bomb.

In Mexico, Colombia, and Peru, the Spaniards found what their court and army at home wanted above all: gold and silver. Therefore they invited the Indians to engage in trading and mining. But to the Spaniards' dismay, the Indians wanted neither to barter for the goods they were offered nor to mine gold and silver under Catholic supervision, so the Spaniards were obliged to introduce compulsory trade and forced labor. For their gold rings and silver artifacts, the Indians were forced to buy horses, Spanish cloaks, and boots—even if they didn't know how to use them. Impoverished Incas were forced to go dressed in silk and to furnish their huts with mirrors. Illiterates in the Andes had the products of the Spanish book-making craft pressed upon them. At the same time a large number of Indians reacted against forced labor in a way that was as passive as it was disastrous: they died like flies.

This is one of the reasons there are so many black people in America today.

Leopold II was an ardent Christian.

The United States, which accommodates 6 per cent of the world's population, today owns or controls 60 per cent of the earth's natural resources and has 1.5 million soldiers stationed at thousands of military bases around the world.

For years the population of Hong Kong was estimated by weighing the collected excrement of its inhabitants.

Ferdinand the Catholic started the inquisition in order to subdue the Jews and Arabs of Spain.

The underdeveloped countries have many trump cards on the raw materials market: oil in the Arab world, tin and rubber in Southeast Asia, copper in Central Africa and Chile, coffee and bauxite in Latin America, gold and uranium in Africa, and untapped mineral supplies in Mozambique, Brazil, and India. But for the present, the Western powers are holding on to these trump cards.

About the year 1000 the Chinese invented the art of printing books. About the year 1450 Gutenberg invented the art of printing books.

The designations Mohammedanism, Hinduism, and Buddhism are Western inventions that lack equivalents in native terminology.

A few examples of contemporaneous development:

In 1965, 113 people were hanged in South Africa, as opposed to 20 in the year 1946.

During the 1960's the Third World acquired 200 million additional inhabitants.

In 1965, 49,000 Americans were killed in auto accidents.

A new trend in poetry called "spatialism"—opposed to all earlier trends in poetry—has been founded in Paris.

Roughly 7½ ounces of newsprint per capita are consumed annually in Burma.

The Swiss eat 2 kilograms of chocolate per capita annually.

The Himalayas rise approximately 3 centimeters every year.

In 1913 per capita income in Southeast Asia rose to about $65; by 1959 it had increased to about $67. During the same period Southeast Asia's share of the world's income sank from 6.6 per cent to 3.6 per cent, but in return the population increased heavily.

Defense costs in the United States are estimated to have risen to $70 billion by June 30, 1967.

Some of the leading airplane factories in the West have invested $20 billion to produce a supersonic plane that can reduce the flying time of jet planes by two-thirds.

By the middle of the 1950's, Asia had managed to get control of 1 per cent, Africa 2 per cent, and Latin America 3 per cent of the world's supply of tractors.

The Java Man and the Peking Man lived at the same time as the Heidelberg Man.

Social Deformation

One of our Swedish writers—Birgitta Trotzig—has said that these days, when she's writing, there is always a face before her eyes. Sometimes she'd like to blot it out, but she seldom can.

The external features of the face change. It might belong to an undernourished child, someone on the street, a colored person, an invalid, a refugee, or somebody hidden in a doorway, but the look on the face is always the same. The face expresses suffering, and regardless of whether the writer is working on a novel set in nineteenth-century Sweden or a collection of essays on Catholic literature, the face is always in front of her and it speaks—up close to her writing hands—of its pain and hunger.

Now everybody sees this face—maybe not every day but surely every other day; you don't have to travel to see it, certainly. There are TV sets, newspaper pictures, Red Cross posters; there are photographs, refugee camps, hospitals, train windows, doorways—the face turns up wherever you go. Statistically it's true that today even a stay-at-home in our cozy Scandinavian welfare state meets Indian farmers, Latin American demonstrators, Swedish narcotics addicts, or Vietnamese children just as often as he meets his own friends and acquaintances. Almost like an intruding cousin, that pained face keeps popping up—seldom in "reality," as we call it, but real enough on the TV or movie screen or the newspaper page: is the voice of a stranger or a good friend on the telephone more "real"?

It may be said that you don't personally meet these people and faces on the TV set or the newspaper page. But you run into them, constantly, and you're confronted personally. At any rate, until you manage to take your eyes off them.

Strolling about Stockholm, the welfare state citizen sees very, very few beggars, few invalids, few "welfare cases," and hardly anybody poorly dressed to annoy him with their embarrassing presence: only the usual hot rodders and Saturday drunks. The ones who have strayed away from the welfare system are more and more frequently sent off to remote institutions, collective homes, hospitals, and prisons, and those places in the center of the city that always attract refuse are energetically being cleared away: beer bars, pissoirs, slums—soon the central prison will be gone too. In other Western cities, to a noticeable extent, the sub-lower class is permitted to occupy gutters and subway stations—a candor that would no doubt appear outrageous in today's leveled-out Stockholm. But if you tag along with the Salvation Army people or a social worker on night duty, you'll find your way to those back streets and alleys that the façade polishers haven't managed to get at yet. And there, as on the posters, in the newspapers, and on the TV screen, the same suffering is staring at you.

The daily presence of the suffering face. That's one part of it.

Another is the fact that it's extremely easy for us to forget this presence. We look away. We accustom ourselves. We find excuses and explanations. We identify the façade of prosperity with what is concealed more and more skillfully behind it. We throw off the pressures of suffering by—among other means—holding up the concept of "alienation" as an alibi to get out of seeing. We're deformed.

Until the next face turns up and claims our eyes.

Today people say that the world is shrinking, distances are disappearing, and the world has become one. But social deformation—sometimes called the self-preservation instinct—seems to follow more old-fashioned rules. It affects everyone, even the most sensitive people, and still takes very definite consideration of geographical distance, for example.

If I'm sitting in a restaurant in London eating a fancy dinner, I know that at a distance of so-and-so many hundred yards other people are pining away at collective homes, hospitals, and nursing homes. Yet this doesn't affect my appetite for one moment, since I don't really see these people, and there's no risk that I'll come across them if I go out to buy an evening paper. They're in safe hands, our underdeveloped Englishmen, so I'm safe too. If instead I'm sitting in a high-class restaurant in Bombay, it probably would be somewhat more difficult to eat in peace.

Only the best people are sitting on the premises, it's true—foreign experts and native profiteers—for nobody else can afford to come in, but the realization that the street outside is filled with beggars and starving people is not equally good for the appetite. It must be nice to be a black-market swindler, but to *feel* like a black-market swindler is disagreeable. Yet the first time it gets really difficult is out on the street when you're surrounded by beggars and starving people: not for one moment can you help being struck by the difference between yourself and them. Not until the geographic distance is completely devoured and you're sitting in the midst of the dung does this social deformation seem to cease its effect.

Finally you see what is happening. And in the same moment you see yourself in a whole new light. The face of destitution unmasks the face of affluence.

But this social deformation has other allies too. If you stay in the locality you'll be bothered less every day, and after a time you'll be prepared to accept the older immigrants' explanation of why the situation is the way it is, by which they mean it will have to stay the way it is. In India, says one writer, original sin consists of "existing, being in the way. This is the wisdom of India, the India of perpetual breeding. [But] In Iran the people are fewer. Existing in itself is not a crime, even though it is a misfortune. The demand for efficiency among beggars and cripples is not unusually high as in India. Generally it's not so overcrowded here. . . . There is always room to walk on by."[1]

How do you manage to walk on by in India?

Perhaps you learn to rationalize in the same way as the wife of the Western expert whom Jan Myrdal met at a reception in New Delhi. Facing death, reasoned the expert's

[1] Willy Kyrklund, *Till Tabbas* (Stockholm: Albert Bonniers Förlag/Aldus, 1965), p. 99.

wife, "Indians don't feel pain as we do. Their philosophy of life is so completely different." It is also fitting to quote the equivocal Mr. Gandhi—so long as the proper passage is chosen—for example, this one on India's princes:

> I feel and know that they have their subjects well in mind. There is no difference between them and me, except that we others are commoners and they are nobles, princes, which God has made them. I wish them well, I wish them all success.

What has particularly surprised foreign journalists in South Africa is that even very sensitive, liberal-minded Europeans assimilate the Boers' self-defensive prejudices within a short time. They have nothing against the blacks, they say; it's just that the blacks aren't ready to help run society yet; and for that matter they're really happiest when they're allowed to live by themselves.

On Minnesota's fertile soil Scandinavian newcomers become Goldwaterites in the same fashion. Nice, respectable, God-fearing Goldwaterites. They have nothing against Negroes, they say, it's just that Negroes aren't ready to help run society. They don't have anything against the Democrats' war against poverty in the United States, they say; it's just that government interference is threatening the finest things that America—despite everything—has to offer: namely, freedom and democracy.

After five weeks in Paris I suddenly noticed one evening that, without any effort at all, I had learned to come to terms with the presence of beggars by my sidewalk café; I saw them without seeing them.

When this social deformation is not aided by geographic distance, it relies upon time. After a while, practically anything at all appears natural if only it is repeated regularly. Or in the striking words of one of our writers who has visited South Africa, "Every day means that nobody notices what is happening every day."[2] The hundredth car-load of prisoners seems to become commonplace for the white South African in the same weird and obvious manner in which the hundredth beggar becomes commonplace for the Parisian. "A man in a raincoat beside me lit a cigarette, and when he exhaled, he looked off in the distance so as not to get the smoke in his eyes, and then he saw the Africans."[3]

It isn't necessary to stay abroad long in order to observe this mechanism. Indeed, it's not necessary to travel at all. The newsreels from the world's theaters of war will soon become commonplace for the TV-watcher, just as the photograph of the face of suffering has become so for the newspaper reader. The difference is merely that the deformation progresses more rapidly when direct body contact is avoided; by the twentieth newsreel, by the tenth newspaper picture the image already appears pale. At home another situation has arisen that seems to accelerate the process of deformation even further: no one can have escaped noticing how similar in kind these films and pictures often are. That emaciated child always seems to have the same big, glassy eyes and the same lifeless expression of fund-raising appeals on his face; the war scenes on the screen repeat incessantly the same confused running and thundering explosions, and it's always equally hard to distinguish between rebels and government troops, between dead soldiers and others just lying there (a fact that leaves us even more at the mercy of the commentators' bias); wherever in the world a burned village is being evacuated, the same bundles of clothing, the same unmovable old people, the same weeping mothers, and the same broken-down carts or pickup truck platforms seem to be put to use.

2 Per Wästberg, *På svarta listan* (*On the Blacklist*) (Stockholm: Wahlström & Widstrand, 1960), p. 22.
3 *Ibid.*

22

Do war and suffering always look exactly the same, or is it the conventions and restricted working conditions of the photojournalists that so often make it look the same?

In time the viewer may be possessed by the odd sensation that these wars and faces exist not in reality, but in a world of their own, an artificial, unevocable, documentary-type world of terror passing daily in review. Eventually the street riot is associated not with the city in which it occurred but with street riots in other newsreels; eventually the child's face is associated not with the person it belongs to or the people it represents but with faces on other emergency relief posters. When the deterioration has finally come to the point that the viewer associates only in terms of films and posters, the process of deformation seems to be complete, and the experience has been replaced for good by a routine registration of details.

Then time and habit heal all wounds?

"The problem of suffering is a wound that ought to be kept open," says Birgitta Trotzig, "a contradiction that must not be reconciled."[4]

But this deformation in the interest of self-defense also employs more treacherous arguments.

Three yards in front of you on the TV screen there's a Buddhist burning and you see with your own eyes that he's burning right then and there; still you tell yourself that this isn't happening now—it's already taken place—and that it happened far away, on the other side of the globe; it couldn't happen here. Scarcely a yard in front of you is a newsphoto depicting torture; still you tell yourself that this torture is taking place a million times farther than one yard away and it already belongs to history. You know that for a person who lives in Stockholm, today it's quicker

4 *Dagens Nyheter*, February 14, 1965.

23

to get to Jakarta than to the North Pole and it's considerably easier to get information from Jakarta than from the North Pole; still you tell yourself that Jakarta is infinitely farther away than the North Pole—on the other side of the globe, in fact.

In a sense you're as right as you are wrong in telling yourself this. Jakarta is closer *and* farther away than the North Pole; the Buddhist is burning before your eyes *and* on the other side of the globe. But it's in the more abstract sense that you are right.

One way for a clever person to strengthen his self-defense is to try some experiments in the psychology of vision. Tribes of people have existed, they say, who did not recognize their closest relatives in photographs that were shown to them; they saw only paper with unknown patterns—patterns that may not even have resembled human beings. Recognizing reality as it's rendered photographically—reduced, usually immobile, and two-dimensional—is apparently not a natural endowment but learning we acquire gradually: if it's a question of contact with reality, it's a matter of secondhand contact with reality. At a possibly later stage of primitive vision, the observer sometimes confuses the representation of reality with reality itself. He becomes, for example, thoroughly frightened that the train in the film will charge right through the movie theater, and Frans G. Bengtsson, the author of *The Long Ships*,[5] is probably not alone in having thought as a child that the camera was an instrument of torture, by means of which flesh-and-blood people were flattened out, made smaller, and put up on the wall as macabre trophies. "That's grandfather."

Normally, at our more sophisticated stage, we are spared both these primitive, extreme reactions. We recognize what we see from the material world, but at the same

[5] Translated by Michael Meyer (Stockholm: Norstedt & Söner, 1954).

time we see it with the distance and skepticism that accompany a secondary vision. The best thing about this distance and skepticism is that we can resort to it when something unpleasant is shown on TV and completely forget about it, staring with open mouths, like children, when something pleasant and exciting is on the screen. The way this works in practice at home is that the lights are on and people are drinking coffee and chatting when the evening news is being televised, and the lights are turned down and people watch the picture intently and hush up all the talk when an adventure movie comes on.

Arnold Toynbee says in one passage:

> There is one world-wide present-day movement that . . . is, to my mind, by far the greatest and most significant thing that is happening in the World today. . . . There is a movement on foot giving the benefits of civilization to that huge majority of the human race that has paid for civilization, without sharing in its benefits during the first five thousand years of civilization's existence.[6]

For the first time in five thousand years, he could have added, anybody on earth can become our neighbor, for daily, through mass media, we who enjoy the benefits of civilization have the means to see the people who "paid for civilization without sharing in its benefits."

But when everybody has become our neighbor, nobody has become our neighbor, and when we have the chance to see the world's destitute every day, destitution becomes banal and we look at it without seeing it. If we're sensitive, we think it is ghastly that so many are suffering, but even if we're sensitive, we would like things to get better for them without getting worse for us at the same time. We cry out in alarm as never before over suffering in the world, but when it comes down to it, we don't want to give up any

[6] *The Economy of the Western Hemisphere* (London: Oxford University Press, 1962), pp. 3–4.

privileges at all. I don't want to give up my income, and you don't want to give up your house.

The people who have received no other privilege than their own destitution know how this social deformation functions, and they have known it for five thousand years: this is why it was among them that the liberation movement got its start. The oppressed people in our own country know that they have to sound the alarm in order for us to hear at all, and the oppressed in the country "World" know that we won't show them serious consideration until they give us a violent reminder.

It was once said that the only language savages understood was the language of weapons, but today we seem to be the ones who don't understand any other language. This is probably why we love Gandhi and Martin Luther King. Warmhearted advocates of peace do not force us to understand.

Western Culture: 1897

British Officers[1]

    Severely wounded: Lieutenant H. B. Ford, with the
31st Punjab Infantry

                             Lieutenant H. L. S. Maclean, with
the Guides Cavalry

    Slightly wounded:

                             Lieutenant G. Swinley, with the
31st Punjab Infantry

---

[1] Winston L. Spencer Churchill, *The Story of the Malakand Field Force: An Episode of Frontier War* (London, New York, and Bombay: Longmans, Green, and Co., 1898), p. 71.

Native Ranks
   Killed: 2
   Wounded: 13
British Officer
   Wounded: Lieutenant E. W. Costello
Native Ranks
   Killed: 12
   Wounded: 29

The Pendulum Swings

Every face is a mirror. When two people look at each other at close range, each one sees his own face reflected in the other's eye. Greatly reduced but perfectly clear even so. Unfortunately, this is the way we seem to go around looking at each other every day: we see only our own image.

Now when someone we meet narrows his eyes when he looks at us, it's no longer possible to see that mirror image of ourselves. There may be sparks from the slits of his eyes, but there's no face to be found. This is not surprising either, for when someone we meet narrows his eyes, we generally think he's glowering, and then we no longer feel we're observing, we only feel observed.

This also seems to be common when two people see each other. Only one of them is seen, or, more accurately, one of them has a gaze so penetrating and perceptive that the other is led to see himself in the light of this gaze. The reason for this is not hard to find. Certain people have power and a high position; others haven't. Certain people are confidently self-reliant with an obedient conscience; others aren't. Certain people stalk about constantly seeing others skulk about constantly being seen.

When all the people who have been skulking about for a long time without seeing suddenly stand up and rivet their gaze on all the people who have been stalking about for a long time without being seen, it's at that moment the pendulum swings.

For three thousand years, writes Sartre, "the white man has enjoyed the privilege of seeing without being seen. . . . Today it is these black [yellow, red, mixed-race] people who are looking at us and our glance returns to our eyes."[1]

The same insight could also be formulated in another way. The world has become one country, and in the country "World," Europe and America are among the few fertile provinces. The world has become a class society and in the class society "World," Europeans and Americans are among the few who comprise the upper class. In all countries in which the population has not completely succumbed, fertile provinces and upper class are regarded with awe or menacing envy. In the country "World," the people with the menacing looks are starting to get very numerous.

The person who only sees is free to consider himself good-looking. But then the game is over. When we are

[1] From Jean-Paul Sartre's introduction, "Orphée noir," to Léopold Senghor's *Anthologie de la nouvelle poésie nègre et malagache de langue française* (Paris: Presses Universitaire de France, 1948), p. ix.

seen, the noble Greek profile and the proud Western face that we've presented successfully to the eyes of the world for so many centuries are distorted instantly and an uglier face emerges, feature by feature.

The high-arched, contemplative brow drops. The clear-eyed, perceptive scholar's look takes on a greedy expression. The youthful, curly fair hair turns gray and straggly. The Christian smile petrifies to eager calculation. The straight, aristocratic nose becomes fleshy or pointed. The thin, refined ear becomes thick. The row of democratically even teeth is replaced by sharp, gnawing teeth. The loving mouth grows gluttonous. The white skin, soft as velvet, turns flaming red and coarse. The firm chin is replaced by a double chin. A bit beneath the chin beats the artery-hardened heart.

We no longer recognize ourselves. We have been seen.

A Portrait of Dorian Gray

*When we looked up we confronted
in the mirror a strange, despicable
face: our own.*
—Jean-Paul Sartre

When Dorian Gray was permitted to see that hideous portrait of himself, he could not be absolved by saying it represented somebody else. He had posed for the portrait, and he knew he would never grow old if the portrait grew old instead. Even so, it came as a shock to him, as we all know. But most of us Westerners are not only shocked: we don't believe our eyes, for we've never been reminded; at any rate, we have never posed for any spiteful, naturalistic portrait painters in the colonies.

On what occasions can these painters have seen us?

Were there perhaps times in history when actions that seemed natural or positive to us appeared negative or absolutely terrifying in the eyes of the others?

It may be helpful to take up the discussion at this point.

Dorian Gray. Before the Spanish King, Queen Elizabeth condemned Francis Drake and John Hawkins for seizing Spanish vessels carrying gold and silver from the West Indies to Spain. She promised to do everything she could to stop this illegal activity.

A Portrait of Dorian Gray. Queen Elizabeth owned large shares of the piracy enterprise of Francis Drake and John Hawkins (both of whom were later knighted).

Dorian Gray. In the United Nations England and France turned against Katanga's separatist efforts during the Congo Crisis and spoke out in favor of a united Congo and the preservation of world peace.

A Portrait of Dorian Gray. During the Congo Crisis England and France were playing two roles. At the same time as they made a case for a united Congo, they supported Union Minière in Katanga—where both countries had financial interests to defend—and thus sided with Tshombe against Lumumba.

Dorian Gray. On the American continent the British acquired early a reputation for themselves for their humane treatment of the Indians. While not infrequently the Spanish and French got into feuds with various tribes, the British maintained peace with the Indians.

A Portrait of Dorian Gray. In North America when the British came across Indians who wanted to keep their land, they killed them. In the other parts of America, on the West Indian islands and along the coast of South America, the British ravaged in a manner which Benjamin Franklin described in the year 1785 with the words: "A highwayman is just as much a thief when he plunders as a member of a band as when he does it alone."[1] A supplementary note is found in Charles Darwin's diary for the year 1835:

> I heard Mr. Caldcleugh say, that sitting by an old lady at a dinner in Coquimbo, she remarked how wonderfully strange it was that she should live to dine in the same room with an Englishman. Twice as a girl, at the cry of "Los Ingleses" every soul, carrying what valuables they could, had taken to the mountains.[2]

Dorian Gray. As was the case earlier in Korea, the United States is fighting in Vietnam to protect—in Asia too—the only forces capable of resisting the menace of expanding world communism: freedom and democracy.

A Portrait of Dorian Gray. As was the case earlier in Korea, the United States is fighting in Vietnam to safeguard its hegemony, to secure the "free" world market (which can only make underdeveloped countries poorer) and—with violence and threat of violence—to prevent China from growing strong in peace. The people of Vietnam and Korea have to suffer for it. Otherwise, these wars have been a profitable enterprise.

Dorian Gray. In Europe the Age of Enlightenment reached its highest point in France in the eighteenth century, when science and culture flourished, a new mercantile middle class grew up, the established order was opened to debate, the absolute power of God's grace was for the first time called into question, peace prevailed, and society manifested a strong faith in progress.

Voltaire stands out as a brilliant representative of this era, tirelessly pleading the case for reason against super-

[1] Hartvig Frisch, *Europas kulturhistorie* (*A Cultural History of Europe*) (Copenhagen: Henrik Koppels Forlag, 1928), Vol. II, p. 353.
[2] *Charles Darwin's Diary of the Voyage of H.M.S. Beagle*, edited by Nora Barlow (Cambridge: Cambridge University Press, 1933), p. 311.

stition and barbarianism, tolerance against all forms of fanaticism, and science against prejudice and theological dogmatism.

A Portrait of Dorian Gray. In France during the Age of Enlightenment a considerable segment of the population of Paris—which was anything but enlightened and had little faith in progress—occupied itself at miserable wages with the manufacture of gilded playthings, silk rosettes, and sweets for the vegetating upper class. Meanwhile the beggars—who comprised 10 per cent of the population of France at the beginning of the eighteenth century—lived "in such an unfathomable squalor that it can be compared with the conditions in the East in our times"; for their livelihood they were "restricted . . . to crime, extortion, and sexual offense."[3] The motto of the Age of Enlightenment— Everything for the people, nothing by the people—was followed to the extent that the privileged were awarded wealth, power, servants, income without labor, higher education, and lenient laws, while the people had to be content with poverty, lack of power, slave drivers, slave wages, ignorance, and capital punishment, which was sentenced for 115 different crimes—those who were lucky escaped with their limbs maimed, their flesh branded, or their tongue or lips cut off. Or in other words: everything (in the way of work) by the people; nothing (other than destitution) for the people.

Voltaire, who stands out as the most cynical representative of this systematic contempt for the people, held the following two opinions on his countrymen: "The people have neither the time nor the capacity for spiritual development. . . . They are oxen who yearn for the yoke, the stick, and a bundle of hay." And, "It seems a necessity that the people be ignorant. If they begin wanting to have a voice in the government, all is lost." This contempt would have

[3] Frisch, *op. cit.*, p. 333.

appeared genuine if these two propositions didn't contradict one another. If the people were really a bunch of oxen, it obviously wouldn't have taken coercive measures to keep them down. This expressed contempt for the manifest weakness of the people seems to be a diversionary tactic, intended to conceal an unexpressed terror of the potential strength of these same people. The only really tangible example of tolerance in the Age of Enlightenment is probably the forbearance on the part of the French people toward their oppressors. Despite the fact that they were treated scarcely any better than the American Indians —whom the French persecuted at about the same time in war after war—they never revolted against those in control of "the eternal justice."

Dorian Gray. The Alliance for Progress is designed to promote the development of Latin America.

A Portrait of Dorian Gray. The Alliance for Progress is designed to promote the development of North America.

Dorian Gray. The nations of Europe and North America stand united today in their endeavor to preserve world peace, above all.

A Portrait of Dorian Gray. Europe is history's bloodiest battlefield. Since 1945 the Americans have taken over the Germans' old role as the world's leading belligerent nation.

Dorian Gray. As an example of the well-known and enterprising English education policy in the Gold Coast, it may be mentioned that the mother country's contribution to education during the period 1913–1931 increased by 900 per cent. During the same period the share of education expenses in the colonial national budget rose from 3 to 7 per cent.

A Portrait of Dorian Gray. In 1931 only every fifth

child in the Gold Coast went to elementary school; .5 per cent of the population attended school at higher levels.

Dorian Gray. In the West the industrial revolution is known as the Glorious Revolution, partly because it was bloodless and partly because it laid the foundation for a rise in material well-being that would rapidly be allotted to the countries of Europe and eventually the whole world.

A Portrait of Dorian Gray. So far as Asia is concerned, this so-called Glorious Revolution was nearly a catastrophe. In a short time the British export of cheap cotton cloth ruined the Indian domestic industry that had long competed successfully on the European market, and in India, Burma, and China, the Europeans now intensified the economic activity and infiltration that would contribute to the wealth of the West and the poverty of the East. It is relevant here to note that neither India, Burma, nor China wanted any of the new European products in exchange for their coveted tea, silk, porcelain, and spices; they wanted payment in silver and gold instead. In order to convince the Asians of the blessings of industrialism, the Europeans were therefore obliged to take up arms. The mere establishment and operation of the English opium export from India to China required three wars.

Dorian Gray. At the beginning of the 1950's Premier Mossadegh, a power-mad, seventy-year-old landowner in Iran, nearly plunged the world into a major new war. Not content with nationalizing the oil and expelling the English firm that had efficiently supervised production for forty years, he also approached the Russians openly and threatened to transform the Middle East into a center for the cold war. Fortunately for the sake of world peace and the balance of power, the hysterical Mossadegh encountered total failure, both in his invitations to the Communists and in his "private" oil production. When the oil wells began to run dry in the absence of the English and the national treasury was empty, the Shah was forced to remove his hapless prime minister and to call back the English technologists, who were the only ones who could get production running once more. This occurred at the last minute, for in 1953 Iran stood on the brink of ruin, and only generous American aid during the crisis saved the country from plunging over the edge. For that matter, it was also the United States that helped Iran to a considerably more advantageous oil agreement than they had previously had with the British.

A Portrait of Dorian Gray. Iran had been discontented with British Petroleum's oil monopoly for many years—since it received only 20 per cent of the net earnings and was not allowed to inspect the books. As a result, in 1951 the parliament decided to nationalize the industry, passing the resolution by a large majority. By threatening to resort to his Russian contacts, Mossadegh hoped to be able to force BP to give Iran a larger share of the profits, but he underestimated the Englishmen's strength. The concern—which normally keeps production down in order to be able to keep prices up—quickly compensated for its losses in Iran by increasing production commensurately in Kuwait. BP also withdrew all its technologists and had the English navy, its main stockholder, efficiently obstruct all oil export from Persian harbors, particularly to the Soviet Union. Mossadegh now used his Russian threat against the Americans, who also intervened. It lay in the interest of the United States to chase the Russians away at once, safeguard the peace, abandon the nationalization of oil, demonstrate solidarity with the English, and, at the same time, pave the way for the American members of the Western oil cartel—all of which required delicate diplomacy. But fortunately in 1953 the brothers John Foster and Allen Dulles —two of Wall Street's leading corporation lawyers and representatives for Standard Oil, among other concerns— had just been appointed Secretary of State and head of the

CIA, respectively. Both of them swung the deal so that the Secretary of State chased the Russians away and the head of the CIA had Mossadegh discharged (a prime minister more friendly to the West was installed); together the corporation lawyers also cooked up an oil agreement that wrecked BP's monopoly, gave the American oil giants 40 per cent of the oil supply, and awarded Iran half of the earnings against the loss of the control of the oil, all at once. At the same time BP was awarded ample compensation, and Iran (read: the landowners), a quarter of a billion dollars in foreign aid. Wall Street anti-Communism had triumphed.

The examples are manifold, for we live in the world's original home of hypocrisy. But now, surely, the association ought to be recognized clearly. Time and again, it's a question of the same face, only seen from different quarters, each time with an emphasis on different circumstances. Often it takes only a small displacement for the entire face to change its mood. Often it takes only a shift from political to economic circumstances.

If the object now were to deal out pro's and con's in sweeping generalities—manipulating history at will in a perpetual game of on-the-one-hand, on-the-other—then we could have dwelt upon these examples, assembling enough extenuating nuance for every last portrait to make the unpleasant feeling go away. But the purpose now is not to see as much of the truth as possible on our own terms but to see as much of the truth as possible on the other's terms, those of the oppressed.

And that's more difficult. Then we whistle a different tune.

With that let us leave Dorian Gray and fix his portrait in our minds instead. To do this is to give it a name.

Some Esteemed Westerners

Foster Cuncliffe, English merchant at the beginning of the eighteenth century.

When Cuncliffe died he received this epitaph:

> A merchant whose honesty, competence, and insight into mercantile things earned himself and his country riches and esteem; an administrative officer who upheld the cause of righteousness with prudence and impartiality;' a good Christian, God-fearing and exemplary in the exercise of all his duties; a friend of virtue, a father to the needy, an enemy only to vice and indolence.

At the beginning of the eighteenth century, when Liverpool functioned as one of the centers of the international slave trade, Cuncliffe was one of the leading slave dealers. He had four ships constantly trafficking in slaves, each one containing 1,120 slaves. "A father to the needy" is no empty phrase, in other words. Cuncliffe was a father to 4,480 needy people per cargo trip.

Herman Josef Abs, German banker and industrialist, contemporary.

President of Badische Aniline & Soda Works, one of the three I. G. Farben enterprises that produced poison gas for the Nazis' concentration camps and ran factories in Auschwitz with camp prisoners for manpower. However, the management of Deutsche Bank is the main occupation of Dr. Abs, today one of the financial leaders of West Germany and thus Western Europe, and during the time of Hitler a leading Nazi financier. As a protest against growing American influence in postwar German industry, Dr. Abs—who is included on the Americans' list of Nazi financiers—has in recent years stimulated independent German and European initiative on the international level, in Latin America among other places. Abs is a member of the board of Adela Investment Co., in which Stockholms Enskilda Bank—likewise blacklisted earlier by the Americans—is represented.

Winston Churchill, English statesman of the twentieth century.

In *The Story of the Malakand Field Force*, the book that marked his successful literary debut in 1898, Churchill, a lieutenant in the colonial army, wrote about the victorious English invasion of North India's mountain regions. In it he says, among other things:

> To the ferocity of the Zulu are added the craft of the Redskin and the marksmanship of the Boer. The world is presented with that grim spectacle, "the strength of civili-

zation without its mercy." At a thousand yards the traveller falls wounded by the well-aimed bullet of a breech-loading rifle. His assailant, approaching, hacks him to death with the ferocity of a South Sea Islander. Here the weapons of the nineteenth century, are in the hands of the savages of the stone age.[1]

Lieutenant Churchill extends his observation:

> Among Europeans power provokes antagonism, and weakness excites pity. All is different in the East. Beyond the Suez the bent of men's minds is such, that safety lies only in success, and peace in prosperity. All desert the falling. All turn upon the fallen.[2]

The arrival of the British was, however, accompanied by notable improvements:

> As the sun of civilization rose above the hills, the fair flowers of commerce unfolded, and the streams of supply and demand, hitherto congealed by the frost of barbarism, were thawed. Most of the native population were content to bask in the genial warmth and enjoy the new-found riches and comforts.[3]

However, the happiness and well-being of the natives does not seem to stop them from rebelling constantly against the superior British forces. This paradox bewilders Lieutenant Churchill, but soon enough he finds the explanation: a "Mad Fakir" has stirred up a wave of Mohammedan fanaticism in the mountain regions:

> The forces of progress clash with those of reaction. The religion of blood and war is face to face with that of peace. Luckily the religion of peace is usually better armed.[4]

During his subsequent career Churchill matured in many respects, as everyone knows, but he remained true to the religion of well-armed peace.

[1] *Loc. cit.*, pp. 4–5.
[2] *Ibid.*, p. 222.
[3] *Ibid.*, p. 37.
[4] *Ibid.*, p. 41.

Jonkheer de Jonge, Dutch governor in Indonesia in the 1930's.

De Jonge used to begin his conversations with Western journalists with the following words:

> We Dutch have ruled here for three hundred years with cudgel and whip; we shall stay three hundred years more. Then we can begin to talk things over.

Samuel Cummings, American businessman, born in 1926.

Head of Interarmco (International Armament Co.) and regarded as the world's largest weapons dealer. This story about Cummings was told by *Der Spiegel* on July 28, 1961.

> Little Samuel loved guns. For every extra cent he got he bought firearms. His mother had nothing against it, for he was at the same time a habitual church-goer in his home-town of Philadelphia, for years the stronghold of the pacifistic Quakers.

At the age of nineteen, Cummings became a soldier, then studied law, entered government service as a CIA agent, and during the Korean War acted as a weapons expert for the intelligence agency. As an apprentice with the Western Arms Corporation in Los Angeles, he learned to keep informed on coups and rebel movements in Central America in order to have weapons consignments ready, but when he went into business for himself, he turned in the beginning to private weapons collectors (a large group in the U.S.). He built an arsenal in Virginia that today consists of eight warehouses and sold firearms by mail order with the help of the same kind of catalogue advertisements that Sears, Roebuck uses for novelty articles: "A find for collectors, terror of the East, designed for use against the West."

Today this idyllic small business is thought to give Interarmco its "solid ground during periods of political calm among the great powers," but the international success of the concern is founded instead upon the infrequency of such periods. It was in 1951 that Cummings began to do business on a political basis, for at that time Guatemala had acquired a Socialist president whom the Americans feared; Interarmco supplied him with weapons. In Cuba Interarmco sold weapons first to Batista, then to Castro. This doesn't seem to have jeopardized Cummings' good relations with Washington: some of Interarmco's largest orders—including modern weapons equipment to Chile, Venezuela, and Iran—have come from the Pentagon. Early in the venture Cummings also managed to establish good contacts with both Eastern Europe and the CIA, among other means, by a kind of double espionage: the Eastern countries received hard-to-get Western arms, the CIA hard-to-get Eastern arms. In Africa Interarmco has supplied the white minorities in Rhodesia, Kenya, South Africa, and Tanganyika with quick-firing automatic rifles, and during the revolt in Angola, it wasn't only NATO but Cummings as well who helped the Portuguese put down the blacks (by himself he armed 200,000 men). It's a relevant fact here that Cummings did not need to consume his American weapons supply for the Angola consignment but was able to buy cheaply from the Bulgarians and Czechs, whose national trade counselors pretended to be innocent of the arms' destination. In Africa Cummings' weapons have been found on the rebel side too, in Sudan for example, but states friendly to the West—and regimes that can pay— consistently benefit most from Interarmco's global weapons trade (now also arms manufacture).

In order to ensure the secrecy around his dealings, to ease the tax burden, and at the same time to come closer to his main Eastern competitors (primarily the Skoda works), a number of years ago Cummings moved Interarmco's main office to Lichtenstein, where laws and taxes limit the free mobility of large foreign enterprises to a particularly small degree. One of the points of the story of capitalism is that during the second world war, Hitler never dared attack Lichtenstein (16,500 German-speaking inhabitants), for I. G. Farben, Royal Dutch Shell, and Standard Oil sat there concocting plans together, over the heads of the great powers. Cummings' latest refuge is Monaco, where, after certain resistance from the aristocracy, Princess Grace obtained citizenship rights for Cummings and thereby international tax exemption. Now in his forties, Cummings usually soothes his skeptics with the somewhat ambiguous words:

> So far as I'm concerned, I conduct trade in arms under just as safe conditions as others deal in soap and coffee.

The president of Interarmco still has a way to go before he can equal the international reputation of his great predecessor, Basil Zaharoff. For his contributions during the years 1914–1918, when he supplied all the fighting countries with arms, Zaharoff was not only granted noble rank but also made a Grand Cross Knight of the Order of Bath, an honorary doctor at Oxford, and a knight of the French Legion of Honor. Cummings, on the other hand, has managed to keep the more sensitive columns of Interarmco's balance sheets secret. It's apparent that the concern is not exactly losing money from the fact that in 1960 the Danish agents alone—and Interarmco has thousands of agents spread all over the world—received a commission of over $185,000.

If there is peace, the commission decreases.

German Archbishop during the Franco-German War, 1870–1871:

> Christian canons are doing a good job.

Swedish diplomat's wife, the present.

As mentioned in Jan Myrdal's book *Turkmenistan,* among the Westerners (mainly Russians) who were working zealously for the dissemination of European toilet culture in Asia was a diplomat's wife who once told the writer:

> . . . during her many years' stay in the Orient she patiently stood on the Oriental toilets and thus urinated in her shoes. When I wondered why she didn't squat down (she didn't wear stockings) she said:
> "I'm no native, either!"
> Culture manifests itself, in other words, in pissing in one's shoes.[5]

Christopher Columbus, Spanish-Italian explorer at the end of the fifteenth century.

Encyclopaedia Britannica had Salvador de Madariaga portray Columbus by describing his legendary feat in these very words:

> At dawn, a land of virginal beauty and fresh colour revealed itself to the delighted Spaniards. With his two captains and the fleet officials, Columbus went ashore carrying a royal banner. He planted it on the shore and took possession of the land in the name of Ferdinand and Isabella. This land—of which he had, of course, no idea—was Guanahani, one of the Bahama Islands, which the Spaniards renamed San Salvador. But everything he saw persuaded Columbus that he was among "the islands which are set down in the maps at the end of the Orient." So, although he saw signs of gold on the noses of the natives, he left in a hurry to see "whether I can come across the Island of Cipango" (*i.e.,* Japan).[6]

[5] Stockholm: Norstedt & Söners, 1966, p. 167.
[6] Salvador de Madariaga, "Columbus," *Encyclopaedia Britannica,* 1966 edition, Vol. 6, p. 112, cols. 1–2.

Allen Lawrence Pope, American bomber pilot in the 1950's.

After his successful participation in the Korean War Pope was stationed at the American military base in the Philippines, from which point he participated on behalf of his country in secret bombing raids over Indonesian territory, intended to expedite the overthrow of Sukarno. In the vicinity of Ambon Island, Indonesian naval forces managed to shoot down Pope's plane and in the course of the salvage operation found documents which revealed that the pilot worked for the CIA.

During the hearing, Pope himself gave a different explanation. He had become interested in dropping bombs during the Korean War, which is why he had purchased a bomber with his own money. Thus, he claimed, he could travel about freely in Asia and bomb whatever target he liked, without having to obey anybody's orders. He just flew around bombing for the sake of his personal pleasure.[7]

Princess K., Russian landowner at the end of the eighteenth century.

In a French collection of memoirs this princess was described in the following way:

> People have seen her make her subjects take off their clothes and flog other subjects in her presence, while she coldly counted the lashes and urged the tormentors to put power into the strokes. People have seen her in intoxicated condition order her servant girls to tie up a serf to a post, strip him naked, and sick dogs on him or thrash him herself. People have seen her snatch the cane out of the hands of one of the women and close in on the unfortunate one herself, whereupon she directed the blows especially toward his most delicate parts, finally to burn off the hair on his head and his body with a lit candle.[8]

[7] David Wise and Thomas B. Ross, *The Invisible Government* (New York: Random House, 1965), pp. 136–138.
[8] From the secret memoirs of Henri Castéra, published in Paris in 1800.

The French author concludes his life sketch:

I have given this beast her title of princess, I will not call her a woman. She is forty years old, of immoderate figure and corpulence. She is still living, and I will gladly give her address to the person who wishes it.[9]

French official in Algeria in the 1950's.

The story of this examining officer during the Algerian War is known only at third hand: The Frenchman's daughter told it to the psychiatrist Frantz Fanon, whom she consulted for certain nervous disorders shortly after her father's death. In turn, without giving away any names, Fanon has reproduced the daughter's account in his book *The Wretched of the Earth:*

"My father was highly placed in the civil service. He was responsible for a very large rural area. As soon as the troubles started, he threw himself into the Algerian man-hunt with frenzied rage. Sometimes it happened that he would eat nothing at all, and not even sleep, he was in such a state of excitement over putting down the rebellion. I saw without being able to do anything about it the slow metamorphosis of my father. . . . The fact was that every time I went home I spent entire nights awake, for screams used to rise up to my room from down below; in the cellar and in the unused rooms of the house Algerians were being tortured so as to obtain information. You have no idea how terrible it is to hear screaming all night like that. Sometimes I used to wonder how it was that a human being was able to bear hearing those screams of pain—quite apart from the actual torture. And so it went on. Finally, I didn't ever go home. The rare times that my father came to see me in town I wasn't able to look him in the face without being terribly frightened and embarrassed. I found it increasingly difficult to force myself to kiss him."[10]

[9] *Ibid.*
[10] Trans. by Constance Farrington (New York: Grove Press, Inc., 1966), pp. 224–225.

Fanon asks how the daughter reacted to her father's death.

> "The funeral sickened me," she said. "All those officials who came to weep over the death of my father whose 'high moral qualities conquered the native population' disgusted me. Everyone knew that it was false. There wasn't a single person who didn't know that my father had the whip-hand of all the interrogation centres in the whole region. Everyone knew that the number of deaths under torture reached ten a day, and there they came to tell their lies about my father's devotion, his self-sacrifice, his love for his country, and so on. I ought to say that now such words have no meaning for me, or at any rate hardly any. I went back to the town directly afterwards, and I avoided all the authorities. They offered me an allowance but I refused it. I don't want their money. It is the price of the blood spilt by my father. I don't want any of it. I am going to work."[11]

Boer wife in South Africa, the present.

> I hope to get my old nannie to go home with me. It won't be easy, either on the boat or at home in old England. I know many people will raise their eyebrows at me for it. But I'm honestly and sincerely attached to my old nannie and the blacks may scheme against me as they will, I've still made up my mind to do what I can to show that peaceful coexistence between the races could be a possibility. I'll never get rid of nannie. If there were only more of her kind, Africa would be a Paradise. . . .
>
> Can you understand why they hate us as they do? Can you understand that—after all we've done for them. . . .[12]

Robert Clive, British empire builder of the eighteenth century.

Among Clive's celebrated contributions in India is the conquest of Calcutta, one of the most important trading

11 *Ibid.*, p. 225.
12 Sara Lidman, *Jag och min son* (*I and My Son*), rev. ed. (Stockholm: Albert Bonniers Förlag AB, Folkbibliotek, 1963), p. 88.

cities of the English East India Company, from Nawab Siradj-ud-Daula of Bengal in the year 1757. The way this came about was that Clive falsified a document, bribed one of the Nawab's ministers to betray his country, and was then able to take the city without serious obstacle. Since the Nawab was apparently captured, the conquest of Plassey in the same year became more of a formality and with that the British were in fact masters of Bengal. The East India Company appointed Clive governor, and he and his men began their administration by obtaining for themselves and the company "compensations" for their slight war losses by emptying Bengal's rich treasure chests. On his own account the governor took £234,000 in cash plus a large estate with annual earnings of £30,000. The result was general corruption throughout the administration.

After his return to England, Clive—now wealthy—was knighted and William Pitt bestowed upon him the epithet "a God-begotten general." In one of Nehru's letters to his daughter Indira (Gandhi), a different opinion is reported:

> On this unsavory foundation of treason and forgery was built up the British Empire in India.[13]

During his second term as governor of Bengal, Clive pacified the population by giving the Nawab increased formal power while the East India Company retained the real power, a form of concealed dictatorship that the British later practiced in several colonies, including Burma and Nigeria. Most important of all, Clive accomplished the feat of giving the company the legal right to collect all the taxes in Bengal and Bihar, a task which the officials of the company performed in exemplary fashion. During the famine of 1770, when one-third of the population of Bengal —several million people—are estimated to have starved

[13] *Glimpses of World History* (Allahabad: M. N. Pandey, 1934), Vol. I, p. 508.

to death, they managed to collect *more* than the full amount of assessment, from the dying and their survivors, among others. At that time Clive had already left India, but Nehru's more general descriptive account included him too:

> There was a shameless scramble for riches and the greed and unscrupulousness of the officials of the East India Company passed all bounds.[14]

In 1774 Clive committed suicide in London.

James Burnham, leading American ideologist in the 1940's.
During the postwar period Burnham pleaded candidly for an American world empire, to be won primarily through an absolute monopoly on atomic weapons in the world.

> This monopoly can be gained and exercised only through a World Empire. . . . The attempt at World Empire will be made, and is, in fact, the objective of the Third World War, which, in its preliminary stages, has already begun.[15]

Burnham also asserted that "monopoly control would at any rate guarantee that not all the earth would be turned into an atomic waste. It would at most be only the other side's section."[16]

---

[14] *Ibid.*
[15] *The Struggle for the World* (New York: The John Day Company, Inc., 1947), p. 55.
[16] *Ibid.,* p. 37.

Is the Western face
beginning to lose its luster now?

Eighteen Judges

Tom Mboya, Attorney General of Kenya:

Too many journalists and sensational writers have [distorted] this scene totally out of perspective, have interpreted Africa as a continent of violence and bloodshed. Being patient and unusually good-humored people, we are amused that this should be the view of white men who have started two world wars and burned up thousands of civilians with atomic bombs, and even now crouch in terror lest their opponents in East or West may loose their huge nuclear armories in their direction. Is this what they call freedom?[1]

[1] *Freedom and After* (Boston: Little, Brown & Co., 1963), p. 215.

It will be a difficult task keeping Africa clear of ideologies. There will be the Cold War growling its thunder around us. There will be professional communists and professional capitalists finding their way into Africa and preaching their irrelevant ideologies. This is why the newly independent states here are battling to define the African goal without being drawn into the Cold War.[2]

Anonymous Chinese in the 1850's:

Impossible that the English are Christian. Then they would not break the Ten Commandments, not take our lands and cities, and not kill our poor people. If they were Christian, they would not break the Sixth Commandment, not sell opium and spread death throughout the kingdom.

General Nihad el-Kassem, former head of state of Iraq, 1963:

What haven't they done to suppress Iraq and ensure themselves of the country's wealth! . . . All our troubles with the imperialists began that day we laid claim to our legitimate rights.[3]

Jesus, Israelite founder of religion:

Beware of false prophets, which come to you in sheep's clothing, but inwardly they are ravening wolves.[4]

Discharged Turkman politician:

I have been in Moscow. I don't understand what they're saying there about Asia anymore. They talk as if poverty didn't exist. As if everything were already on the right road. And I realize that much wrong was done under Stalin. I know that myself. But Moscow has forgotten the world's poverty. I don't like what's in our newspapers anymore. It's not true. They don't tell how aw-

[2] *Ibid.,* p. 169.
[3] From an interview in *Le Monde,* 1963.
[4] Matthew 7:15.

ful the world is. And therefore perhaps the young people over there don't understand anymore why we Turkmen joined the revolution.[5]

Kwame Nkrumah, former head of state of Ghana, 1963:

We were trained to be inferior copies of Englishmen, caricatures to be laughed at with our pretensions to British bourgeois gentility, our grammatical faultiness and distorted standards betraying us at every turn. We were neither fish nor fowl. We were denied the knowledge of our African past and informed that we had no present. What future could there be for us? We were taught to regard our culture and traditions as barbarous and primitive. Our text-books were English text-books, telling us about English history, English geography, English ways of living, English customs, English ideas, English weather. Many of these manuals had not been altered since 1895.[6]

Krishnalal Shridharani, Indian religious philosopher:

The very notion [of missionary evangelism] implies a superiority complex as well as an impulse of self-righteousness. Now that might be tolerable in other fields, but when it is brought into the realm of religion and the spirit, it looks very strange to the Hindu. To the Hindu philosophers, nothing is more irreligious than a holier-than-thou attitude—an attitude which of necessity provides the driving force of evangelism. One cannot describe it as a human desire to share with fellow men things that are found personally precious. Such a desire would turn into fellowship, into discourse, never into a drive for conversion. In this respect I feel that all the great religions of the world have one thing to learn from Hinduism [and, it may be added, from Buddhism, Taoism, and Confucianism]: a humility born of a profound philosophic insight into the relativity of knowledge of ideals. . . . I think that in this Hinduism is more in harmony with the spirit of modern

[5] Myrdal, *op. cit.*, p. 167.
[6] *Africa Must Unite* (New York and Washington: Frederick A. Praeger, Publishers, 1963), p. 49.

science than almost any other great religion. It is forgivable to insist on *one* God, but to insist upon *The* Prophet and *The* Law is intellectually wrong. The assertion of Louis XIV that "I am The State" is quite innocent compared to anyone's assertion that "I am The Law". . . . This exclusiveness is antispiritual inasmuch as it is overweening in the light of the limitations of human perception.[7]

Fidel Castro, head of the government of Cuba, 1959:

The formidable problem that confronts the world consists of the fact that it has been put in a situation where it must choose between capitalism, which leads people to starve, and communism, which solves economic problems but suppresses those freedoms and rights that are valued so highly by mankind.[8]

Abdum Salam, scientist in Pakistan, 1963:

From the horizon of Moscow or New York the risk of a final nuclear catastrophe appears painfully close. But in Khartoum or in Karachi the visible death of daily starvation lies a good deal closer. Fifty per cent of the inhabitants of my native country earn and live on about ten cents a day. Seventy-five per cent have less than fifteen cents a day at their disposal; fifteen cents for two meals, for clothes, housing, and education (to the extent there can be talk of such things at all). For us the unsolved conflict between East and West appears as a luxury that only rich people can afford to pursue.[9]

Carlos Fuentes, Mexican author:

You bombed the first decent houses, the first schools, the first hospitals of Cubans who never before, during the long American protectorate over Cuba, had a roof, an alphabet,

[7] *My India, My America* (New York: Duell, Sloan and Pearce, 1941), pp. 338–339, as cited by F. S. C. Northrop in *The Meeting of East and West* (New York: The Macmillan Company, 1946), p. 413.
[8] From a public statement, May 21, 1959.
[9] Cited by Hans Magnus Enzensberger, "Europäische Peripherie," in *Kursbuch,* No. 2, 1965, p. 167.

or their health. And you did it in the name of liberty, democracy, and free enterprise. What do you want us to think of these nice-sounding words when in their names a population is murdered and the first proofs of concrete welfare are destroyed?[10]

Ezekiel Mphahlele, South African writer:

Where persons have been oppressed as a race group, the Church has sought safeguards and concessions for the individual, evading the necessity and responsibility of group action. And while it fixed its gaze on Calvary or kept up an aloofness from political realities, the road has been slipping back under its feet. It never seems to have occurred to the Church that right under its nose has been growing a calculating white barbarism, among those it considered as the hereditary custodians of Christianity, custodians who need mission stations in their very midst. I cannot but reaffirm what I said in a B.B.C. talk in 1955 on the African intellectual: that to us, the Church has become a symbol of the dishonesty of the West.[11]

Chinese spokesman during the Korean War:

One of the master planners of the Japanese aggression, Tanaka, once said: "to conquer the world, one must first conquer Asia; to conquer Asia one must first conquer China; to conquer China one must first conquer Korea and Taiwan.... American imperialism ... plagiarizes Tanaka's memorandum, and follows the beaten path of Japan's imperialist aggressors!"[12]

Malcolm X, black Muslim preacher in the United States:

I'm the man you think you are. And if it doesn't take legislation to make you a man and get your rights recognized,

[10] "The Argument of Latin America for the North Americans," in *Whither Latin America?* (New York: Monthly Review Press, 1963), p. 16.
[11] *Down Second Avenue* (London: Faber & Faber, 1959), p. 221.
[12] John Spanier, State Department Bulletin XXIII (July 10, 1960), pp. 86–87.

don't even talk that legislative talk to me. No, if we're both human beings we'll both do the same thing. And if you want to know what I'll do, figure out what you'll do. I'll do the same thing—only more of it.[13]

Julius Nyerere, head of state of Tanzania:

The foundation, and the objective, of African Socialism is the Extended Family. The true African Socialist does not look on one class of men as his brethren and another as his natural enemies. He does not form an alliance with the "brethren" for the extermination of the "non-brethren." He rather regards all men as his brethren—as members of his over-extending family.

Ujamaa, then, or "Familyhood," describes our Socialism. It is opposed to Capitalism, which seeks to build a happy society on the basis of the Exploitation of Man by Man. And it is equally opposed to doctrinaire Socialism, which seeks to build its happy society on a philosophy of inevitable Conflict between Man and Man.[14]

There are few greater truths than the Bible statement "To him that hath shall be given, but from him that hath not shall be taken away even that which he hath." Economic strength breeds strength; money breeds money. Without these things ill-health, ignorance and hunger prevent a man from standing upright and talking as an equal to his brother.[15]

Getulio Vargas, former head of state in Brazil, 1954:

I fought against the exploitation of Brazil, I fought for the people, I fought a straightforward game. The hate, the outrage against me has not made me downhearted.

A law against improper profits was stopped in the con-

[13] Answer to question, Militant Labor Forum, January 7, 1965. In *Malcolm X Speaks* (New York: Grove Press, Inc., 1965), pp. 197–198.
[14] From the booklet "Ujamaa: The Basis of African Socialism." Cited by Tom Mboya, *op. cit.,* p. 170.
[15] From Nyerere's article "African Nationalism and the Common Man," *Revolution* (Lausanne, Switzerland: Edition La Cité), Vol. I, No.· 4–5 (Aug.-Sept. 1963), p. 115.

gress. When I recommended social justice and an increase of the minimum wage, the hate broke out against me. I wanted to create national freedom by extracting our riches through Petrobas [state oil concern] and it seemed to meet with success, when a diffuse agitation was got under way. Even Electrobas [state electrotechnical concern] was opposed so that its future seemed hopeless. They don't want the workers to become free. They don't want our people to become independent.[16]

Chinese student:

All that you in the West believe in are mere superficialities. . . . The basic truth about your country is that the capitalists exploit the people, and your life is therefore bound to be unhappy. You may have your own cars, you may be able to travel and enjoy yourselves, but at a deeper level your unhappiness is the true reality, and it's right that our newspapers should select the facts that correspond with the essential truth. But when your journalists describe China—they write what amounts to a libel, even when their reports are based on facts. These unhappy facts do not correspond with the essential truth about us. Our real inner happiness lies in the knowledge that we are not exploited.[17]

Jawaharlal Nehru, former head of state in India:

Christianity is politically the dominant religion today, because it is the religion of the dominant peoples of Europe. But it is strange to think of the rebel Jesus preaching nonviolence and *ahimsa* and a revolt against the social order, and then to compare him with his loud-voiced followers of today with their imperialism and armaments and wars and worship of wealth. The Sermon on the Mount and modern European and American Christianity—how amaz-

[16] Written shortly before Vargas took his life. Cited in Caleb J. Anderson's *Vår otrygga värld* (*Our Insecure World*) (Stockholm: Rabén & Sjögren, 1965), p. 128.
[17] Sven Lindqvist, *China in Crisis*, trans. by Sylvia Clayton (New York: Thomas Y. Crowell Co., 1965), p. 98.

ingly dissimilar they are! It is not surprising that many people should think that Bapu [Gandhi] is far nearer to Christ's teaching than most of his so-called followers in the West today.[18]

Frantz Fanon, doctor from Martinique:

Let us . . . leave this Europe where they are never done talking of Man, yet murder men everywhere they find them, at the corner of every one of their own streets, in all the corners of the globe. For centuries they have stifled almost the whole of humanity in the name of a so-called spiritual experience. Look at them today swaying between atomic and spiritual disintegration.

And yet it may be said that Europe has been successful in as much as everything that she has attempted has succeeded.

Europe undertook the leadership of the world with ardour, cynicism and violence. Look at how the shadow of her palaces stretches out ever further! Every one of her movements has burst the bounds of space and thought. Europe has declined all humility and all modesty; but she has also set her face against all solicitude and all tenderness.

She has only shown herself parsimonious and niggardly where men are concerned; it is only men that she has killed and devoured.

So, my brothers, how is it that we do not understand that we have better things to do than to follow that same Europe?

That same Europe where they were never done talking of Man, and where they never stopped proclaiming that they were only anxious for the welfare of Man: today we know with what sufferings humanity has paid for every one of their triumphs of the mind.

Come, then, comrades, the European game has finally ended; we must find something different. We today can do everything, so long as we do not imitate Europe, so long as we are not obsessed by the desire to catch up with Europe.

[18] *Loc. cit.,* p. 134.

Europe now lives at such a mad, reckless pace that she has shaken off all guidance and all reason, and she is running headlong into the abyss; we would do well to avoid it with all possible speed. . . .

Let us decide not to imitate Europe; let us combine our muscles and our brains in a new direction. Let us try to create the whole man, whom Europe has been incapable of bringing to triumphant birth.

Two centuries ago, a former European colony decided to catch up with Europe. It succeeded so well that the United States of America became a monster, in which the taints, the sickness and the inhumanity of Europe have grown to appalling dimensions.

Comrades, have we not other work to do than to create a third Europe? . . .

For Europe, for ourselves and for humanity, comrades, we must turn over a new leaf, we must work out new concepts, and try to set afoot a new man.[19]

[19] *Loc. cit.*, pp. 252–255.

Is it beginning to be apparent
that there are other faces, other eyes,
other ways to see?

Who Are We?

There is in the West such a strong tradition of self-criticism that for a moment it's possible to make ourselves believe we should be especially well prepared to accept the criticism of the Third World. We should reflect—calmly and objectively—upon the uncongenial face that Frantz Fanon and the others have pointed out and called "Europe" and "The West" in order to see how it conforms with what we actually have accomplished. Not with our glorious ideals and intentions, but with our actions.

But there's a vast difference between criticizing one's self and being criticized by others. Americans have an extraordinary talent for unrelenting self-criticism, but if an Englishman says one unfavorable word about the United States, they get offended and start vindicating themselves. How much criticism can a Frenchman bear to hear from a German, a Czech from a Pole, or a Swede from a Norwegian?

But by all means: the criticism of neighbors—like European wars—generally keeps within the bounds of common Western values. The fundamental is not called into question. It's worse when Eastern Europeans criticize Western Europeans, or the Soviet Union criticizes the United States, for then it becomes apparent that even such everlasting values as democracy can be interpreted in different ways. Hence, we do not accept Eastern criticism either but call it vulgar Marxism or Moscow propaganda and go on instead to talk about freedom of speech. For that matter, how many people reading this book are sitting, waiting for a "Western" assurance on my part—that I'm not a Muslim, that I'm not a Chinese communist, or such— in order to accept my criticism more confidently?

But worst of all is when the criticism comes from Africans, Asians, Latin Americans, and miscellaneous island dwellers in the Pacific—for this touches not only upon the whole foundation of our culture but also upon the superiority complex on top of the Statue of Liberty's crown. In principle, since the world has become one country, there's no reasonable need for us to take the criticism any differently than if it had come from the victims of the welfare state, from the unemployed in West Germany, from black people in the United States, from small farmers in Sweden, from low-income groups in the Soviet Union, or from Gypsies in Hungary, but we don't see things this way. As victims of geography books and Western ethnocentricity, we see things differently. What if these underdeveloped billions were to come and say there is something wrong

with our view of humanity, with our technological development, with our religion and morality, with our writing of
history, with our view of the world, with our way of living,
with our way of living off others? What if they were to
come and say that in all these areas there's an appalling
gap between our theory and our practice and that they may
even possess better or equally worthwhile alternatives that
we have every reason to come to know and accept as
guides? Those people who have so much to thank us for!
I would suspect that the majority of Europeans and Americans still find it very easy to understand how George III
reacted in 1793, when the emperor of China declined his
invitation to import English merchandise with the following self-righteous words:

> "Wondrous and precious objects do not interest me. I . . .
> have no use for your country's manufactures. It behoves
> you, O King, to respect my sentiments and to display even
> greater devotion and loyalty in the future, so that by per-
> petual submission to our Throne, you may secure peace
> and prosperity for your country hereafter. . . ."[1]

How did George III react? He let it be known he would
show the Chinese.

For the sake of simplicity, let us proceed from the fact
that cruelty, egotism, and the hate of foreigners are dis-
tributed evenly over the surface of the earth. Yet the critical factor then remains that it is we Westerners who have
the power, and that the others are suppressed.

To be suppressed is to see one's self constantly through
others' eyes, to have to listen constantly to others' criticism. The Africans seemed to have lived so long with the
self-image that the Europeans stuck firmly to their faces
that they now have to pinch themselves hard in front of
the mirror to believe that the face remaining behind the

---

[1] Nehru, *op. cit.*, p. 520.

mask after all really is theirs and is real. On the other hand, to have power is to escape being seen by others, at least from above or from the same level, and only the person who thus escapes being seen can allow himself the luxury of retaining his sense of superiority.

Only then can you safely delude yourself that as a Westerner you go about in the world representing not a form of humanism, but humanism, not a form of development, but development, not a form of civilization, but civilization, not a form of atheism, but atheism, not a form of the modern view of art, but the modern view of art, not a form of cultural radicalism, but cultural radicalism, not a type of research, but research, not an attempt at impartial news reportage, but impartial news reportage, not a world center, but the center of the world.

Naturally, we could also have refrained from all these delusions. For example, we could have applied our proud scientific tradition to fathom all these absolutes and metaphysical constructions. But we have not done so, for they've served us well in our meetings with other nationalities. In the same way that our missionaries have been well-served by the inflated delusion that Christianity is not *one* way, but The Way and all people should follow Christ above all prophets.

It's no more complicated than that; it's a matter of superior power. We happened to come upon the method of constructing modern weapons and steam engines first and made sure the whole world knew it.

But then the power starts coming loose at the joints or is shifted farther and farther to the west and east so that Europe proper is left to fend for itself: then it's no longer possible, for all these delusions then lose their foundation, and our European windowpanes are filled once more by critical, girded eyes. This hasn't happened since Arabs, Turks, and Mongols stared at us through the murk of the

Middle Ages, and that was a long time ago. We're not accustomed to it, in other words. Consequently, we don't believe our eyes, we bury our heads in the sand, rush mindlessly in to "help," take a pose of innocence if we've donated to the Red Cross, act as if it were always a question of the familiar Western struggle between East and West, or join forces in terms of economics and trade policies to retain our superior power at any price.

In short, I believe we are exceptionally *ill*-prepared to accept the criticism of the proletarian countries. Who cares what happens to the rest of the world, so long as "we" aren't the ones to suffer.

With a bright outlook and the prettiest, most peaceful of intentions, our industrial magnates, pressure politicians, gunboat captains, secret agents, Buddhist missionaries, government bribesters, trade delegations, district supervisors, international bankers, labor recruiting officers, mineral prospectors, peace negotiators, and military leaders crisscross all the continents of the Third World, and decade after decade their faces glow with unwavering youth, health, and goodwill. But inside the huts the portrait of Dorian Gray is growing old.

The voices that were assembled earlier to deliver their "verdict" on Europe and the West could obviously have been selected in other ways. If instead, for example, the heads of state of the Philippines, Malaysia, Turkey, Ethiopia, Morocco, Venezuela, and Argentina had taken the judges' bench, a verdict considerably more friendly to the West could have been delivered, for these men would not have dared anything else; in return the eastern part of the West would have been in for an anti-Communist drumfire considerably worse than is currently the case. In the same fashion—though in reverse—if Mao Tse-tung, Ho Chi Minh, Kim Il Sung, and Fidel Castro (of today) were permitted to predominate: the United States and Western Europe would have been judged considerably more harshly, Eastern Europe considerably more leniently. But of course, if the intent is to listen to the verdict of the proletarian countries, there's not much sense in having the matter decided by judges who have voluntarily or involuntarily taken sides in the Western struggle between East and West, for these men obviously represent not only the Third World but the first or the second as well. All of the eighteen judges I've chosen to quote—whether socialists or bourgeois nationalists, politicians or scientists, writers or religious philosophers—have in common the fact that they represent no other part of the world than their own. (Possibly two of the Chinese voices constitute an exception, but naturally the one great power of the Third World has to be included.)

Leaders who refuse to take sides on the terms of the Western powers-that-be often have a hard time of it, and of the eighteen judges mentioned here, so far two have been deposed, two have been shot to death, one has been crucified, and one has committed suicide. Which one of the independent African leaders is next in line: Sekou Touré, Nasser, or Nyerere?

Frantz Fanon has been given the final comment, which in many respects sums up—and heightens—the others' criticism. Fanon's image of Europe as the executioner and deadly enemy of the proletarian countries seems to have made a very strong impression not only on political discussion in Africa but on that in Asia and Latin America as well. *The Wretched of the Earth* is among the most influential books of the 1960's.

Obviously a European or American responds less enthusiastically to this icy image. But what is there to do? Undeniably, it would be easy if it were possible to do as the International Court in The Hague: declare the plaintiffs incompetent and with that let the whole matter drop. But this isn't likely to work, for the Third World has already seen too much subterfuge of this kind. But even so, the verdict deserves further discussion, surely? Certainly no one can ask us all to swallow such an unspeakably bitter medicine in Christian humility just because we happen to be born in the West? Without protests and appeals for mercy in exceptional cases?

Then let's discuss the matter. Mustn't the verdict be modified by specifics and qualifications, so that a dividing line is drawn, for example, between East and West, between dictatorship and democracy? And don't important exceptions have to be made? Shouldn't European labor movements be exempt, for instance? Or intellectuals and scientists as a group? Or the great mass of ordinary people who don't know what has happened and what is happening? Or people of the church and the Christian mission? At any rate mustn't the more or less neutral, small countries of Europe be exempt? This deserves further consideration, point by point. Is there perhaps a possibility to escape the verdict of the Third World?

The Dividing Line Between East and West

Here the verdict doesn't seem to be unanimous, but the policy line of the majority appears inexorable. They will not agree to any Janus division of the Western face, least of all to a division into a half that is beautiful and democratic and a half that is ugly and communistic.

The entire face is white and the world is filled with white people, from the Urals to California.

The entire face is prosperous and industrialized, and the world is filled with prosperous, industrial nations from the Urals to California.

The entire face is imperialistic, and the world is filled with imperialistic great powers from the Urals to California.

The entire face radiates power and aggressiveness, and power is concentrated in the world to the nations that most frequently make war, and these nations too (except Japan) are located between the Urals and California.

Against this, there is not much objection to be made. And with this, from the viewpoint of the proletarian countries, it is stated categorically: all of us in the West belong to the rich, white strata of oppressors in the world class society. Russians as well as Americans. Czechs as well as Belgians.

Certainly industrial prosperity is considerably more conspicuous in the West than the East, but Western Europe in return contains more ample measure of both extremes—unabashed luxury in the North and agrarian poverty in the Mediterranean area. In the same way there are no citizens of the Soviet Union who are as well off as Wall Street's multimillionaires, but in return, there are no Russians who are as hard up as the Indians and the starving Mississippi black people in the United States, either.

It's hardly possible to proceed further with historical arguments. The concept of the West (or Europe) as a complete entity east of "the Iron Curtain" is scarcely two decades old and is already starting to collapse, while the concept of the West as one continuity all the way from the Urals to California has several centuries to its credit. There doesn't seem to be any historical support to relegate capitalism and communism to separate worlds or groups of culture. "Both marxism and liberalism," writes C. Wright Mills in *The Marxists*, "embody the ideals from Greece and Rome and Jerusalem: the humanism of the renaissance, rationalism of the eighteenth century Enlightenment."[2] Marx, as a matter of fact, was a German, as everyone knows.

So much for the picture before us.

[2] New York: Dell Publishing Co., Inc., pp. 13–14.

74

But *if* the judges wanted to draw a line between East and West, then one thing is certain: the ugliest features would wind up on the side of the West.

The people in the Third World know what Czarist Russia *and* the Soviet Union have done in order to subdue a gigantic empire in Asia, but they also know that unlike the Western powers, the Soviet Union has not sought out colonies, military bases, and trading stations outside its country's borders. They know that one single confirmed imperialist on the Eastern side is matched by five or six confirmed imperialists in Western Europe alone, and they know that not only the United States but Australia, Canada, Rhodesia, South Africa, and Japan as well stand on the side of the Western Europeans, and they have extraordinarily strong historical reasons to be afraid, of South Africa and Japan in particular. They know that, broadly speaking, the Western powers have parted with their colonies, but they know too that West Germany is doing a great deal for herself today in Latin America, just as France is doing in Africa, and England in Asia, to secure or procure *economic* empires. First and finally, they know that today the United States is utterly peerless as the world's most powerful, active, and dangerous imperialist.

In a comparison of war activities, the Eastern side gets off just as lightly, for the countries that have started the majority of wars, conducted most colonial wars, and today undertake most armed intervention around the world are all Western countries. If the judges' classification is strained—the Soviet Union belongs to Europe by virtue of its white affluence while China belongs to Asia by virtue of its yellow poverty—and China is counted among the Eastern countries, then the balance becomes just slightly better. What counts of course is not that China is threatening *in words* to destroy the United States and Japan and parts of the Soviet Union as well; what counts is what

China *does,* and in her actions China—for a hundred and fifty years perhaps the most frequently warred-upon, devastated, and degraded country on earth—has devoted herself primarily to defense. Especially against these very countries: the United States, the Soviet Union, and Japan. Moreover, if China is counted among the Eastern countries, it is necessary to count that warring country Japan among the Western countries—and then the lack of balance becomes even more striking.

But even so, the difference between democracy and dictatorship must speak in favor of the Western side, surely?

It may seem so for us living in Europe and America. But the people of the Third World do not live in Europe or America. They live in the Third World. If Africans and Asians had their choice between living in the U.S. and living in the U.S.S.R., I think the majority would choose to live in the U.S., at least if they were allowed to paint themselves white first, but now they live where they live. In the world's slum. What we do inside our own borders, whether we oppress the citizens or give them prosperity and personal freedom, is pretty immaterial from the viewpoint of the eighteen judges. What is crucial for them is what we have done and are doing *against them,* in our country or theirs.

And even in this respect there exists, it seems, a difference excruciating for the West. The Russians clamp down hardest on people at home. The Western powers clamp down hardest on people away from home.

I'm going to return to the dubious aspects of the Western distinction between democracy and dictatorship, but for the sake of the discussion, perhaps we can agree that the Western powers reserve freedom and democracy for domestic use and the Russians reserve subjugation and police rule for domestic use. What is crucial now and will remain so for the proletarian countries is that neither democracy nor the police state seems to enter into any of the countries' exports to underdeveloped countries. (Even *within* her own territory the Soviet Union has treated the Asiatic population considerably more leniently than the actual Russian population.)

What the Western powers have offered the Third World so far, as we know, is not freedom but subjugation, not democracy but dictatorship, not support for the oppressed masses but support for the oppressors of the masses, not aid to the necessary transformation of society but aid to tidy up the status quo with hospitals, missionary schools, dam construction, private enterprise, contraceptives, and moderate parliaments. What the Soviet Union has concurrently offered the Third World—outside her gigantic Eurasian empire—is neither police rule nor democracy but support to oppressed groups and revolutionary forces, to land reforms and national industries, to liberation armies and communist parties. Or else they do nothing at all— and even this is better than doing harm.

Thus the fascist traits that the Western powers' big capitalists, trade politicians, military men, and secret agents so fortunately seldom show off to their countrymen, they allow the world's proletariat to see all the more clearly. And the socialist traits that cadres of newly bourgeois leaders of the Soviet Union's class society so dismally seldom show to their countrymen they let the world's proletariat see quite a lot of.

We don't think about this detail so often in the West. That there is a difference between being at home and being away. For some reason we take it for granted that the people sitting in the Southern Hemisphere painting our portrait shouldn't pay any attention to the uncongenial traits we continually display for them but bear only in mind the congenial traits we display for the most part at home in

Europe and the U.S. And when they paint the Russians' portrait they're supposed to think only of Stalin's slave camps. But not even the most benign painter can be asked to immortalize a model he's never seen—and completely neglect the model he has practically sitting in his lap. Nor can the judges be asked to regard the Russians' socialistic contributions to the proletarian countries as pure communist bluffs and at the same time regard the Western powers' capitalistic contributions as pure expressions of our democratic temperament. Instead, we have every reason to be *grateful* that in their portrait of hate, they let Eastern and Western traits blend together. This way we're the ones who get off most lightly.

A person could turn the question around and wonder why the judges don't make an exception in favor of the Eastern side instead.

Many people do, without a doubt, most particularly when it comes to ideological comparisons, but the factors of white affluence and superior power seem to be crucial to the general verdict. As we have seen, for Abdum Salam the game between East and West seems itself like "a luxury that only rich people can afford to pursue," and when Tom Mboya talks about the nuclear weapons race and when Frantz Fanon talks about the space race, two manifestations of this game, they do it in approximately the same fashion as poor people sometimes talk about millionaires' parties. They don't rejoice when Scott Carpenter or Gagarin takes off into space, and they don't say "world peace is ensured" when the superpowers each produce another hydrogen bomb or atomic submarine; instead they speak of madness and extravagance, which it is a matter of, obviously. Who is the guiltiest in this prestige war that gorges billions and serves only to widen the chasm between poor and rich countries? Clearly, the United States and the Soviet Union are both involved, more or less drooling with a lust to compete, and the proletarian countries need know no more than this to be frightened off.

Now not one of the eighteen judges has a single positive word to say about capitalism, while a good number of them speak out in favor of socialism. Isn't this a significant difference? Without a doubt. While capitalism has remained a foreign, parasitic element throughout the Third World, Marxist ideology has come to stay. Those who speak out in favor of socialism are also quick to add that they want no part of any "European Communism" or "Moscow agreement"; they want to develop their own form of socialism—Maoism in Asia, Fidelism in Latin America, *Ujamaa* socialism in Africa, Muslim socialism in the Arab world, etc. It remains to be seen how efficient these alternatives are, but what has happened already is that China, North Korea, and Cuba have made considerable progress in building a socialist form of society without slavishly following the Russians, and individual African nations have begun finding roads to socialism that lead neither to Moscow nor to Peking. What this spreading of socialism has made particularly clear is how "European" Soviet socialism is, to what length it has estranged itself from the destitute proletarian situation that constitutes the basis of every form of social revolution in all the underdeveloped countries. For each year that passes, the Soviet Union seems to lose ground in its role as a socialist prototype. Instead, China gains ground (but not all socialists of underdeveloped countries will follow China, either).

Above all, our judges seem to have realized that throughout the Third World, Russian socialists are not at all content with supporting rebels and building steel mills, but—exactly like capitalists in the West—they also want to draw the proletarian countries into their own sphere of power and make them pawns in their Western chess game of power politics. When Americans—in the name of free enterprise—brand all kinds of rebel movements and opposition groups as Communists or Moscow lackeys, the Russians stand with open arms and offer their services to the rejected parties—and whichever embrace an underdeveloped country selects for its sustenance, in the process it loses its independence, politically or economically.

With increasingly hollow pathos it is asked in our lattitudes, "Will the forces of freedom or of oppression triumph in the world?" For the proletarian countries—and thus for the world—this is a secondary question, an exclusory dispute on constitutional practice and political techniques that can only detract attention from the one question that's a matter of survival: Will the rich triumph for good in the world or will the impoverished billions have a chance to build an existence worthy of human respect? From the perspective of this question it doesn't look as if West Europeans, Russians, and Americans were competing today to help the underdeveloped countries develop themselves; rather it looks as if West Europeans, Russians, and Americans were competing today to *stop* the underdeveloped countries from developing themselves.

The white man has founded the Common Market and Comecon, SEATO and the Warsaw Pact, CENTO and the Alliance for Progress on the motto "United we stand, divided we fall." When the poor countries—which have a considerably more desperate need to unite for strength and independence—try in the same spirit to create an African trade alliance, an Asiatic market, a Latin American military pact, etc., then the industrial countries do everything possible either to weaken and sabotage these attempts or to coax the underdeveloped countries into *their* trade alliances, into *their* markets, into *their* military pacts, into *their* commonwealths, for this is the surest way for them to retain their hegemony. Divided the underdeveloped countries fall. Or as Julius Nyerere has expressed it:

In the world society we individual States of Africa are almost in the position of beggars talking to millionaires. We don't like it. We are all endeavoring to develop our own economies, but the more we try the more we are forced to realize that only through African unity can we really break out of the vicious circle of poverty.[3]

From the viewpoint of the proletarian countries, in other words, it is a very good thing when de Gaulle criticizes NATO, and Rumania, Comecon; when China criticizes the Soviet Union, and the United States, France; when West Germany begins competing with the United States in Latin America, and China with the Soviet Union in Africa; when West is divided and East is divided, for this increases the proletarian countries' chances to trade, borrow, and accept aid without ending up in the Western trap. But can they at the same time avoid the destructive dismemberment of their own continents?

Without using racial arguments or those of psychological retaliation, the matter thus seems to be clear. Simple rational argument is quite sufficient for our judges in the Third World to let all their white supporters blend together in one single, despicable form: the rich Westerner who protects his own privileges at the expense of the world's proletariat.

For us living in the West there seem to be only two things to do in this situation. Accept this all-European verdict or request special legal treatment whereby West gets a *more severe* sentence than East. There we stand with our democracy.

The Labor Movement

Here it's possible to be brief, for the failure of the labor movement in the underdeveloped countries is visible at

[3] "African Nationalism and the Common Man," *Revolution* (Lausanne, Switzerland: Edition La Cité), Vol. I, No. 4–5 (Aug.-Sept. 1963), p. 115.

long range. During the war in Indochina it wasn't only the Social Democrats but the mighty Communist Party as well that kept silent or stood behind the policy of the French government. It makes no substantial difference whether a Labour or Tory government is in power when it's a question of England's bases east of the Suez or a matter of the government's attitude toward South Africa and Rhodesia. On no crucial points have any labor governments in Europe or America sought to curtail the freedoms of private enterprise in the Third World; and on the side of the opposition, the West German Social Democrats have demonstrated their approving attitude not only to NATO but also to the Ruhr. So far as the trade unions are concerned, they have promoted the cause of international solidarity throughout the West in *words,* but in their actions they have devoted the postwar period either to safeguarding their "own" workers to the exclusion of all underprivileged and/or immigrant labor or else to limiting international solidarity to the army of workers in the West who are already relatively well off. In the East they have looked after their own house for the most part, and in most places in the West they have accepted the expansion of private industry as an essential requirement for increases in salary. When they haven't gone the full course and contributed directly with CIA money to the workers in Central America and Guiana.

The Afro-Asian observers who recently visited the last meeting of the Socialist International thought they'd landed in a rich man's club, for Willy Brandt talked mainly about the necessity of "saving" NATO and the British talked about the necessity of a strong Common Market. The observers thought the motto "Workers of the world, unite!" had been given a new interpretation in a direction detrimental to them: "Workers of the *wealthy* world, unite!" Which is why they left the meeting.

This does *not* mean it would be immaterial from the viewpoint of the proletarian countries whether the position of the labor movement were strong or weak in the West, for in Europe the little initiative that is taken to stop the wheels of colonialism and imperialism from turning is generally taken, just as now in Vietnam, by labor. But the labor movement cannot be exempted from the sentence of the underdeveloped countries.

The Intellectuals

In *Confessions of a Disloyal European* Jan Myrdal writes:

> ... The unconscious one does not betray. He walks secure through life. But we who are a part of the tradition—the Europeans—and who carry on the tradition we have betrayed with awareness, insight, and consciousness, we have carefully analyzed all the wars before they were declared. But we did not stop them. (And many amongst us became the propagandists of the wars as soon as they were declared.) We describe how the poor are plundered by the rich. We live among the rich. Live on the plunder and pander ideas to the rich. We have described the torture and we have put our names under appeals against torture, but we did not stop it. (And we ourselves became torturers when the higher interests demanded torture and we became the ideologists of torture.) Now we once more can analyze the world situation and describe the wars and explain why the many are poor and hungry. But we do no more.
>
> We are not the bearers of consciousness. We are the whores of reason.[4]

This verdict is even more severe than the one signed by Frantz Fanon. Myrdal seems to put such great demands on intellectual awareness that only an extremely small minority within each intellectual professional group can

4 New York: Pantheon Books, 1968.

lay claim to being called aware. Certainly it also deserves to be said that the majority of scientists and teachers, doctors and lawyers, writers and critics, technicians and economists, politicians and opinion leaders are unaware and unintellectual in the sense that they seldom know more about war, torture, and hunger in the world than what it says in the papers; seldom do they produce any analyses of the "world's situation," for they let themselves be engulfed by their fields of specialty. Perhaps the Myrdal family might be included among the exclusive elite who are capable today of "analyzing the world situation" and "explaining why the many are poor and hungry." But this wouldn't do either, for neither Alva, Gunnar, nor Jan Myrdal has managed to put an end to the hunger or prevent the wars; thus, they too would be "the whores of reason."

I question whether these abnormally high demands don't counteract Myrdal's critical purpose, for if 99.9 per cent of all the people who are intellectually active can be said to have failed, then a person can pretty well put up with being included among the failures, most particularly if the greatest stress is put upon the type of radical actions that prevent war, for the same 99.9 per cent of all intellectuals know very well they have no chance at all of carrying out such actions. In this regard the majority of politicians, economists, and military men also lack the necessary power. One would also be obliged to include Marx among the prostitutes. So let's settle for putting the stress on awareness and solicit only such actions as the majority of intellectuals can carry out: obtaining information, analyzing events (at least secondhand), arousing opinion, protesting, describing what is happening, etc. Even so, intellectual casualties seem to be very high.

The flagrant examples announce their presence immediately: opportunists in the fields of science and cultural affairs during the time of Stalin, collaborators, war chemists, counterfeiters of history, and race biologists during the time of Hitler. When Frantz Fanon studied psychiatry at the University of Algiers, the instruction was led by Professor A. Porot, a Frenchman, who after studying the North African's psyche for thirty years had come to the following conclusion:

> The North African is a criminal: his predatory instinct is well known; his intense aggressivity is visible to the naked eye. . . . The Algerian has no cortex: or, more precisely, he is dominated, like the inferior vertebrates, by the diencephalon. . . . The hesitation of the colonists in giving responsibility to the native is not racism nor paternalism, but quite simply a scientific appreciation of the biologically limited possibilities of the native.[5]

In a publication in 1955, *Psychologie normale et pathologique de l'Africain*, a Dr. A. Carothers, one of the World Health Organization's experts, attempted to extend Professor Porot's observation to include West, East, and South Africa too:

> The African makes very little use of his frontal lobes. All the particularities of African psychiatry can be put down to frontal laziness. . . . The lack of integration of the frontal lobes in the cerebral dynamic is the explanation of the African's laziness, of his crimes, his robberies, his rapes and his lies.[6]

The underdeveloped countries cannot count intellectuals like these among their supporters. But to what extent can they count on others—on us? In the youth of the atom bomb there were several physicists who stood up to protest and discuss the matter, but today, when considerably more natural scientists and technologists are engaged in

[5] Fanon, *op. cit.*, pp. 242–244.
[6] *Ibid.*, pp. 244–246.

the nuclear industry, the space industry, and the war industry as well, we very seldom hear such protests, from either Moscow, Paris, or Los Alamos. Evidently the research scientists feel at home in their prominent positions or else they're complaining in silence. The thought that from the viewpoint of the proletarian countries there might be anything improper or at least debatable about their occupation seems to have trouble impregnating their well-paid brains, otherwise they surely would have said something. In the West the majority of engineers and natural scientists are bought up by industry and commerce, and as we all know, many are put to work constructing luxury articles instead of practical goods, supersonic planes instead of safer jet planes, expensive packages instead of inexpensive products, mere objects that confirm the chasm between rich and poor in the country "World." These intellectuals do not have the power to alter the development, certainly, but sometime it would be amusing to hear leading technologists say something else in public besides "We are guiding progress," "If it weren't for us, there wouldn't *be* any prosperity," or the like.

In nine cases out of ten a corporation lawyer or a person with an M.A. in Business Administration who gets an offer from, say, Unilever asks about two things: salaries and working conditions. If the answers are favorable, I suppose he takes the job—without finding out where and how the concern gets its raw materials or what its monopoly status in West Africa implies politically. The underdeveloped countries might come into the picture by way of the Amsterdam personnel director's proposal of sojourn to one of the Latin American offices, and at this the M.A. in Business Administration or the corporation lawyer brightens up, since he's never been there.

Let's not forget that most intellectual occupations are socially respected and well paid, and are, as a rule, recruited from the higher classes of society. And not only diplomats and top executives but more subordinate engineers and medical students as well seldom agree to serve in underdeveloped countries unless they are allowed a standard of living that makes the local population perceive the foreigners as lords. Away from home, they stand on the side of power and status quo just as they did at home.

Generally, in order to find intellectuals who shun neither political dealings, sacrifices of standard, nor demonstrative action, we have to go far down in the years, to students and others in like situations who have not yet been absorbed by production and therefore have "time" to protest against the spread of nuclear weapons, pass out bulletins on Vietnam, join the Peace Corps, or write articles viewing India's desperate poverty with alarm. In this company are also found miscellaneous, unattached intellectual folk—writer, painter, and journalist types— especially signing petitions. Of course, this kind of activity is often dismissed as opportunistic or politically ineffective. Yet even though it's fully realized throughout the Third World that these young protesters can seldom influence the people in power, it is evident that their acts of solidarity are often appreciated. Especially in Vietnam. Perhaps a genuine chance of being exempted from the verdict is beginning to emerge here.

But there is another side to the question.

I think it's important to emphasize that intellectual awareness of the face of suffering cannot be gauged exclusively or even primarily in the current terms of "commitment": political orientation, protest activity, ideological stand, etc. What is produced by the increasingly obtrusive presence of the world proletariat is an international realization that spans the entire intellectual terrain, an awareness of the world as one country, an awareness that can penetrate and erupt not only in politics and cultural controversies but also within historical research and economics, within religious philosophy and archeology, within ethnology and sociology, within literature and art criticism, in the daily press and on television, in schools and museums, in magazines and book publishing. In approximately the same way, I imagine, as the awareness of Sicily (sometimes) manages to penetrate and influence the politics, literature, education, and social research of rich Northern Italy; or as the awareness of the destitution of the northeast provinces of Brazil (seldom) leaves its mark on the intellectual activities that are restricted to the southern provinces and large cities.

Is this kind of international realization common? It seems not. Not much is done to disseminate it either.

In history class at school Western children are required to study mainly about our kings, our presidents, our revolutions, our world wars; in religion class all foreign religions are dismissed in one-hundredth of the space that is devoted enthusiastically to Christianity; English, Spanish, and French seem to compete constantly, in vain, with Russian in Eastern Europe, Spanish competes constantly in vain with English, French, and German in Western Europe, and only freaks study Chinese or Arabic. In higher education, economists in the East seem just as confined to Marxist issues as economists in the West are confined to capitalist issues; religious scholars study Asia's religions with Christianity—more or less emphatically superior—as a point of departure; sociologists seem to be engrossed by problems of welfare; archeologists by Rome and Athens; and literary scholars by domestic or European subjects. At the present time a wave of interest in underdeveloped countries seems to be pervading Western mass media, but despite this wave, mass media constantly eschew the poor countries' own news bureaus, magazines, and radio stations or choose to have their material filtered by reliable agencies stationed in East or West. And when people interested in underdeveloped countries look anything up in handbooks of cultural history or politics, they find everywhere a Western perspective of the world predominating completely. Political debate in the Soviet Union today seems to be concentrated on domestic agriculture and industry; parliamentary debate in Scandinavia revolves resolutely around the 99.7 per cent of things deemed more important than the Third World, and in Europe esthetic debate restricts itself with dogged resolution to the European tradition, exactly as is still the case with the Swedish Academy's Nobel Prize committee. In the field of translations, the situation looks a bit brighter: Maspero, in France, and Penguin, in England, devote entire series of books to problems of the underdeveloped countries, but for one thing, this is a drop in an unabating, surging sea of Western books, and for another this is generally a question of European or American books *about* proletarian countries and not books *from* proletarian countries. Of course, both kinds are needed, but in the latter area, it seems, almost everything remains to be done, throughout the full range of literary subjects: Indian historical research, Southeast Asian theology, African teaching methods, Chinese sociology, Latin American economics, Central Asian prose and poetry, Arabic debate on the relationship between Islam and socialism, Brazilian esthetics, African scholarship on Christianity, Central American mythology, theory of dance in Thailand, East African social psychology, Asiatic scholarship on Europe. . . .

In short, a Western ethnocentricity that has prevailed for centuries seems to be holding its ground effectively against most forms of intellectual world awareness. Point by point, advances have been made and are being made, but on a broad scale and in depth little seems to happen. Perhaps the old wives' tale still exists in incessant hyperbole that the interesting science, art, and exchange of ideas are to be found only in the West?

In several intellectual domains in the West, moreover, people still seem to spend all their time working their way out of a national or sectarian consciousness. European politicians, writers, and churchmen, for example, all seem to perceive the step from province to continent as such an enormous seven-mile step that on arriving in Brussels, Munich, or Geneva, they must feel as if they'd reached the center of the earth. Belgian trade delegates shake hands with French trade delegates, members of the Danish avant-garde shake hands with members of the West German avant-garde, Roman cardinals shake hands with Greek Orthodox bishops, and Calvinists from the Alps shake hands with members of Swedish mission societies from Dalecarlia, whereupon, with an exhausted, global, Common Market smile, all the parties collapse into their ecumenical armchairs.

In the United States and in Western Europe in particular, economists seem to be among the few advanced exceptions, at least in terms of volume of research. While before the war, as Gunnar Myrdal has pointed out, cultural anthropologists dominated the modest social scientific research that the West conducted on underdeveloped countries, today the initiative has passed into the hands of economists. But Myrdal is also of the opinion—expressed in 1964 in *Vår onda värld* (*Our Evil World*),[7] among other works—that the major part of this research on underdeveloped countries, conducted in the shadow of the cold war, is influenced by opportunistic haste, deformed by a consideration for commercial competition, and sterilely fixated with Western models—"Western concepts and theories prove to be an expedient way to rationalize oppor-

[7] Stockholm: Rabén & Sjögren, 1964, pp. 52–53.

tunistic interests." According to Myrdal, when this is supplemented by a tactical or well-meaning tendency to mitigate anomalous states of affairs, the result is often as equally a "false conception of reality" as that which characterizes Soviet Russian research on underdeveloped countries.

Even on the home front the scientific nature of humanistic and social research is a delicate subject, but precisely when "foreign" parts of the world are drawn into the research field, the pretext of objectivity becomes particularly hard to maintain. I think it was René Grousset who pointed out that a scholar of ancient history may seem to develop a completely convincing and rigorous historical criticism so long as he restricts himself to Greece; as soon as he gets into the relations between Greeks and Persians, though, his partiality is uncharitably revealed, for he is capable only of observing Persepolis from Athens, never Athens from Persepolis. The customary subject division between sociology and anthropology seems to give an indication of what a long way we have to go to a "de-Westernized" view of humanistic and social science. When, for instance, will we get to read an anthropological dissertation that gives a picture of England or Sweden in terms of marriage customs and death rites, tribal relationships and religious practices, leadership cult and initiation rites, folk dances and weather conditions? When will we get to read a sociological dissertation that attempts to survey Madagascar or Polynesia in terms of group dynamics and social control, alienation and role expectations? Probably not until the Third World, in this respect too, begins to take us seriously in the West: as objects of research.

Who knows, perhaps it is these very people—whom our scholars of the humanities and social sciences in particular have helped brand in terms of "primitive culture," "primitive religion," "outskirts of culture," "outside the center of events," "lower level of civilization," "stagnation," "inner disintegration," "forgotten by progress," "frontal laziness," etc.—perhaps it is scholars from these "retarded cultures" and "primitive peoples," who will best be able to determine the extent to which our "universal" science of humanity and human society is partial, prejudiced, blinded by tradition, and unscientific.

I would like very much to take up one more aspect of the intellectuals' claims to being exceptional.

It would be hard to picture the Swedish mystic Willy Kyrklund leading a political demonstration or writing inflammatory articles, but the way to the face of suffering is not one but many. In *Till Tabbas*, his book from Iran, Kyrklund tests the way of analyzing landscape, comparing religions, entering into the spirit of language and the spirit of cultural history. It's not facts and social problems in the usual sense he's aiming at but tone of voice, details, faces, the inside of the faces. Some of his finest passages deal with sun-dried clay, with Iranian poetry, with opium, with sand, and with the relationship of gender in the Persian language to a pantheistic, universal empathy.

Generally the Western traveler in poor countries is so intent on seeing as much as possible in a short time that he relies exclusively upon planes, express trains, and taxis, and later, when he is writing, one notices that his pen has flown or ridden in a taxi too, for it functions quickly and efficiently, like a jeep, and the face of suffering spins by in the text, exactly as it did on the trip. Kyrklund, however, who is never separated from his language, yokes a sluggish ox to his style and his pen.

> All culture arises from confrontations. There are different ways for people to confront each other. The most common way is with weapons.[8]

8 Kyrklund, *op. cit.*, p. 133.

Generally the Western traveler in underdeveloped countries prepares for his trip by reading a travel account written by one of his countrymen or an up-to-date analysis in English, at best one that situates itself on the side of the people. And later, when he is traveling, he leaves his European touring party only to look up certain "addresses" he has obtained, of colleagues in the vicinity or of Western diplomats. Kyrklund prefers to situate himself on the side of the people in a more concrete way—by learning their language ("Camel's-back-breaking classical Arabic"), abstaining from addresses and Western guides, and relying instead upon books that are written on the scene; in fact, he seems to travel alone. Sartre has asserted that it's not possible to read Robbe-Grillet in an underdeveloped country, but some Iranians, it seems, know Hafiz or other Persian authors by heart and not infrequently are initiated into the mysteries of Sufism or Parsism.

In the field of literature, what I have called international realization does not seem to be restricted to a certain type of "engagé" writer or a certain type of "engagé" writing either. On his winding paths the inner-directed Kyrklund develops this kind of realization to as equally high degree as the outer-directed Jan Myrdal does on his straighter paths. (Other examples could be selected, but these two Swedish writers happen to have stimulated me most during the work on this book.) It has become popular to point out some controversial political work and say that *this* is literature's road to the world's destitution, but the roads to anything that is still so painfully unfamiliar as the world's destitution cannot justifiably be either too many or too rugged. The face of suffering can be seen from all the perspectives of art as well as science.

But the object now was not only to see, but also to be seen, and when the eighteen judges see the people who have described them, it doesn't seem to make any difference who they are. Kyrklund doesn't appear prosperous, yet when he's wandering in Tehran during the time of the oil crisis, the excited population scream and throw rocks at him. He sees no reason for surprise. Certainly, he could raise the objection that *he's* no oil magnate, but the people's looks remind him that he's on their side only so long as no rocks hit him; whenever he wants he can break off his visit, seek refuge in the Swedish Embassy, or go home to Western prosperity to lick his wounds (and sell the rights to 'his book on destitution for a high price). A tradition that has given him freedom and (relative) prosperity has at the same time given them oppression and poverty.

For his part, Jan Myrdal has devoted almost all of his *Confessions of a Disloyal European* and a few other books to elucidating these things: To what degree Western intellectuals are implicated in what has happened and what is happening, how little their solidarity usually amounts to when the going gets tough, how easily they let themselves be hoodwinked, how instinctively free and secure they often feel within their intellectual specialty—as if the other people's glances didn't take in these professions too. Myrdal showers just as much abuse upon intellectuals as Sartre ever did, but he doesn't do it in order to exclude himself. Hence, I'll cite two quotations:

> What surprises me is not that even intellectuals allow themselves to be corrupted, but that they are so cheap. If a trip costs $80 for ordinary people, at the embassies there can be a line of intellectuals who want to get invited. This is no longer the treason of the clerks. It is their self-destruction.[9]

[9] *Söndagsmorgon* (*Sunday Morning*) (Stockholm: Norstedt & Söners, 1965), p. 197.

I had got a gold filling in a lower left molar in 1944. Germany had payed for Swedish exports with gold at that time. I often wonder whose tooth that is chewing in my mouth. A Jew from Lodz, or one from Amsterdam?[10]

Many people who write literary accounts of underdeveloped countries seem so busy entering into the spirit of the conditions of suffering that such crass observations are never allowed to sully their feelings. Many appear to stake so much on identifying with destitution that they easily forget their own well-fed face; many seem to be so fraught with the commitment they feel today that they won't admit to the commitment they didn't feel yesterday and thus not to their history, their dependence, or the limits of their loyalty either. Many are so completely captivated by the people they see around them on the trip that they seldom notice—in approximately the same fashion as missionaries and explorers—they have sought out suffering not only to share it unselfishly but also in order to deepen their own spiritual struggles, to become aware or to be saved themselves, or to pick up credits for *themselves*, in heaven or on earth. In short, they forget that there are two faces, one to understand and identify with, one to recognize painfully.

But I have to put a stop to this now, before the desire to criticize is driven to such lengths that "unfettered" intellectuals are made out to be no better than finance kings and gunboat captains. This would be almost as grotesque as putting the European labor movement in the same boat as raw-material-chasing commerce and industry. If the people of the Third World cannot count on a (limited) loyalty, at least from the representatives of labor and the minority of intellectuals who haven't sold out, then where would they be able to find it in the world of the rich?

[10] *Confessions of a Disloyal European* (New York: Pantheon Books, 1968).

The eighteen judges do not appeal directly to the intellectuals, either. Nor are intellectuals excluded, and when one acquaints one's self with the verdict, it is easy to read in it an exhortation that seems addressed precisely to the cadres of the educated: look at yourselves in the mirror and reconsider!

The Church and the Christian Mission

Concerning the church, the verdict seems so unanimously harsh that it can be supposed that only truly sophisticated theology may find holes in it. But what about the missionaries? In building hospitals and schools, the Christian mission has been responsible for a few of the extremely rare Western contributions that have not been detrimental to the oppressed. At the same time, from the start of colonization, the mission has been associated with violence and with business ventures. The conquistadores were on fire with ardent faith, exactly as the French navy officers in the "newly discovered" Indochina. If this type of belligerent, business-like missionary has gone out of existence, the people in Africa and Asia know by this time that for every humane missionary there are ten businessmen or officers who all—at least if they're Americans—enthusiastically proclaim themselves to be Christians while greedily helping themselves. Thus, not all the blacks, yellows, and reds always manage to see clearly that the missionary and the other people are not affiliated. Today the people of Africa and Asia often turn toward religions that don't remind them of the white man's empire (Islam in Africa, Buddhism and Islam in Asia, etc.). This does not prevent the take-over of the good missionary habit of building hospitals and schools by Hinduism, among other religions, yet at the same time it is the Indian judges who dissociate themselves most decidedly from "the aggressive narrowness" of the Christian mission's appeal—"Go ye therefore, and make disciples of all the nations"—as well as from the built-in intolerance—"I am The Way. . . ." If the methods of the conquistadores appear un-Christian today in the eyes of most missionaries, no one can deny that on this point particularly they took Jesus more at his word than contemporary social-working colleagues. The conquistadores didn't build any hospitals, but they did turn many people into disciples of their religion by manual force, and even today—as all of us know—the Christian faith is thriving in Latin America, supported especially by large landowners.

I'll return to Christianity, but one thing is clear regarding the growing multitudes in the West who believe themselves to be secularized or de-Christianized because they've abandoned the manifest forms of religion. When these people have turned their criticism against the Christian mission, the mission has seldom had difficulty dismissing this criticism on the grounds that it is uninformed. It will be more difficult for the mission to dismiss the criticism of Africans or Indians, for these people criticize from experience.

The Small Neutral Nations

Shouldn't countries such as Austria and Yugoslavia, Finland and Sweden be exempt? They haven't taken part in the hunt for colonies; they're not engaged in oppressing distant peoples; nor are they a party to the military bloc formations of the West. Isn't it exactly this type of country —decent, neutral, and striving for peace—that the underdeveloped countries can count as their allies and U.N.-sympathizers in the cold war period? If any Western states may be exempt from the verdict, these people probably ought to be in the best position, having tried in Europe to create the same thing that many underdeveloped countries are trying to create in their part of the world—a place in which to live between the power blocs.

This sounds enticing—the question is only whether it is true.

Let's take Sweden as an example.

Sweden Is Included

The way our society is constructed, war in Asia is money in our pay envelopes.[1]

—*Jan Myrdal*

Since olden times in Sweden, we've been puffing on an extraordinarily good cigar.

At once we can pride ourselves on belonging to illustrious Western civilization—let be in a rustic periphery—and protest in innocence that we haven't a thing to do with the darker sides of Western civilization, with the Crusades,

[1] *Aftonbladet,* July 31, 1966.

with the Inquisition, with imperialism, with the colonial wars, with fascism, with neo-colonialism, with militant anti-Communism—with all those things that have given Western civilization so much of its wealth and power. We live up here, down there is the Continent, the cradle of culture is rocking in Greece (more and more vehemently), directly beneath us in the South we have the Queen's Australia, to the West lives Uncle Sam, in East Berlin the Iron Curtain is rattling, and that's the world. That's the whole world. The rest of the globe is just an annex and warehouse to which those other Westerners—not us—sometimes travel to fetch things, for example, slaves, raw materials, and religions.

But when the people in the Southern Hemisphere come into the picture the cigar goes out. When they point and say "you upper-class whites," "you egotists," and "you exploiters," then there we stand. Of course, we try to put our best face forward—the well-scrubbed (through 150 years of peace), colony-less, professionally candid, folklorishly quaint face we show to our tourists—and anxiously refer them to the other people, to the sullied, to the ones who did colonialism's dirty work and raked home the most brazen big profits. But it doesn't seem to work. For we're upper-class whites, too. We're egotists, too, for no matter how much we learn about the connection between starvation in the world and our rising standard, we just keep raising our standard anyhow. We, too, are exploiters, although usually secondhand: we're the ones who stick out the siphon when our Western trading partners take out their colonial hoses; we're the ones who hold out our hat when Americans, Germans, and Frenchmen make it rain gold and dollars over Western Europe; we're the ones who get a cheap ride on the sustained industrial boom that has transformed so many agrarian Western societies into flourishing industrial nations by concurrently transforming twice as many more rich, non-Western countries into monolithic cultures producing slaves and raw materials. Through the centuries-old, worldwide battle between oppressors and oppressed, we're the ones who have always taken the part of the oppressors, sat at their table, sold them weapons, let ourselves be Anglicized or Germanized to blend into the company better and benefit constantly from their profits. When any of the oppressors in recent years have disgraced themselves in the eyes of world opinion, we've naturally raised our U.N.-Christian brows, but all the while we've continued, unconcerned, to benefit from their profits. In Scandinavia the clean political hand never pretends to know what the dirty financial hand is doing.

I, too, am among those who are grateful that they happened to be born in this sheltered and *comparatively* decent corner of the world. As an Indoeuropean, of course, one might have been born in India. What I'm trying to say is something else again. By uniting herself economically *and* politically with the Western powers, militarily neutral Sweden has accepted and directly contributed to (1) economic imperialism and (2) political anti-Communism—both of which have most seriously affected and are affecting the Third World in particular. Our neutrality is only skin-deep. Our innocence is not even skin-deep.

1. Economic Imperialism

People complain about Sweden's "isolation," but from the viewpoint of the underdeveloped countries, on the contrary, Sweden is isolated too little. We're a member of six major Western trade alliances[2] and are working energetically to get into the Common Market. By means of these

---

[2] The European Free Trade Association, the Council of Europe, the Group of Ten, the Organization for Economic Cooperation and Development, the General Agreement on Tariff and Trade, and the Group of Twelve (of shipping countries).

alliances, the trade situation of the Third World is usually impaired—totally regardless of whether the alliance in question is "political" or not. Portugal's membership in the European Free Trade Association tells the whole story.

Tom Mboya says laconically of the Common Market: "It is Western Europe's effort at survival."[3] However, the acute risk doesn't seem to be that Western Europe will die but that, with the help of the American Business boom, Western Europe will so energetically undertake to survive that the Third World will die instead. The mutilation called Balkanization is already in progress.

Sweden has economic ties not only with the Soviet but primarily with a large number of European countries. To England we export a great deal of ore; from England we receive not only so-called colonial commodities but also part of the prosperity that the British founded by exploiting Asia and Africa. In terms of politics, we believe ourselves to be free to criticize factually the possible shortcomings of the British and French commonwealths, but in terms of economics, we're living high off the leadership of the Europeans.

In the area of arms export, Swedish war industries are not allowed to sell weapons to just anybody at all, but the export of guns to Australia was not broken off until that country had already been at war in Vietnam for a time, and not too long ago arms manufactured by the Swedish firm Husqvarna were encountered among the Cuban exiles in Florida. The policy is that no warring nations are to receive arms, and on one point, at least, the policy seems to be followed: no liberation movements are allowed to buy arms. On the other hand, even corrupt regimes seem to have an easy time obtaining arms, if only they lean toward the West, while even good regimes are excluded if they lean

[3] *Freedom and After*, p. 185.

toward the East; in general rich countries are favored. The Third World, in other words, doesn't seem to get any great benefit from Sweden's steel, and this has always been the case. In the seventeenth century Louis de Geer saw to it that Sweden annually supplied the Dutch East India Company with a large number of iron cannons for Asiatic use, and during both world wars of the twentieth century, German gunsmiths got the major share of their iron ore from Swedish mines. Or maybe the Swedes didn't know what the steel barons in the Ruhr intended to use Lapland ore for? Gunnar Hägglöf, the Swedish ambassador in Paris, has described the great degree to which our "iron diplomacy" contributed in keeping war away from Sweden. In this manner our peaceful, out-of-the-way corner has taken a rather active part in both colonial wars and world wars; sometimes for the Germans, sometimes for the Allies, but always on the side of the rich West.

How do people in our cozy welfare state respond when such facts are mentioned? In most cases with pride, it seems. Sweden is included in the big picture; Sweden is playing a part in world politics. Recently I heard a history professor talk in this kind of tone about Louis de Geer's export of cannons, and not infrequently it sounds the same in the newspapers, among foreign correspondents as well as among sportswriters.

Apart from arms, Swedish foreign trade is free, and as a rule the companies that have business with underdeveloped countries seem to be allowed to do what they find appropriate without any conspicuous Swedish authority poking its nose into everything. Instead the state has begun poking its nose into everything in a way that's more pleasant for business: by supporting export to underdeveloped countries, giving export credit guarantees, etc. During the last election campaign, Sweden's Prime Minister Tage Erlander was of the opinion that Swedish aid to underdeveloped countries was actually twice as large as is stated in the national budget, for he included credits to industry, among other things. Is he also going to label the activity of LAMCO (Liberia-American-Swedish Minerals Company)[4] as aid to underdeveloped countries perhaps? Low costs for labor and raw material plus miscellaneous tax exemptions have laid the groundwork for LAMCO's high profit, a contribution that's not going to benefit the people of Liberia, to say the least.

It does happen that Swedish newspapers complain about the Federation of Swedish Industries or our trade with South Africa; however, a top Swedish financier was appointed chairman of the board of the Adela Investment Company,[5] an international firm that—along with some fifty West European, American, Canadian, and Japanese commercial banks and large enterprises and stockholders —is going to provide Latin America with industrial capital, then the same newspapers kept quiet just as frenetically as the Russians usually do when it is a question of police intervention and political shake-ups.

Anyhow, it's certainly not uninteresting, is it, that Sweden's leading banks and big companies have got together with some of the financial giants of the Western world in this way to strike a blow for the economic development of Latin America? The kind of blow the Adela Investment Company intends to strike in Latin America is apparent from the statutes. The investments are to be made in such countries as can demonstrate "an advantageous invest-

[4] According to *Scandinavian Times Newsmagazine* (No. 6, 1965–1966, p. 42), LAMCO "took its beginnings when a U.S. mining man named Johnston Avery came to Stockholm, armed with a prospecting concession on 'a whole country of iron ore.' "—Trans.
[5] According to *Scandinavian Times Newsmagazine* (*ibid.*), "the idea was first conceived by Senator Jacob Javits, as chairman of the NATO parliamentary economic committee, in association with then Senator now Vice President Hubert Humphrey."—Trans.

ment climate, a good political stability, and sufficient guarantees for the development of a large private industry." The most stable military dictatorships seem to be in the best position, in other words. Recently a complementary effort was made on behalf of Brazil in the form of FINASA, "a development and investment bank" that is to "promote industry and trade within the private sector." Sweden's Enskilda Bank is included here, too, just as are Baring Brothers in London, Dresdner Bank in Frankfurt, and the Morgan banking group in New York. This was printed in Swedish newspapers, but no comments appeared. None at all.

Is it this type of initiative Erlander is thinking of, perhaps, when he talks about "making way for a transfer of capital to the underdeveloped countries"?

A few years ago the president of the Swedish Association of Engineers and Architects made this interesting comment:

> We know that for the past one hundred years we have been able to count on the material living standard doubling every twenty-five years. We are discussing whether we can increase the pace, perhaps, so that in the future we'll get it to double in twenty years. The technologist thinks he sees very striking results from his work: he sees before him great opportunities for development, and his work is directed toward rapid development. This effort is completely in accord with the wish often expressed by the government and parliament for the most rapid rate of progress possible. LO [the Swedish Federation of Trade Unions] declares that increased production is the basis for increased real wages. So far as general purpose concerns his work, the technologist finds himself in good company.[6]

If we remove the technologist from this good company and insert the owner of capital instead, I believe this is a

[6] Bertil Sjögren in *Dagens Nyheter*, June 28, 1966.

correct description of the values shared by Swedes in the 1960's.

What the free business community wants—increased production, increased export, increased earnings—is largely what the Social Democratic government, the bourgeois parties, and our associations of wage earners, including the trade unions, want too. If production does not rise, the national income cannot rise, and if national income does not rise, the government will not get any leeway for its reform work, and the trade unions, no leeway for salary increases. On this point political and economic interests seem to coincide happily.

The only question is, who's going to pay?

The administrators of Swedish industry—they insist themselves—will have to do what the Japanese and West Germans already have done in order to meet the iron-stiff competition: undertake efficiency engineering, restrictive trade practices, and joint planning on home ground and at the same time seek out new markets, cheaper manpower, and cheaper raw materials abroad. New markets still seem to be found at rather close range, in Eastern Europe among other places, but where are there cheap laborers and raw materials? Earlier there were plenty of cheap workers in Europe, in the England of child labor, for example, but increasing prosperity has made them rare, and today our personnel directors have to travel all the way down to southern Italy, to Greece, and to Yugoslavia in order to find real, European proletarians. But obviously the largest collection is in Africa and Asia. The cheapest raw materials are also in the Third World. If the industrial countries ask 28 cents or more for their sugar while Cuba and Brazil settle for 6 cents, we'll clearly support the underdeveloped countries by buying from them. Then if our industries build subsidiary companies, they get the benefit of the low price level on both manpower and raw materials, obviously on the precondition that the countries in question can give guarantees against acts of nationalization and favor private investments with tax exemptions and the like. Moreover, within the framework of European trade allowances, it's just that much easier to take advantage indirectly of the low prices and wages of the underdeveloped countries; the Western countries take advantage of their colonial contacts.

It seems, in other words, to no immaterial extent, to be the Third World that has to pay.

It may appear a bit hard to understand what all this has to do with social democracy, trade union activity, and aid to underdeveloped countries, but the key concept is increasing prosperity, and commerce and industry hold the key to increasing prosperity. According to Professor Erik Lundberg:

> Sweden can supply greater economic aid to underdeveloped countries . . . if the productivity within private commerce and industry is accelerated and if the ability of export to compete is strengthened sufficiently to give them a surplus in the balance of payment that corresponds to our obligations to underdeveloped countries.[7]

Exactly. We have to earn money off the underdeveloped countries in order to be able to finance our aid to underdeveloped countries.

Sweden, in other words, seems to have wound up in the rich man's squirrel cage. For good?

2. Political Anti-Communism

Fortunately, the kind of one-eyed anti-Communism that draws down such a tight iron curtain between the concepts of democracy and dictatorship that all capitalist

[7] "Lösningar i långsam takt" ("Solutions at a Slow Pace"), *Dagens Nyheter*, July 7, 1966.

states become acceptable and all socialist states unacceptable seems no longer to be representative of Swedish opinion. So I'm not going to have our schoolbooks in social science or American TV programs such as "The Roots of Madness" (on China) set in pillories, but will take up instead a more nuanced book, *U-länder i omvälvning* (*Underdeveloped Countries in Transformation*),[8] written for adults by the economist Birger Möller.

In the last chapter Möller gets into the one-party systems that have become common in Africa's new states and that clash with our parliamentary concepts. Can such regimes be accepted at all by a judge who sets out from "generally democratic, humanitarian, and progressive" basic appraisals and on whose scale of values "democracy now or at least eventually, humanity, and the abolition of poverty" rank first? Yes, it's possible, Möller thinks, but first the following seven demands must be met:

1. Widespread oppression must not occur.
2. Allowance shall be made for divergent opinions within the party.
3. The decision-making process within the party must be democratic.
4. Change of leadership should be able to take place by means of other methods than violence.
5. The party must work successfully for a rapid economic and social development of the country.
6. A one-party system must be necessary for the sake of national unity.
7. The regime must accept the idea of a multi-party system in the future.

The demands are many, and, not unexpectedly, the casualties are high. The author considers approving Tanzania, but even here there is room for doubt. Ghana and Cuba may seem to be in fine shape at least to point 5, on the country's rapid development, but that annoying adverb "success-

8 Stockholm: Albert Bonniers Förlag AB/Aldus, 1965, pp. 231–240.

fully" eliminates them too; Nkrumah and Castro ought to have "succeeded" better. China and North Korea should easily meet the fifth demand, but on the other hand, they're already out of the running since they were knocked off on the first points. For the rest, Möller suggests that an eighth demand ought to be met too: the one-party states should be located in Africa (or at least not be "Communistic").

It is an ingrained habit in our latitudes in making international comparisons to disregard carefully what is bad in our own government and to use what is good as a weapon against other governments. So I don't think very many people spontaneously perceive Möller's well-meaning list as a manifestation of Western arrogance. But if we imagine that the chief of a one-party state, for example Nyerere in Tanzania, took it upon himself to figure out in a similar fashion what must be demanded, in his opinion, of a multiparty system in order for it to be approved, then most people, at least, would call *that* list arrogant. For example, if it looked like this:

1. Financial dynasties and exploitation of other countries may not occur.
2. Economic equality and equality before the law should prevail.
3. Every party must consider what is best for all the people and not be dominated by shortsighted or selfish group motives of power politics.
4. The army, the church, and the secret police may not possess political power.
5. The ruling party must rapidly work successfully to abolish unemployment, affluent production, oppression of minorities, land speculation, bossism, etc., and rapidly accomplish industrial democracy.
6. The development of welfare must be adjusted to the people's real need and not be carried so far that other people suffer.
7. The government must accept the idea of disarmament and socialization in the future.

Here the demands are a bit more extensive, but even so, perhaps some consideration may be taken for the fact that this list primarily involves rather well-to-do countries? In any case, the casualties are high. The majority of Western countries would collapse a good deal more suddenly than Sweden, especially the United States, Italy, West Germany, and Belgium; on the other hand, it's not easy to point out any single demand that Sweden *undoubtedly* can be said to meet. Many underdeveloped countries to which Swedes generally seem favorably predisposed because they have parliaments (and, thereafter, they might be corrupt, like India, or led by the nose, like Malaysia) manage hardly any better.

But isn't this opposite list unfair, one-sided, excessively severe, and full of holes? Yes. But it's also modeled to resemble Möller's list.

Let me draw attention to some priorities. At the top of Möller's "scale of values" stand democracy and humanity —the abolition of poverty comes in third place; first among the "basic appraisals" stand the democratic and the humanitarian—the progressive ones come in third place; first among the seven demands comes freedom from oppression, freedom of opinion, and democracy—economic development comes in fifth place. It is this fixation with form instead of with content that I believe is representative of today's less militant form of anti-Communism.

We inquire so eagerly after parliamentary forms that the primary question—whether the country is governed for the benefit of the people or for the benefit of a minority— becomes a secondary question. We inquire so eagerly after humane methods that the primary question—what the methods are used for—becomes a secondary question.

And the underdeveloped countries suffer worst from this fixation.

It's bad enough that we in Scandinavia and the West

have devoted a large part of the postwar period to one-eyed moralizing over the lack of freedom in Eastern Europe, and that today we see everything that is positive in these countries as a sign of "liberalization" and "Western influence" (while the rest is "lingering" Communism or the like). But reasoning in this formalistic fashion when it's a matter of the underdeveloped countries is worse: this is defending the status quo by sticking our heads into the sand. Land reform is fine, we say—only no totalitarian central direction. Strong management is fine, we say—only not socialistic or communistic oppression. Control of the country's resources is fine, we say—only don't throttle private initiative completely. The reality we shy away from in this manner is the fact that the majority of underdeveloped countries find themselves in such a desperate situation that only really profound measures (not by us but by them) can get them on their feet, and really profound measures cannot be carried out without individuals, minorities, and democratic forms having to suffer. Nor do we seem to want to face the fact that capitalism and parliamentarism have been fiascos in most underdeveloped countries that tried to adapt these systems, while different kinds of socialism and one-party rule have often been successful.

In Sweden business and government go hand in hand to such countries as Ethiopia and Pakistan, where anti-Communism is sufficiently strong, the risk of revolution is small, Western industries are provided good terms without being threatened by acts of nationalization, and underdevelopment on the whole is guaranteed a long life. Close ties with reactionary Liberia rather than any ties at all with progressive Guinea. Diplomatically, Sweden recognizes West Germany and South Vietnam but not East Germany and North Vietnam. Seventy-five per cent of our trade takes place with Western Europe, 10 per cent with underdeveloped countries, and 5 per cent with Eastern Europe. The countries outside Europe to which we export most are, in order, the United States, Australia, South Africa, Canada, and Japan. The underdeveloped countries to which we export most are India, Argentina, Brazil, and Mexico. From 1959 to 1964 our trade with underdeveloped countries has decreased steadily while Eastern trade has been at a standstill. With West Germany alone Sweden has more exchange of trade than with the underdeveloped countries and the Eastern countries put together. The step to the Common Market appears not to be far. Perhaps not to NATO either?

Worried Americans usually say that Sweden's socialistic tendencies jeopardize the country's neutrality, but they don't need to worry. It's Sweden's capitalistic tendencies that jeopardize her neutrality.

Gifts—and Gifts in Return

In the course of thousands of years Europe and America have collected a good deal from the other parts of the world. The birch tree, the pine, the bear, the elk, the alphabet and writing, the habit of conducting world trade, the coin, the compass, the art of printing books, despotism, surgery, gunpowder and the cannon, the windmill and the iron industry, the use of precious metals, glass and porcelain, indigo and quinine, mathematics and philosophy, religious dualism, slavery, the prophets, spices and narcotics, coffee and tea, potatoes and rice, cotton and rubber, gold and silversmith crafts, stone buildings and city planning, tulips and tobacco, feudalism, torture, and the concept of tolerance can be mentioned as examples. You could also mention agriculture, Christianity, and a large share of our population.

For many of these gifts and much of this learning Westerners have expressed their thanks at regular intervals.

For Christianity, by making war for more than 350 years upon the Oriental people who were foolish enough to accept a different religion.

For the coin and the habit of conducting world trade, by exploiting the other parts of the world by means of money and trade monopoly.

For the use of precious metals, by plundering South America, Africa, and Asia of precious metals.

For the concept of tolerance, by conducting crusades in the Far East, slave hunts in Africa, cultural demolition in India and China, inquisition in Latin America, Indian massacres in Central America, Negro slavery in the United States, Christian missionary activity among Muslims, Hindus, and Buddhists plus persecution of Jews within the borders of Europe.

For the barbarian custom of drinking coffee and tea, by spreading through Asia and other continents the cultivated habit of drinking whisky and Coca-Cola.

For invaluable food supplies, by creating or fomenting in the Southern Hemisphere an ever increasing demand for food supplies.

For sculpture, goldsmith craft, ceramics, and diamond cutting, by plundering the richest countries of their treasures in these areas.

For slavery, by appointing Africa as Europe's slave supply and from this source filling the needs of the American and Asiatic colonies for cheap manpower.

For a system of reckoning time, by supplying the non-

Christian peoples with a chronology that would annually remind them of their heathen status.

For despotism and tyrants, by supporting or introducing them in the poor countries that had none.

For the use of opium, by cultivating it in India, prohibiting it in Europe and America, and all the while introducing it by force into China.

For gunpowder.

As everyone knows, culture and civilization flourished in Egypt, Mesopotamia, India, and China while the Europeans were still hewing stone. The learning and useful information that have benefited the West by this means through the course of thousands of years have also been given a more generic expression of gratitude, namely, by setting upon all culture and civilization that have flourished and are flourishing outside the West the same label: primitive.

Now to the gifts in return.

Freedom and democracy have been given to the Philippines, Indochina, Malaysia, Nigeria, and Central America, among other places.

People's democracy, to Armenia, Georgia, Turkmenistan, and Kirghizia, among others.

Parliamentarism, to Indonesia, India, South Africa, and the Dominican Republic, among other countries.

Free enterprise, to the Middle East, the Congo, and Brazil, among other places.

Modern school instruction, to the Gold Coast, Morocco, and Indonesia, among other countries.

Free association with the Western bloc, to those parts of the world that haven't been offered free association with the Eastern bloc.

Science and technology, to the Arab world, Japan, Vietnam, and Polynesia, among other places.

Law and order, to Kenya, Rhodesia, Cuba, and Guatemala, among other countries.

Equality, to Panama, Honduras, Angola, Turkey, and Iran, among other countries.

Foreign aid, to Saudi-Arabia, Turkey, Formosa, South Vietnam, Peru, and Liberia.

Nuclear weapons.

Victim or Executioner

In his foreword to Henri Alleg's book *The Question,* Sartre writes:

> If nothing can protect a nation against itself, neither its traditions nor its loyalties nor its own laws, and if fifteen years are enough to transform victims into executioners, then its behavior is no more than a matter of opportunity and occasion. Anybody, at any time, may equally find himself victim or executioner.[1]

[1] Trans. by John Calder (New York: George Braziller, Inc., 1958), pp. 14–15.

Sartre is thinking of the French in Algeria. He could have been thinking of the Dutch in Indonesia, of the British in Burma, of the Portuguese in West Africa, of the Russians in Eastern Europe, of the Japanese in China, and of the Chinese in Tibet. He could also, further back in history, have been thinking of the Persians in the Mediterranean area, of the Greeks in the Orient, of the Mongols in Asia, of the Spaniards in South America, of the Europeans in China, and of the Germans in Europe.

Nowhere·in the world or in time do the big powers seem to have spared their victims. They have only, according to "opportunity and occasion" and national traditions, stopped at different degrees of oppression, from remote thought control and mild censorship to secret torture and open massacre.

Perhaps this should be kept in mind even in an unfair appraisal. If the Arabs hadn't lost, if the Turks hadn't lost, if the black people hadn't lost—what is there then to say that they would have treated the Europeans and Americans better than the Europeans and Americans now treat them? It's "no more than a matter of opportunity and occasion. Anybody, at any time, may equally find himself victim or executioner."

There is a current example of this that, I believe, can be worth dwelling on.

The Example of Vandestan

The rather unknown protectorate of Vandestan off the east coast of Africa has a population profile that digresses a good deal from the usual in Africa. Ninety-three per cent of the inhabitants are *Europeans,* 5 per cent are Asians (mostly from the nearby Arabian peninsula), and only 2 per cent are Africans. Nonetheless, Vandestan is an African protectorate; the emperor of Ethiopia has sovereignty over the area.

European farmers and sailors colonized Vandestan as early as the beginning of the sixteenth century, found the climate suitable for settling, and divided the most fertile land among themselves. In the mountains certain mining (copper, later cobalt) was begun. In the seventeenth century Asian merchants invaded the trading centers along the coast, and a lively interchange came about between Europeans and Asians. Despite some skirmishes and periodic want in connection with epidemics, on the whole peace and prosperity prevailed up to the end of the nineteenth century, when itinerant scholars from Ethiopia and Kenya discovered Vandestan. Many of these were veterans of the successful war against the Italians, others were exiled Kikuyus who had served in Ethiopia's army, and some were missionaries of Islam.

"We have come to the land of the Crescent Moon, where no black man has ever set foot," wrote Ras Mengala, the Kikuyu leader of the expedition, in his diary.

The travelers found that the European natives were at a relatively high level of culture; they were literate and Christian, had built schools and mine elevators, conducted worship service on Sundays, lived in small families in picturesque wooden houses, and selected their chiefs by means of a complicated voting process ("government"). They were light in skin but nevertheless not Italians; they came from farther north and west. Some had red hair. In many quarters the soil was well cultivated, and no oppression of the Asian group seemed to occur; on the contrary, mixed marriages were seen. In addition there were hospital cottages and level fences around each house. All these inhabitants were called Vands.

However, Dr. Mengala pointed out, the picture was not entirely bright.

They keep slaves, called day wagers. The elders are not venerated, but isolated from the tribe at a certain age. When the offspring are of sufficient maturity to be circumsized, they are instead given wine, which is said to come from the bloody body of Jesus. In the schools much is studied, but only to a low age ("confirmation") and nothing at all about Africa, Islam, or character training. Dance and song rare, the worship of ancestors unknown. Although Christian, the churches are never round, neither do they have cloisters. We were consternated when we saw how little takes place on a collective basis among these pale, seldom smiling strangers. People replied with a European proverb, "Self is the best servant," yet they kept servants too. Personal zeal to take action is esteemed more highly than consultation, knowledge of sundry subjects more highly than experience, indeed, even gold more highly than love, all of which is imprudent, primitive. Few own much land, many own little or no land.

Although difficulties awaited those who wanted to missionary, sow seed, or live in peace in these regions, it was clear from that moment that it would be irresponsible of the Africans to leave Vandestan to its fate. Ethiopia also found the ore attractive.

By the time of the colonizers' arrival, two years of crop failure had forced a large number of landowners to leave their land temporarily, and the Africans were immediately able to annex this acreage, which was overrun with weeds. Certain grazing land they took for bush country and plowed it too. Effaced or unsuitably drawn boundaries were replaced by new ones. The rumor of rich Vandestan spread quickly on the mainland, and soon the free land was gone, so that the last to arrive were forced to buy land from the Vands. To their good fortune, it proved a good deal easier to take possession of large land areas than small ones, owing to the fact that deeds of transfer were signed by powerless tenant families who professed to be owners (they often ran off with the purchase price). The native land proprietors, generally residing far from their property, demanded their land back and organized the "Home Guard" (Vandestan lacked a regular army) against the black "trespassers" who insisted that the deeds of purchase were valid. When disturbances broke out at the same time at the mission stations—where the Muslims initiated their activity by having European girls circumcized—and in the harbors—where African "merchants" (sometimes criminal elements) introduced double tariffs on all commercial products, one for Europeans and one for Asians—troops had to be called in from Ethiopia to ensure peace in the country.

The Home Guard presented unexpectedly gallant resistance to what was at that time Africa's strongest army. It was not until after five years of fighting, which harvested the lives of tens of thousands of victims (including more than three hundred Kikuyus and two Islam missionaries), that peace negotiations could be taken up in Mnodik in the year 1904. Vandestan was given semi-colonial status within the empire of Ethiopia; all opposition flags were exchanged and the European Home Guard was integrated into an all-Vandic army. The Africans, thereafter called Vandestans, were assigned all the land they had earlier annexed or "purchased" and control over the mining operations plus a ninety-nine-year lease on all harbors and transport roads. The victors apportioned the exchange so that the Ethiopians took over the mines and transport roads plus the lands of the southern provinces. In return well-to-do Vands were given the opportunity to repurchase land from the Africans by clans, while families without means were offered the chance to remain as contract workers on the land they had earlier owned or to move to the mining district. Moreover, the natives were permitted to retain their popularly elected government, provided that six of the ten seats were yielded to the Vandestans and three of those remaining to the Asians. When the Europeans protested at being reduced in this manner to a powerless minority in their "own" government, two new members were appointed whose exclusive job was to look after the natives' interests. When this concession as well called forth bitter protests (the new members were Vandestans too) and the general governor did not manage to get help sent in from the mother country—Ethiopia wanted to have grain and ore first—the aggressive Europeans were returned their original government, this time supplemented by African and Asian observers. In order to ensure the Vandestanic leadership and at the same time protect the rights of the minorities, the Africans set up a council of elders (CAD), consisting of seven Vandestans and two Asians, upon which the government (VAF) could unload some of their burdensome duties, the executive power among others. The VAF retained the legislative power (except in matters of security), but the CAD reserved for itself the right to ratify proposed legislation. The demands now posed by the Europeans for representation as well in the elders' council, in which the Asians had two members, could not be approved, partly since they already dominated the VAF, and partly since they still lacked elders with administrative experience, but in return they were permitted to retain their beloved "king." The Vandestans contented themselves with providing the latter a resident councilor, upon whom the king was allowed to discharge a sufficient number of powers to be able to devote himself primarily to public speaking (up to 1942) and inaugurating the railway lines. A similar plan to preserve tradition was introduced in all the larger districts where the Vands had their own governors ("prosecutors"); when these died or were promoted to the schools of the elders, their posts were inherited by Vandestanic provincial residents. In the villages the African chief who had the most land was appointed sheriff.

When a makeshift kind of order had been established in this manner and the natives slowly began to get used to their "black masters," the CAD could carry out the development program it had decided upon for the colony as early as the year 1917, an ambitious plan that contributed more than anything else to Vandestan's reputation as a model African colony (compared with Sudan). Over a ten-year period the plan was designed to remedy current unsatisfactory conditions, and over a fifty-year period, to prepare for the self-government of the white people's majority. The program contained five main points:

1. Redistribution of the land previously divided unequally for gradual conversion from individual cultivation to community use.
2. Democratization of the society by extension and amalgamation of the small European families to large families of the African type.
3. The establishment of freedom of religion, with Islam as the main religion.
4. Training of Vandic elders, chiefs, functionaries, military men, mining foremen, and muezzin for successive replacement of the African cadre.
5. Establishment of Amharic as the official language.

The land reform, which required the relocation of close to a hundred thousand natives, signified an effective breakup of the large European landowners' power, which was taken over instead by the Vandestans, especially by chiefs who had relatives inside the CAD. The rich Europeans whose lands had not been disposed of earlier had to pay for the cost of carrying out the reform by now having their property confiscated. They were also required to cede the acreage that the Africans didn't think they needed themselves to less fortunate fellow countrymen and Asians, whereby the largest and most fertile areas went to former tenant families, those who had previously sold their employer's land to African pioneers. At the same time many farms were merged to facilitate the transition to communal agriculture, to which the Europeans were unaccustomed. For a long time they interpreted communal ownership as "forced collectivization" and tried in various ways to sabotage the consolidation, which is why the CAD was obliged during a transition period to extend capital punishment to apply also to "crimes against the land laws." In order to ensure the just character of the reform, the newly formed Vandic clan farms were forbidden to enlarge their acreage by purchase or annexation, while concurrently an annual rental fee was demanded from each farm; other rules held for the Africans. The risk that the natives would lose their will to work was prevented by setting the fee high; those landowners who achieved insufficient harvests two years in succession were threatened additionally by expropriation.

Vandestanic functionaries first served as collection men, but when their presence stirred up bad blood among the Europeans, they were replaced by Asians and, to a greater extent, by Europeans who had converted to Islam (they received high fees).

More difficult to execute was the extension of the small families to clans, a Kikuyu reform. The Europeans were fantastically monogamous and regarded the formation of large families as a "heathen" departure from the Bible's "holy family" (three people). Moreover, unlike the Asians, they lacked a sense of being related outside the narrow family circle, moved away from their parents early, never took advice from the eldest of the relatives, and could live for years without even meeting their brothers and sisters. No marriage guarantee in the form of a dowry occurred, but young couples were expected to stand on their own legs from the start. According to an old custom, the newly formed small families then competed in collecting the most possessions, and did so until their death.

To inject respect for communal ownership into such a self-willed tribe was hard enough; to inject a sense of belonging to such "distant" relatives as paternal grandparents and cousins was doomed to fail. The CAD chose a more practical line of action. The natives were allowed to retain their monogamy, but a law was established prohibiting cohabitation for households smaller than twenty persons. This meant, according to European standards, that at least three families would be accommodated under the same roof, and since only a few European clans seemed to include this many members at a reasonable distance from each other, many unacquainted people had to move in together. The CAD was careful not to drive families of different skin color together, but they did not realize that the whites had originally come from different European stocks and in several cases shared neither language, religion, nor customs. The VAF, which had registered a case in which one English, one Spanish, and one Norwegian family were forced to share a household, were of the opinion that this mixture of people was both "unpsychological" and needlessly expensive, especially since the majority of wooden European houses required costly annexes in order to hold twenty people (the CAD made clay and straw available to them). When the mother country grew alarmed at the same time by the decreasing export of grain during the relocation period, members of the CAD began to speak out for a revision of the reform, but the majority held firm that being divided up into small families constituted a much too serious threat to the unity of Vandestan for it to be tolerated. The VAF managed to get a measure passed providing that the families of mineworkers be left in peace, and that within the farm populace the number of languages and religions not be allowed to rise above two per household. However, with these restrictions the program was carried out—when necessary with the help of the army— which took twelve years (1922–1934).

Freedom of religion was a more popular reform, but because of the migration, this too was delayed. In many villages the natives had built at least one place of worship, but since they were forced to move in many cases, it happened that newly built villages with predominantly Catholic or Reformed population could offer the faithful only a Pentecostal revival tent or a Hindu temple. Therefore, several religious structures had to be rebuilt and in doubtful cases divided up into two religions. Since many newly formed clans lacked housing and the rapidly growing main religion lacked mosques, more than half of the natives' places of worship were rebuilt, partly as housing, partly as mosques. (Many of the old schools of the Europeans met with the same fate.)

None of these measures agreed with the Vands' ideas of religious freedom, and the "church housing" in particular gave rise to disturbances, including repeated murders of missionaries. We do not know whether the so-called Vachili Massacre of 1937, when the entire population of a village was shot after one such murder, managed to calm the population, but the CAD won at least temporary respect for its interpretation of the concept of religious freedom: primarily the freedom to profess one's faith in Islam. Instruction in Christianity was replaced by instruction in Islam; in those villages where the number of inhabitants justified only one place of worship, this was to be a mosque; for admission to higher offices a profession of faith in Islam was required. In order to facilitate the dissemination of the main religion, prohibition and a month of fasting were introduced for all citizens of the country (non-Muslim Vandestans excepted); at the same time the day of rest was moved from Sunday to Saturday, Ethiopia's sabbath.

In the religious area, too, the endeavor of the colonial power to preserve the unity of the realm sometimes came into conflict with the ambition of looking after the needs of the minorities, but, on the whole, the CAD abstained from direct intervention in the religious practices of the European sects. Although generally the Vandestans had emigrated from the Ethiopian provinces faithful to Islam, the fact that Ethiopia has been a Christian empire since olden times obviously played its part. They were content to abolish superstitious practices, the drinking of wine in the "Holy Communion," the training of Salvation Army soldiers, bulky reproductions of the tortured body of Jesus on the Ark of the Covenant, the partaking of "the Christmas ham," etc. Circumcision, sanctioned even in the Christian orthodox church in the mother country, became compulsory for men as a complement to the de-alcoholized communion rite (bread and donkey milk). At the same time, with consideration for the main religion and the country's security, Christian missionary work and pilgrimages to countries other than Saudi-Arabia (the natives lacked the right to travel) were forbidden. When new churches were to be built, they had to be round.

All this sowed dissension between Europeans and Asians but also between Indians and Arabs. The Hindus were affected very severely by the religious "Africanization," while the Arabs—Muslims from ancient times— were naturally favored.

At least formally, the establishment of Amharic as the official language was an easy matter. Beginning with Ramadan of 1926, all school books, announcements, and printed newspapers had to be drafted in Amharic; use of the European dialects was permitted only in private conversations. Letters that were not written in Amharic were returned or discarded. But it developed that not only the Vands but also a great many Vandestans had difficulty understanding announcements and signs, so a certain multilingual status has been tolerated. For admission to higher offices, however, language learning was required of the natives; a sharp eye was also kept on the postal laws, which is why Europe was informed so late regarding their Vandic descendants.

The training of Europeans to become elders, policemen, muezzin, etc., proceeded rather painlessly as long as the instruction was concentrated on pure skills. But as soon as language and confession of faith entered into the instruction, problems arose. Few Vands were attracted by Islam, and they were so firmly rooted in their European language habits that they seemed beyond help. Prospective clergymen were spared from converting, but in return they were required to learn Amharic as well as Geez, the sacramental language of Ethiopia, which was taught only at the clergy's seminary at Harar, to which European theologians could not afford to travel. The four-year teachers' seminary in Addis Ababa was also too expensive for most whites; only the African cadre of teachers was able to increase. Because of the high standards of the European cottage hospitals, the natives were permitted to handle the training of doctors and nurses themselves, but since the authorities lacked the means to build new hospitals for the growing population, the doctors could never set aside time for instruction. Until 1953, Vandestan lacked its own institutions of higher education. Judges as well as technicians had to be educated in Ethiopia, where only Vandestans could afford to study. At the same time the number of European prosecuting attorneys was decimated because the overaged and the deceased were succeeded by Africans, and the demands upon language and religious knowledge in the schools of the elders were fixed so high that the majority became "repeaters" and died before they had time to pass the examination or else they had grown so weak that they could no longer get elected into the CAD. Ethiopian scientists have linked the early senility among Europeans with their particular structure.

In 1925 approximately 3,000 Vands held higher offices;

by 1955, owing to these circumstances, the number had decreased to 382 (of which 140 were Asians). Before the general elections in 1956 the VAF maintained that in this fashion the Africans were knowingly preventing the rise of a Vand intelligentsia and consequently the approaching self-government of the whites. Many Vandestans, however, believed that the whites were closing their eyes to the real reasons for their tragic stagnation by emphasizing only surface reasons for their repeated misfortunes. The real reasons were they could not adjust to the African way of life; they were not ready to take responsibility; they often shied away from work, and they evidently could not get along without the help of the Africans. For its part, the CAD admitted that the demands upon the white leadership had been raised with the years, but alleged a different explanation from that which the VAF gave. From the outset the Africans had eagerly supported the education of the natives, but when it became clear that the Europeans lacked maturity and suitability for higher offices (for instance, they had allowed the collection service to degenerate to an outright blackmail business directed against their own people!), the same course could not be pursued without threatening the collapse of the entire society. The Vandestans were quite simply forced to take over, otherwise order would have been turned into chaos. The Vands would get another chance soon enough anyhow, but to coerce their self-government would be "knocking them down more than helping them up."

The Vandestan that went to the polls in 1956 was in many respects a society different from the one the African expedition discovered after the war of independence against Italy. During the European period certain small industries had been started, but since Ethiopian companies wanted the ore for their own account and practically all the cotton and sisal had to be exported in order to finance the import of Ethiopian industrial products, all manufacture soon died out because of the raw material shortage. Since the prices of raw materials were kept low and imported industrial goods rose continually in price, Vandestan—despite its cheap manpower—each year became more and more dependent on Ethiopian loans and assistance; in 1956 the national debt amounted to more than a billion Ethiopian dollars. Inflation, corruption inside the administration, plus the flight of capital limited the prospect for economic development further. But the most difficult problems were encountered in the countryside.

It had never been the Africans' intention to create a new landowner class of rich chiefs. On the contrary, they had intended a fair distribution of land, but when the CAD made exceptions for Vandestans, they had in fact cleared the way for a feudal oppression that the chiefs were not long in exploiting. When the joint tenant farmers had trouble paying the rental fee, the chiefs offered them long-term loans at exorbitant interest rates; when the debt shot up higher and higher, they were forced to make repayment by ceding land. As a rule, two years of crop failures were sufficient for them to dispose of all the land. In this way the years of crop failure in the 1930's brought about in one blow a more sweeping transformation of the conditions of ownership in the countryside than two decades of laborious reform work. Seventy per cent of the land of the Vandic clans was transferred to African property. A good many clan members, for that matter, did not find out about what had happened until they returned a couple of years later from the new war of independence against Italy. At that point they had to choose between slave contracts with a chief or unemployment; some were wearing medals, several were invalids. In the majority of villages the chief-sheriff now reigned supreme, and today there are entire provinces (some fifty villages) ruled by a single landowner. The Kikuyus' ambitious clan system had thus collapsed, and the major share of the rural native population were now actually serfs, as were the mining populace as well.

An Egyptian journalist who visited Vandestan in 1962 was particularly surprised by two peculiarities, "the crossbred architecture" and the European population:

> What is a mosque from one side is often a missionary building from the other; in many dwellings you walk into a wooden house and come out of a mud hut. The Europeans live here. If you've seen their well-fed, industrious kinsmen in Kenya you'd think these Europeans belong to a different race. Many are bloated with malnutrition or wasted by diseases. They often work fifteen hours a day, but to all appearance, mechanically and without pleasure; as soon as the black overseer looks away they loaf about. Their clothes are often ragged and their homes, dirty. Despite the fact that they have nothing, they often steal from one another. The eyes of many of the children are permanently damaged by trachoma. There are aggressive elements in the countryside too, but when the chief appears most of them start smiling and holding out flowers, for the chief is the only one who's allowed to produce communion wine and other strong beverages. The women, too, give off a sweetish odor. If it weren't for the skin color, you would be sure you had met Negroes.

That same year, 1962, the International Red Cross started a collection primarily to fight TB in Vandestan; the government of Ethiopia gave a generous nest egg of $20,000.

It was also in 1962 that the terrorist activity of the so-called Vandals seriously drew the eyes of the Continent to the little colony off Africa's east coast. The terrorism had begun in connection with the election, when the Vandic nationalist parties managed to capture 75 per cent of the reported votes and yet did not get the majority in parliament; the electoral system was constructed in this fashion. Through several months the wave of terror spread over the country. African chiefs and prosecuting attorneys were found mutilated in front of their palaces; more than one missionary of Islam was placed upon the Ark of the Covenant with a knife in his back; entire families were murdered at night in their beds. In each case the culprits disappeared without a trace. People argue about the way in which the Vandal movement arose, but ever since the 1920's, those Vands who could not confess their faith, study their language, administer communion, or develop their political views had assembled in secret societies; here was a natural breeding ground for extremism. But outside influences, perhaps from Kenya, perhaps from China, may also have entered in. It is clear that the terrorism gained ground among the Europeans in the mining district, where traditionally the Vandic Salvation Army has had a strong position, and then spread to the countryside; even many aggressive Hindus were won to the movement; in 1963 the cities were drawn into the wave of terror.

What was tragic about the Vandal movement was that to a great extent the natives suffered as well. Fratricide turned Europeans against Arabs and Hindus against Europeans, thus spoiling the long-standing minority policy of the CAD definitively. It could also be said that an animosity suppressed for years was now flaring up. European doctors who cured only rich Vandestans, Arabian collection men who exploited the small farmers, Christian ministers who did errands for the authorities, European officers, mine overseers, muezzin—on a large scale all these groups fell victim to the knives of the Vandals. But even impoverished Vands, who could not possibly be accused of "collaboration," were more and more often found incomprehensibly, meaninglessly murdered. In 1963 the government declared a state of emergency throughout Vandestan, whereby the army was given the authority to arrest, imprison, or execute suspected Vandal sympathizers without a trial. When a village sheriff was found murdered the whole village was usually razed to the ground; when a Vandal was taken prisoner, his clan was imprisoned too.

In this fashion, many, many more Vands were afflicted by the army than by the Vandal movement. Despite this, as late as the spring of 1964, the wave of terror had hardly been weakened, and many Vandestans fled to the mainland.

Ethiopia's delegate to the U.N. General Assembly stressed that, like the Mau Mau in Kenya, the Vandal movement was probably a Communist-influenced extremist movement completely lacking the support of the popular majority, and within a short time, Ethiopia was counting on peace being restored to such a degree that the Vands could get their promised self-government; however, this was on the condition that the U.N. would not interfere in Ethiopia's domestic affairs by sending troops to the country. After vehement discussion the General Assembly referred the questions to the U.N. Security Council, where Ethiopia managed relatively soon to convince two of her foremost trading partners—the United States and Great Britain—that for the present, the U.N. should not intervene. Meanwhile, in the Parliament of Vandestan, the representatives of the African Democratic Party were maintaining that the Vandals' ravages comprised "the definitive proof" of the necessity for an assured control over the country. Even the Vandic Nationalist Party repudiated the Vandals but directed their criticism primarily against the army, which was thought to have used the Vandal terrorism as an excuse for a "regular mass murder" of Vands.

Today the situation in Vandestan is rather confused. The ravages of the Vandal movement have ceased, but as several of the leaders are still at large, it is probable that the movement has not given up but been transformed into a Vandic guerrilla army. Gatherings of troops have been observed in the mountains, to which a thousand or so deserters from the regular army have probably fled, and arms have been smuggled in from the north (from the Arabian peninsula, perhaps also from Europe). In political terms, a striking discord prevails. Frightened by the wave of terror, the white nationalist party has begun to work for a peaceful compromise solution, and the leftist groups within the party have broken away and now support the guerrillas in the mountains more or less openly. In the parliament, where the left is not represented, the conservative party goes by the slogan "Vandestan for the Vandestans," while the democratic party of the government (formerly the CAD) is attempting to win the nationalists to an "emergency relief program" across party lines, intended as a quick cure for the unsatisfactory conditions the years of terror created (ravaged villages, wrecked machines, epidemics, demolished schools and mosques). In this manner the nationalists have ended up between two fires, criticized vehemently from both right and left, but they hope to regain the support of the majority through their program for "civilized living conditions for the Vandic majority." All the while the rumor is being spread in the mountains and the mining district that the nationalists want to buy independence for the price of the mines on which Ethiopian companies have concessions, and the guerrillas have started making advances in the north.

The question is, since the opposition has been divided, whether independence does not appear more remote one year before the end of the grace period assigned in 1917 (1967) than it did after the election in 1956. Unemployment now takes in 15 per cent of the population; by the very fact of the school reform, illiteracy has increased drastically; there are nine prisons for every cottage hospital; a strong police force has been sent in from Ethiopia, and the mood in the country is tense. Finnebiorn Olsen, one of the most respected European nationalist spokesmen in Parliament, is seeking to soothe tempers on a provisory basis by appealing to the blacks:

> We Vands have the greatest respect for the old Ethiopian culture, and we know what you've managed to accomplish by virtue of it, both in the mother country and here in

Vandestan. But you must understand that we can't satisfy ourselves only with this, when at the same time you remind us daily that what we do is worse, that our culture is inferior to yours, that our language ought not be taught in the schools, that our form of Christianity must be adjusted to the Orthodox Church of Ethiopia in order to be practiced freely. We need to be told some time that what we do and what we represent is good enough the way it is, by virtue of our human dignity and our own cultural tradition!

I know there are Vandestans who think we Europeans are lazy or aggressive by nature, but when you once came to this land we all love, we were neither lazy nor aggressive; we tilled our soil, and we kept peace with our Asian brothers. I know too that you see us as colored, because our white skin hits you in the eyes. Your dark skin hits us in the eyes too! But does it say anywhere in the Koran that northern races should be treated worse than southern ones? Does it not say instead that all people should live as brothers to one another?

We Vands hold great admiration for your beautiful shamma, and we realize that hotels and restaurants prefer to see well-dressed guests inside their doors. But when our own costumes are clean and in good condition, why are we then never considered "well-dressed" and let in, we who are not allowed to wear the shamma? We also admire those fast trains you have built here in Vandestan. But why must we always be crowded into the worst and smallest cars, while your beautiful cars often travel empty through the country?

We know that the road to freedom is hard and long, and after the years of terror we also know this: never more violence! But peaceful means are not signs or policemen stopping us with the words: "For Vandestans Only." Peaceful means are doors that are opened to black as well as white, and if these doors are not opened, then perhaps we will also lose our faith in freedom!

In opposition to this the leftist groups outside Parliament raise the objection that peaceful means open doors for blacks only.

Western Culture: 1968

New York is New York. Is there anywhere else?
Headache pounding like a drum
Give Life Meaning
Put a Tiger in Your Tank
Invest in Marco Island—The Fairy Tale Island
    off Florida's West Coast
The Everything Card
Why do blondes have more fun?
Radiation Detected From Missing H-Bombs
**We're Looking For Executive Material For
    Progress At A Fast Rising Pace**
Put a Tiger in Your Tank

Better Living Through Chemistry
She was raped, drugged, and shackled with chains
Think of Your Figure
Bus Hits Train—10 Killed
All This Can Be Yours!
Realistic Christianity
Twenty Thousand—He Was Worth It!
Put a Tiger in Your Tank
We Try Harder!
Swiss Still Display 21-Jewel Economy
Comfort as Never Before
This Dreamhouse Can Be Yours . . .
 If You Have $27,000!
You have a friend at Chase Manhattan
Put a Tiger in Your Tank
Torture Killers Extradited
El Exijente—The Demanding One
Stre-e-tch Your Coffee Break
Peace Feelers: A Trap?
Put a little fun in your life
Put a Tiger in Your Tank

Crime pays here!

The Scenes of Suffering

German East Africa, the present Tanzania, 1905. A rebellion among the black put down by the Germans: 10,000 dead.

Amritsar, India, 1919. British troops shoot directly into an unarmed, protesting crowd: 379 dead, 1,200 injured.

Surabaja, Indonesia, 1945. The Allies, with the British and Australians in the forefront, liberate the Dutch East Indies from the Japanese to pave the way for the returning Dutch, find an Indonesian government functioning, let the Japanese stay in order to fight it, get the Indonesians against them, start the actual war against the Indonesians, and in one decisive blow—with the Allies forcing Indian troops to fight for them—take the harbor city of Surabaja on Java, after which the Dutch retake their old colonial command.

Sétif, Algeria, 1945. When the French ordain a general celebration of the victory of the Allies, oppositional groups raise the Algerian flag instead and, during the conflict that follows, kill 88 Frenchmen. In revenge the French kill, in Sétif and its environs, between 5,000 and 10,000 Algerians.

Madagascar, 1947. The Malagasy attempt an uprising, and the French reply with massacre: 90,000 dead.

Korea, 1950–1953. According to American reports the war took the lives of 2 million military personnel plus 3.5 million civilians.

Guatemala, 1954. The United States invades Guatemala from Honduras, overthrows President Arbenz, who is eager to nationalize, and safeguards additional American financial interests by executing all the union-affiliated inhabitants they could get hold of.

Rivet, Algeria, 1956. The French militia invades the little village of Rivet by night, rouses 40 men from their beds and kills them.

Angola, 1961. The Angolese rebel; the Portuguese reply with arms from NATO and Interarmco: 30,000 dead.

Bagdad, Iraq, 1963. Against General Kassem, who is eager to nationalize, the CIA inspire an uprising that is successful after a bloodbath: several thousand dead (including Kassem).

This just in the way of a few examples.

Now Europe, the bloodiest battlefield of the twentieth century, is so studded with scenes of suffering that it may appear to be terrorist tactics to gather stones from other parts of the world to make the burden even heavier. Nor is it true that we in the Western world belittle or forget our own scenes of suffering; rather, we often remind people of their existence. Don't we constantly say to ourselves and each other: Remember the Moscow trials, remember Guernica, remember Czechoslovakia and Greece, remember Belsen and Buchenwald, Auschwitz and Treblinka, remember Hungary in 1956?

Yes.

But reminding people of these things is a comfortable form of masochism, a pointless self-criticism that hardly can make a scratch on our own democratic skin. Of course in these cases the powers of evil, the ones who bore THE GUILT, are selected and labeled in advance: fascism in its most visible forms, Stalinism in its crudest forms. It's a part of this pathetic game that at every reminder of these Western crimes we're supposed to emphasize in a contrite tone of voice that we all share in the guilt, that no one goes free, and that the same seeds of evil can take root again, perhaps in our own soil, and obviously this is absolutely right. The only catch is that we think we know that we *ourselves* are neither Nazis nor Stalinists, which of course we aren't, either, and thus the self-criticism loses its point.

Recently a European daily newspaper had a series of articles on "The War That No One Dares Talk About." Very predictably, it had to do with one of the most written-about wars in modern times, the Spanish Civil War, a war that all Europeans (except a number of Spaniards) dare talk about with no inhibition at all, for the central question of guilt in this case was solved to democratic satisfaction at an early stage. Such illusionisms are also a part of that pathetic memory game: in dead seriousness we're supposed to impress on people's minds that these scenes of suffering are actually unknown and uninvestigated, that we constantly forget them and that one of the most important tasks of mass media is to increase our knowledge and awareness of what is happening. When a gigantic series on Churchill is not running on TV, then the serious department of our radio is dominated by (European) events of World War II, and when the magazines are not devoting special numbers to Stalinism and the Spanish dictatorship, the daily papers are roaming for the hundredth time through the Warsaw Ghetto or analyzing Eichmann's personality. Now if by means of such tricks we could force the West Germans, above all, never to forget what they did, naturally it would be a splendid gain, but this probably wouldn't work, for obviously the West Germans prefer to strengthen their war power, develop their industry, build up an economic colonial empire, and for what remains, eat sausage and drive cars as never before. We can't blame them for that either, for we Americans, Frenchmen, and Swedes have not only devoted ourselves to reminding them of their concentration camps, we have also helped them, economically and militarily, to become a dangerous big power once again, and we've succeeded considerably better with the latter. In practice those pathetic gestures to suffering also acquire a different function from that which is usually named. The lamentations over the slave camps of the thirties and the ghettos of the forties help draw the public's attention away from the happenings more unpleasant and more controversial for "the democracies," for example, from today's fascism in the Ruhr.

The advantage of this Third World list of scenes of suffering is that it doesn't allow manipulations and subterfuges of this sort. Here the victims are innocent Asians, Africans, and Latin Americans who were only fighting for their rights, and the guilty ones cannot be stuck away in any of the admitted European pigeonholes of shame, the Nazi or the Stalinist one, for those who have been in the forefront are "honorable" people of our own caliber. The democratic English, the highly civilized French, the (prior to 1914) highly respected Germans, the congenial Dutch, the freedom-loving Americans, and the peaceful Australians. Possibly the Portuguese in Angola constitute an exception, despite the fact that they were struck by very worthy NATO weapons. But instead, then, let's bring up the Belgians, a democratic people who, during the period 1876–1908, managed to put between five and eight million Congolese to death and who often showed proof during the Congo Crisis that the spirit of Leopold II is still alive.

On the whole these evil deeds seem hard to explain away. But perhaps we can be spared by classifying them under the heading "The Age of Colonialism," which is now fortunately over? That line won't work either. The Congo Crisis did not take place that long ago, any more than did the war in Algeria and the coup in Iran; it was in 1965 that the Dominican Republic was invaded; it's quite recently that the British were at war in Aden, and it is at this very moment that Americans and Australians are fighting against the people of Vietnam. If we want to be sincerely self-critical, it's to these scenes of suffering that we ought to dedicate our laments. It is also from these scenes that the oppressed people have come to know us Westerners, and should we lose the desire to remind ourselves of them and return instead to our "own" concentration camps, then at least we can be sure that the oppressed people don't intend to follow our example. They do not intend to forget what we've done to them, and as soon as they have the opportunity, they're going to remind us.

Remember East Africa in 1905.

Remember Amritsar.

Remember Surabaja.
Remember Sétif and Rivet.
Remember Madagascar.
Remember Korea and the Congo.
Remember Guatemala and Santo Domingo.
Remember Angola.
Remember Bagdad in 1963.

New Habits

If everybody thought just as much of his fellow men as he did of himself it's possible that there wouldn't be any oppression by the rich of the poor or any oppression by the white-colored people of the other colored people. Perhaps there wouldn't be any Third World. Perhaps there wouldn't be any collective destitution. And everywhere the face of suffering would be visible, admitted, and addressed. But now everybody thinks of himself first of all, and the richer and more powerful a people become, the more eagerly they seem to set their property stamp on the world: that's mine.

Compassion proposes and selfishness disposes. The U.N. proposes and Washington disposes.

Habits—I wrote in the beginning of this book—keep us from becoming aware of the destitution in the world, and I was thinking, among other things, of the habit of figuring all distances in miles so that it becomes only the suffering around our doorstep that counts. I was thinking of the habit of quickly banishing that unfamiliar, "remote" face to a monkey cage for Sunday spectators, a Coney Island of feelings. I was thinking a little later of the habit of regarding the small nations of Northern Europe as some kind of isolated islands in the world sea, out-of-the-way places that have thawed out the world without other people's help by virtue of their industriousness, their ingenuity, their natural riches, and their Social Democrats. Such habits and deformations are powerful, but it is selfishness, not least, that gives them their power.

Indeed, these habits are in our favor. They make it easier for us to disregard other people without feeling guilt. They make it easier just now for me to finish writing this book in peace and quiet, for the person who always has destitution before his eyes writes nothing in peace and quiet.

With that said, enough about selfishness. In this context I prefer to stick with such factors of life as permit themselves to be changed, and habits permit themselves to be changed.

That we have succeeded down through so many years in the fantastic artifice of looking past the world's destitution depends in many respects surely upon the toughness of certain Western habits. But if old habits keep us from seeing, only new habits can teach us to see. When a convention is broken down (in social life as in art) there is sometimes accorded a wonderfully charged moment when our eyes feel free and our senses kaleidoscopically open, a moment that generates unheard of dreams, but this freshly redeemed "direct" encountering can never be made permanent, it can only be channeled into a new convention. The dream of a life liberated from convention is just as vainglorious as the dream of an art liberated from convention. New conventions are demanded.

Which new habits can help us become aware of the faces before us, the other people's and our own?

I've amused myself by putting together a provisory list, a wish list, if you will.

1. *The habit of daily finding out how things are going in the world in the same way as we daily inquire how our closest relatives are feeling.*

This sounds simple. But on the whole, so long as the ordinary man traveled to his capital city once a year and otherwise read the local paper, minded provincial animosities, listened to the king or president on radio, scared the children of the Russians, bought Christmas seals, and regarded everything situated outside his continent (or capital) with the eyes of Columbus or Charles XII, this habit was not within reach. But now, since so many Westerners have acquired access to such effective isolation-breakers as money, TV, language learning, world war along their borders, cars, internationally oriented national newspapers, charter flying, Dag Hammarskjöld, foreign fellow workers, vacations, and intercontinental conversation topics, at least the external prerequisites exist for such a habit to be established.

Only let's not form illusions too quickly. For us in Sweden the internationalization of the living conditions of the rich often seems only to mean that our own chauvinistic image of the world is rolled out over the continents. On TV: Swedish battalion preserves the peace in the Congo. On the newsstand display poster: 7,000 Dead (little headline)—Swedes Out of Danger (giant headline). In factory toilets: Go home to Sparta, Greek Devils.[1] On the sports pages: The Swedish Mettle Stabs. On the vacation photograph: Erik and Ingrid in front of Jesus' grave. In *Expressen*, our most popular tabloid: Swedes Help Hong Kong Survive. In restaurants on the Canary Islands: Swedish Schmorgasboard. When U Thant or Chaplin is interviewed: What's your opinion of Sweden? In India: Swedish powdered milk cheats starvation death. Or in other words: how are things going for *Sweden* in the world? But British and Americans will recognize their own ethnocentricities in these examples. Though more practiced in international affairs, Britain and the United States don't seem to be significantly better, otherwise they would hardly have gone to so much trouble trying respectively to persuade the whole Commonwealth to drink five o'clock tea and to swathe the whole globe in an aroma of Coca-Cola and prairie stables. For their part the Russians are doing all they can, with the best of intentions, to demolish Central Asian architecture by supplying their republics there with Soviet palaces of terror.

I shall return to this hard-to-establish habit.

2. *The habit of reckoning time in relation to the year Zero (the present Anno Domini) so that what comes before is called B.Z. and that which comes after is called A.Z. (in French av. Z. and après Z.; what would that be in Chinese and Arabic?).*

Perhaps, preferably, a person should be General-Secretary of the U.N. in order to suggest something so worldwide as a new chronology; my excuse is that I only want to secularize the existing Christian chronology. Wouldn't such a reform be worth thinking about?

Finally, Buddhists and Muslims would be spared from

1 Such graffiti, expressing hostility toward the growing numbers of foreign workers in Sweden, have appeared in industrial plants.—Trans.

saying that Buddha was born in the year 563 before Christ and that Muhammed was born in the year 570 Anno Domini. Finally, the majority of the world's population, although excluded from the Western tradition, could see the New Year in without being reminded of the hegemony of Christianity or the domination of colonialism.

I would suppose that other people, for example, representatives of the growing Western cadre of atheists and agnostics, have touched upon the same thought before, but not until recent years has the thought of secularization acquired what is probably necessary for a reform, namely, a scientific justification: scholars of religion have been forced to move Anno Domini to the year 6 (possibly the year 7) B.C. If one proceeds from the *actual* birth year of Jesus, in other words, one would have to re-date all of history, have Caesar get murdered in the year 38 B.C. and World War II end in the year of Our Grace 1939. This would be very unpractical. One possibility in this fluid situation would be to introduce a completely new chronology, but even this would be unpractical. For that matter, there doesn't seem to exist any chronology of any scope that lacks connection to a definite religion or cultural sphere, and to replace a Christian measurement with a Muslim measurement, for example, would hardly mean any improvement from a Buddhist point of view. Instead there is—as ordered by Radakrishnan, U Thant, and Bertrand Russell—a secularized year Zero, at which point no people or religions seem to have got their toes stepped on.

I mean it seriously: Buddha was born in the year 563 B.Z., Jesus was born in the year 6 B.Z., Muhammed was born in the year 570 A.Z.

3. *The habit of associating the concepts of travel and traveling even with such means of conveyance as do not involve movement of the body.*

149

4. *The habit of using artificial sense organs such as the telephone, motion picture camera, phonograph, etc., as "natural" complements to our inborn sense organs.*

This sounds less essential, perhaps, so a more explicit commentary.

The bicycle and the automobile are our fortified shanks' mares, the wings of jet planes are our flying arms, the teleprinter and the telegraph our more rapid writing hand, the telescope and zoom lens our sharper eye, the radio our improved ear, the telephone and the microphone our new voice of thunder, the radar our extended tentacles, the diesel motor our stronger lungs, the laser beam our sharper nails, the computer our infallible memory, the television our eye and ear perceiving the essence of the entire world.

We must see it in approximately this way if we conceive of technology as the servant and armor of the human being, as a complement to his senses and extremities. But to *experience* the matter in this way—to experience the telephone conversation as a way to travel different from walking or flying but nevertheless as a way to travel, or to experience that which appears on the TV screen as just as "real" as what we see with our "own eyes," firsthand—that is more difficult.

It demands training, habit, perhaps an expanded sense of reality.

How do you travel by means of the telephone? Walking up to the phone is like going to a railroad station. You buy a ticket by looking up a number in the telephone directory and get on the train by dialing the number; with a click the train starts off and goes on its way on the track during the regular ringing. When it clicks in the receiver again and you hear the voice of the right station master, the end of the line has been reached. Sometimes the journey is long and you have to change trains; you hear foreign voices talking; you switch to new tracks. Sometimes you get off at the wrong station and have to wait for a new train. It also happens that the journey just keeps on, station after station, ring after ring, and your hope that the train will finally stop becomes more and more futile; nervously you pull the emergency brake but the train just rushes on, farther and farther into empty space. In order to terminate such a trip there is finally only one alternative, to jump off; you're left sitting by a quiet, deserted embankment.

How does a person travel by means of television? You set off for the air terminal by going to the TV set; with a twist of the dial you reach the airport; on the way from the set you get on board the plane and settle yourself in the armchair; when the sound comes on, the plane drones off like a Mercury rocket; when the picture comes on you are already there, in the midst of Saigon's tumultuous throng. All this goes on at an unreal speed, but on the streets of Saigon the journey continues at a "more human" tempo; as one of many travelers, you then walk and drive around, with a camera as an eye.

Imagining the mass media trip in this way, childishly if you will, can make it easier to humanize the monstrosities of technology, to make technology accessible for our feeling, to make it *ours*. What else can be of assistance here?

The awareness that for hundreds and thousands of years, mankind has undertaken fabulous journeys in the imagination, without any means of transportation at all, should serve to help. If it is possible to travel to the South Pole while you're lying sleeping or to Lima while you're sitting daydreaming it should not be harder but easier to feel that you're traveling when you get to see the real South Pole at the movies or put a piece of music from the Lima of reality on the turntable. An Indian, whose only means of transportation are a plow and a faith—where do his travels take him?

In terms of perception, we have now, fortunately for people who are nearsighted, accepted eyeglasses as a natural part of the human face, and perhaps it may soon be possible to humanize the hearing aid in the same way: "naturalized" from an inhuman, disfiguring metal tumor on the face to an extra sense, a well-embellished outer ear. Loving couples once thought they had to sit up close to each other in private in order to be able to declare their love to one another; today they let unknown telephone operators in distant cities listen in on their intimate long-distance whisperings or send off glowing, typewritten declarations of love by special delivery. In this fashion even "cold," "impersonal," "artificial" technology can be made warm and human, a letter carrier of love after the precedent of the homing pigeon.

Judging by this and other evidence, it need not matter greatly what kind of material the new means of transportation and supplements to the senses are made of, what speed they have, and which elements they move in. What is crucial for the senses is the way in which the inventions are used and regarded.

If you are accustomed to crawling, it feels highly unnatural to walk; if you are accustomed to riding a bicycle or a horse, it feels unnaturally fast and frightening to drive a car—but then you perceive the car as an alien monster and yourself as its helpless victim. Judging by the assured facial expression of the trained motorist, he perceives his chariot as his own overcoat, the tires as his own galoshes, and hence 60 m.p.h. as his "natural" marching speed, in approximately the same fashion as the knight of the Middle Ages saw the horse as an indispensable part of his gear; it was not a horseman waging battle on a horse but a new type of centaur, a six-legged runaway sheet-metal locomotive. Why should it be impossible to use and enslave mass media in the same spirit? Actively make them our own by making the choice of programs ourselves, clarifying the pictures, interpreting the voices, commenting upon the words, and as an invisible free passenger, traveling along? It's not the fault of the television but the fault of our primitive TV habits that we passively submit so often to the discretion of the screen and uncritically allow ourselves to be fed, staying forever in the armchair at home. We are unaccustomed to it, quite simply. When it comes to telephone habits, we already seem to have come a good bit further.

The objection can be made that the TV traveler feels nothing of the pains of the journey and the responsibility of the trip and thus only travels secondhand; how could he make the means of transportation or even the·journey his own? But compare him with the steamboat traveler, who in an extrinsic sense is equally extraneous. Turning the responsibility and navigation worries over to other people does not for a moment stop the easy-chair dozer on the upper deck (or in an airplane) from experiencing the fascination of the trip. On the contrary: he is at greater liberty than the pilot to see what he wants and, with or without the help of his fellow passengers, to create his own journey. Or compare him with the newspaper reader who normally glances past the majority of *The New York Times'* continents of words without entering into the columns himself, yet when something interests him, he stops and, as a matter of course, starts traveling along, interpreting, evaluating, interrupting the correspondents, making the text his own.

Nevertheless, the mass media trip is inevitably doomed to be a secondhand journey, isn't it? What we see and hear, of course, is always seen and heard by others; we are served up their terminated, agglomerate travels. Maybe. But here too there is room for doubt and reservation, for the border between the first- and secondhand journey has become markedly mobile. Just as a reproduction of the Mona Lisa at home in an art book can be experienced more freely and more intensively than the original at the Louvre, the TV trip to Saudi Arabia can seem to make more of an initial impact than the most ambitious pilgrimage to "town and byway." The vacationing West German family exploring in Tunisia—"far from the great tourist trek"—seem from the start to have insured themselves against any discoveries at all by packing their Volkswagen full of German words, German people, German family worries; and how many of prosperity's chartered travelers in Turkey or Egypt travel for one moment firsthand, without letting themselves be directed by travel agencies, herded by guides, indoctrinated by guidebooks, radar-guided by prejudices they brought along, misguided by the opinions of the group, stunned to blindness by the cities' throngs? Most people seem to take along their armchair from home wherever they travel.

I wonder whether on the whole we don't harbor an inordinate confidence in our inborn senses and an inordinate distrust in the technological supplements to our senses. Even the most ruminating stay-at-homes are accorded the rank of travel if only the body is set into motion by car or plane; not even the most open and independent trip at home by means of a book or television is accorded the rank of travel.

Now if a portion of our confidence in primary vision and bodily transplantation were transferred to mass media, perhaps we wouldn't need to stand powerlessly and regressively provincial before the tremendous reduction that technology particularly has made the globe undergo (for those of us who can afford technology)—Tehran and Khartoum within a day's journey, pagodas on TV, African revolution songs on radio, magazines from Latin America, hour-old news from the whole world several times daily. Perhaps we could establish habits that would enable this fact to enter the range of our feelings, so that it would also be possible to experience, so that it would also be possible to live with, so that it would also be possible to grasp it and look it in the race: the fact that the world has become one country.

In ideological debate the concept of alienation has acquired a negative significance since, with Marx, it has been associated with setting the workers at a distance from the ownership and control of production in the capitalistic society. Obviously, this form of alienation is something evil, and it's also possible to criticize it vigorously, for a different social order is quite conceivable. A better order. But in working life now one already encounters a form of alienation that seems equally inevitable in both socialistic and capitalistic systems of production, namely the "foreignness" in relation to the finished product that seems to affect all industrial workers at a certain level of mechanization. And what it is not possible to do away with cannot readily be criticized in the same way. Instead one has to learn to live with an alienation like this, to procure methods to allay and disarm it, to try to regard it as the price of something good, which in many respects, of course, it actually is. The situation is exactly the same, I believe, with the technological alienation that our new forms of travel and sensory supplements have brought with them. If we want to have the whole world within comfortable reach we have also to pay the price for this benefit: a certain impairment of the sense of reality, a certain dilution of the sense of proximity, a more and more indistinct boundary between primary experiences and secondary experiences.

Undoubtedly there is a factually justified horror of technology's nimble creations: two of the most important means of communications are of course world war and the atom bomb. And from the *development* of transportation and communications technology (toward the supersonic plane, odorama, phonovision, trips to the moon, air-cushioned buses, and other insanities) there is not a great deal more to be hoped than that it stops, that is to say, is turned toward projects more useful for the world as a whole. The world proletariat has already paid for enough of the West's luxury production, and for our own part, the mass media we already have are quite sufficient.

I'm not dreaming of traveling *exclusively* by means of mass media. That would be tantamount to never—except on some surprising occasion by telephone—exposing one's self to the unavoidable bath of socialization. Not only private enemies of light and scoptophobes but our business-men as well seem to hold this in greater terror than any-thing else: being deprived of the dusk-dim refuge of their spyhole and being wrenched personally out into glaring inspection, finally to be seen and judged themselves. How-ever, even we who are spared from supplying industry with cheap manpower seldom have the time and money even to remove ourselves bodily from our silk Western straitjacket and to take wing, letting the world unfold be-neath us, but we do have both time and money for news-papers, radio, TV, telephone, and a book or two. If a person has ever traveled bodily—it doesn't need to be far, only far enough and sufficiently unprotected by touring groups so that he's had time to be seen and branded by the people he's seen and branded himself—then I imagine too that the stay-at-home means of transportation can keep the flame alive for a good long time by forcing his consciousness of the world's existence and proximity to be revived daily. If the other people had the same opportunities, they would be able to see us as we now see them. But it's not equally necessary for them to see us, for they haven't hurt us so much that they have to use all means accessible to understand what they've done. We're the ones who must understand.

I say this with a certain personal emphasis, for I've ventured to write a book that is occupied a good deal with the problems of the Third World without ever having set my foot outside Europe. Even so, I believe I have traveled. I've traveled as that hybrid of viking and freeholder that our time's engineers have produced: the peasant viking who simultaneously travels and stays on the farm. Or in the words of the Upanishads: "Although sitting still he journeyed on."

5. *The habit of applying such expressions as "confront," "meet," "see with your own eyes," and "on the scene," also to the solitary encounters and stay-at-home viewings of alienated traveling.*

6. *The habit of talking about "discovery" and "voyages of discovery" when people from any country at all discover any other country at all.*

When Europe became Europe the greater part of the world was already discovered. When European imperialists started stationing their national flags throughout Asia and the "New World," in most quarters they first had to remove the flags of other discovering peoples. When Livingstone and Stanley pushed their way forward through "darkest" Africa they reported discovery upon discovery, both of countries and of people; the idea that these tribes would have discovered anything themselves never occurs to us. When European missionaries and businessmen "discovered" Indochina in the fifteenth century a good 1,600 years had gone by since the Chinese discovered Indochina. Columbus, as everyone knows, did not discover America (or India) in the year 1492, but neither did he discover the Caribbean island where he happened to go ashore, for the Caniba people had forced themselves upon the people there earlier. For that matter, it does not seem to be clarified whether the inhabitants of San Salvador constituted an aboriginal population.

The Gauls rejoiced when they invented soap, for they didn't know the Sumerians had used soap three thousand years earlier. But we know. There's no longer any excuse for the colonial-European blindered habit of inquiring only where the white man set his foot and what the white man discovered. There is no longer any excuse to keep on inventing the bicycle, along with the Russians.

Once the Asians discovered a woodsy little land area that has now been cleared away and called Europe. Once people whose faces were light brown, yellow, or black discovered that there were people on earth whose faces were pink.

7. *The habit of distinguishing between Christian atheists and Hindu atheists, between secularized Muslims and secularized Buddhists, between Muslim disbelievers and Christian disbelievers in the same way that we distinguish between Christian, Hindu, Muslim, and Buddhist believers.*

8. *The habit of using the prefix "world," the noun "world" and the adjectives "general" and "international" only when they are justified.*

An elementary intellectual hygiene, it may be thought, but seldom observed. Some examples:

The World Market. In nine cases out of ten this refers to the market of the Western industrial countries; in the tenth, to the markets of the Western industrial countries plus the markets of the Eastern industrial countries. For the present the underdeveloped countries will have to try to hold their own in these markets or die.

World Trade. Generally the trade that the Western powers dominate. Even in statistical surveys trade of the Communist countries is often disregarded.

The World Bank (or International Bank). All the Communist countries plus a large number of newly created Afro-Asian countries lack membership in the World Bank, in which those countries that invest the most money have the most say-so, primarily the United States. In return three non-members of the U.N., namely West Germany, South Korea, and South Vietnam, are included in the World Bank (read West Bank). The same is true, on the whole, of the International Monetary Fund, the International Finance Corporation (IFC), and the International Development Association (IDA), purely West-dominated U.N. agencies.

The International Court. Since the members here are not selected permanently, as in the economic specialized agencies, but are newly elected by the U.N. General Assembly and Security Council every ninth year, there are at least theoretical prospects that the court could become "international" in the same sense as the General Assembly: including a sufficient number of representatives from the different blocs of the world to avoid political partisanship. However, thus far the court in The Hague has been dominated by the Western powers, partially to the detriment of the Eastern bloc, above all to the detriment of the Afro-Asiatic bloc.

World War. If one calls the Western Civil War of 1914–1918 a world war, the American Revolutionary War, which engaged just as many great powers, should be called World War I and the war of 1939–1945, World War III. If one requires that a major conflict activate great powers in at least three parts of the world, preferably including Asia, in order to be called a world war, the war of 1939–1945 stands out as World War I. Possibly the outbreak of that war should perhaps be moved back to 1937, when Japan attacked China, and the month of armistice moved up to August 1945, when the United States dropped her first atom bombs on Japan.

Out There in the World. There's trouble out there in the world, say the Dutch, when the Germans and the French quarrel over Lorraine.

World History. If a Chinese historian were to portray world history for his countrymen according to the same methods that Western historians usually use, he would begin by taking up first of all, under the heading "Antiquity" or "The Classical Period," the Indua culture and the other early civilizations in the vicinity of China. Secondly, he would discuss Mesopotamia and Egypt, dwelling on the spread of Buddhism throughout the world. The later, peripherally situated Greek culture would not be taken up in this connection but, together with the Mayan and Aztec cultures, would be assigned to the brief survey in the subordinate section "Other Early Cultures." The chapter on "The Bright Middle Ages" would deal mainly with the building up of the Chinese world empire, the victorious progress of Islam and the Chinese religions throughout the world, the great Asian discoveries within technology, astronomy, mathematics, the art of writing, philosophy, etc., and the crucial struggles between Chinese and Arabs on the hegemony of the civilized world. The addendum "National Migratory Movements in the West" would briefly take up the Huns' and Romans' aggressive invasion of Northern and Southern Europe, by reason of which the Huns would be thanked for having discovered Eastern Europe, and the Roman Empire would be designated as powerful but unfortunately much too isolated to be able to play a part in the continuity of world history. The chapter "The Battle of the Silk Road" would begin with the tragic dismemberment of China's western empire in order to lay emphasis on the Mongols' aggressive invasion throughout the world. The chapter would proceed to the humiliation of China under Genghis Khan, the defeat of the Khorezmer realm and the Turkish empire, the Arabs' battle against "The Christian Peril," the discovery of the African continent plus the rise of the Great Mogul Empire. A note in reference to the constant European tribal wars would compare the "unchanging" West with the "dynamic" East and seek the reasons in Europe's lack of a civilized religion and a long culture tradition. "The Age of Enlightenment" would take up the expanding world trade in silk, spices, and porcelain, the flourishing of Indian, Persian, and Chinese culture, and the Arabs' trading empire, but even the first traces of Western trading activity would be noted. In the chapter "The White Invasion" (beginning in the middle of the eighteenth century) the European barbarians would for the first time receive dominant attention, though not for their wars and revolutions in Europe (Napoleon's "hordes" would be mentioned, however) but for their increasingly successful endeavors, with arms, science, and the new type of trade policy inconsiderate of the civilized world, to subdue Asia (and Africa). Nor in "The Modern Age" would any European events such as the "First World War" draw attention away from "The Liberation of the World," that is to say, the rebellion of the Asian and later also the African peoples against Europeans, Japanese, and Manchu emperors. Surely the internationally crucial consequences of the European wars, in particular of the Russian Revolution, would be pointed out: revolution in China, Iran, and Turkey; nationalism in India, Burma, Indonesia, and Arabia; industrial development initiated around the world.[2] Finally, the world war would be portrayed not as the Germans' but primarily as that of the Japanese, and secondly, as the war of the Western colonialists; because of the latter's uninterrupted or resumed fighting, neither would the war be denoted as finished in the year 1945, but as continued for twenty-three more years, surging from one theater of war to another, from India to Burma, from Indonesia to Korea, from Kashmir to Aden, up to today's date in Vietnam.

General Art History (from the Renaissance to our time). If not only "the capital cities of World Art" in Western Europe are included but also Russia and the Balkans, we are thankful; if America gets a section of her own, we are fortunate; if Latin America is devoted anything more than a summary postscript to the Spanish section we open our eyes wide; and if one word is said to the effect that Asia, Africa, and Oceania possess anything at all in the way of art beyond the classical art preceding the Renaissance or the "primitive" art that European artists have happened to stumble upon when they've been hunting for their origin, we hardly believe our eyes.

World Literature. Common name for European and American anthologies in which 95 per cent of the text is devoted to Western literature and 5 per cent to other literature. Since the time of Goethe we have also been speaking of world literature in more visionary terms as a kind of monolithic literary culture to which all the people of the earth are thought to present their contributions. However, any such literature or culture is hard to imagine, since no

[2] In *What Is History?* the English historian E. H. Carr writes: "The Russian Revolution of 1917 provided a further and decisive impulse. What was significant here was that its leaders looked persistently, but in vain, for imitators in Europe, and finally found them in Asia. It was Europe that had become 'unchanging,' and Asia that was on the move." (London: Macmillan & Co. Ltd., 1962), p. 143.

common development of culture exists on earth, but only a great number of literatures and cultures that essentially follow different lines of development.

International Perspective. Common headline when a Swedish commentator on the arts goes through the contents of one Danish, one Finno-Swedish, and one German literary review. In the same spirit people talk of *international trends* when a new French "ism" is mentioned in Finland, or when electronic studios are built for composers in both West Germany and Switzerland. More comprehensively—that is, in terms of provinces in our part of the world—people talk of an *international modernism* when a Western fashion within literature, sculpture, or music is concerned.

Now *international* is a vague term that permits itself to be stretched in many directions, and obviously we cannot constantly attach conditions for its use that are as rigorous as when it is a question of (supposedly) global U.N. organizations. But when people speak of international modernism (or of contemporary art or of modern literature) they often imply the idea that this art and literature are dominant in the world as a whole or that the art and literature created in other parts of the world and foreign to us aren't really "modern" and don't really belong to "the contemporary age." The implication is that in various ways these foreign creations are "retarded" or "behind," bound to culture traditions that have already been "passed by" in the "leading" countries of art. In order to play a part in "the international development of art," the artists in these retarded parts of the world, it is suggested, will probably have to follow the example of the Japanese and several Latin Americans and "adjust" to the more "advanced" esthetic technique and the more "relevant" approaches for "the contemporary age" that characterize Western art and

163

literature. In short, people imply that the underdeveloped countries are underdeveloped countries in cultural respects too.

But even when such appraisals are *not* implied, it appears most sensible today, when the globe has begun to dwindle down to one country, to reserve the words international and internationalism for worldwide things and otherwise settle for more limited and adequate designations (Western, European, West European, Scandinavian, American, etc.).

International realization isn't something a writer or anybody else chooses freely, but to a high degree it is something dependent upon the prevailing climate of the times. That so many writers and social critics of the radical left can work rather freely today with a global perspective depends to no little extent, for example, upon the fact that the postwar period's narrow asylum between the power blocs has now been widened (and, unfortunately, the power blocs with them), not only in Europe but above all in the Third World. Consequently a provisory view of the West *from the outside* has been made possible. But an equally important benefit is perhaps that the increased freedom not only encourages an internationalism of a political kind but seems to open global thinking in many shifting directions. The pressure from the outside is certainly not *weaker* today than it was in the forties, but the European pressure from the war and the cold war was to a great extent a political pressure that seemed unilaterally to "favor" a kind of writer who is reliably aware of the times, just as it also could attract an inquisitorial terrorism of confession. The pressure from the Third World seems to hold an appeal to each and every person to take a step out of that blindered Western narrowness so that he sees a patch of the world outside and thus himself and his own patch of the world in a new light. The appeal is rigorous since destitution stands rearing menacingly behind it, but even so, the appeal is open, for nothing is said about how the step is to be taken and on which field.

No *type* of writer or writing seems to be excluded or disfavored beforehand by the appeal. Consequently there no longer seems to be any excuse to pretend as if exercises in European or American avant-gardism or in a Western community of cultural interests would be manifestations of *international* awareness.

9. *The habit of calling a looting expedition a looting expedition and not a popular migration or crusade; of calling imperialism imperialism and not trade, round-the-world voyages, or missionary work; of calling wars of aggression wars of aggression and not military assistance, the dissemination of culture, or struggle for freedom; of calling annexation annexation and not liberation of the people; of calling breach of the U.N. Charter breach of the U.N. Charter and not defense of freedom; of calling superior power superior power and not a balance of power; of calling neo-colonialism neo-colonialism and not aid to underdeveloped countries; of calling oligarchy oligarchy and not popular democracy or parliamentarism; of calling exploitation exploitation and not world trade or world revolution; of calling Soviet communism Soviet communism and not socialism; of calling American capitalism American capitalism and not democracy.*

What was that comment on South Africa? "Every day means that no one notices what is happening every day."[3] Every day means that nobody reacts anymore when black people are jailed, cities are bombed, people are oppressed.

But this can be only half the truth. In order for any-

[3] Pär Wästberg, *op. cit.*, p. 22.

thing to be able to influence our appraisals and our actions in a permanent way, it must, in one way or another, become an everyday occurrence for us. Everyone prizes an intensive experience of involvement, to really see and become upset. What happens when the first intensity has cooled we readily conceal, disappointed and embarrassed. But that an involvement is channeled is no less important than that it arise, otherwise it vaporizes in the same moment that the intensive experience vaporizes and there remains a memory with a glow that only emphasizes the grayness of our cooled-off, present state. All this seems to depend upon what we value most highly: the passion or the contact with another human being, the strong sense of involvement or the interest for the cause, the bath water or the baby. If we value the passion and sense of involvement most highly, we take the step from love to friendship unwillingly and instead yearn impatiently for new Vietnam kicks. But if we want to espouse the cause itself, so to speak, there is every reason to try to attach that once intensive involvement to feelings we have more frequently and duties we pursue daily, for only if the involvement is channeled can it become a part of our continuing life.

That's why I'm talking in such detail and so avidly about new habits.

I'm going to quote a passage by Béchir Ben Yahmed, publisher of *Jeune Afrique:*

> This is one of the most remarkable and most important phenomena of our time: the more news service is developed and disseminated, the less its influence becomes. We no longer react: we passively accept.
>
> Scandal has become a daily addiction: for a few seconds it arouses our attention, perhaps we comment upon it. Then we go on to something else.
>
> What newspaper still believes that it is possible to hold

the reader's attention to the scandal taking place in Vietnam?[4]

This is certainly true: we seldom react on a level with what is happening. To sigh or to passively stare when a Buddhist lights fire to himself cannot be said to be an adequate reaction. Even so I think Béchir Ben Yahmed has missed what is really a positive new aspect of contemporary news-gathering; namely that mass media have started to become just as self-evident a part of our daily life as eating meals together, smoking, looking at familiar faces, walks, secrets, or smiles.

Formerly, news bulletins from the outside world were sensations and exotic wonders to which people reacted vehemently for the simple reason that the bulletins were as few and far between as holidays and as stunning as the circus coming to town. Everybody ran out and gawked. Everyday news at home, on the other hand, was more banal. It consisted of the man of the house coming home and asking his wife 350 times a year: "Anything happened?" And 340 times a year the wife answered: "No, nothing special." Now what has happened is not that the news at home has grown less banal ("Cindy got the sniffles") but that by moving into our homes, the news from the outside world has grown equally banal. "Was there anything on Huntley-Brinkley?" "No, nothing special."

Evidently there are risks in this new arrangement. Not the least of which is the fact that world news is exposed to a familiarly prattling idyllization that impudently disarms what is alien to us. "Why, Nasser looks exactly like Uncle Stanley." In olden times the bearers of urgent messages never had to fear such things when they sprang forward on lathered horse. But the idea that we

[4] *Jeune Afrique*, No. 254, November 1965.

should now react with greater passivity and care less about what is happening is contradicted by the facts. The example of Vietnam, "the first TV war," speaks not for the eventuality that a heavier flood of news would put the public to sleep but the opposite.

I think it's worth remembering that, despite everything, the majority of people keep up with newspapers, radio, and television quite voluntarily. Despite everything, a certain activity is demanded to catch programs and keep up with news articles. It doesn't seem particularly plausible that the majority of people in industrial countries would lay out so much time and money for mass media if passive staring were the only dividend they could hope for.

Obviously it's true that few people gape, wide-eyed, when atrocities are shown on TV or are reported on the radio, but gaping, wide-eyed, has never been a sure sign of involvement or interest: generally it's only a sign that a person experiences something as unusual and remarkable, and neither military coups nor napalm bombs remain unusual and remarkable for long to the routine user of mass media.

But precisely in this there still lies a danger, surely, that feeling will be worn down, the ability to react will be blunted. Yes, undoubtedly. Namely, the same danger faced by each and every person who has a job, is married, or has friends. Feeling is worn down *in the presence of everything you care enough* about to have it surrounded by habits. Certainly it's hard for the journalists, for the hundredth time, to write something freshly experienced and "engagé" about Vietnam, but this kind of fakir trickery is not what the daily readers are asking for, either, for by this time they are justifiably fed up with Vietnam too. What they want from the journalists is about the same, I should think, as what the chronic invalid wants from his relatives when, for the hundredth time, they visit his sickbed: not that they turn up the whites of their eyes and work up a newborn interest for his ailment, which he knows they've already squandered all their accessible feelings on anyway, but quite simply that they put in an appearance; that they come around with any possible news, preferably factual; that they care about the *contact* itself, even after duty and routine have entered into the forms of contact. If this sounds overly mild we ought to remember that it is often precisely the person who has heard the doctors assure him a hundred times that the disease is under control and that the patient soon will be well who the hundred-and-first time exhausts his reserve of patience and bawls out the head physician or starts carrying aggressive Vietnam placards. This potential alternative for action also lies beneath that seemingly indifferent, everyday question:

"Anything happened?" "No, nothing special."

This is only half the truth, as I said, but I stress this half because I believe that precisely in the presence of the face of suffering there is an excessive faith in the importance of the *dramatic* experience and presentation, especially in literary connections.

Certainly a shock presentation is needed in order for our eyes to be opened at all; to be sure, few people have yet discovered what everybody sees every day. Every person who has lived with another human being for long knows that intensive reminders are sometimes needed so that the habits of intimacy do not petrify for good, a sort of sudden echo of falling in love the first time and yet not an echo but something "new."

But it's not often that life is so open-ended. Even writers and travelers in underdeveloped countries live for the most part *between* such moments of high tension and seldom *in* them. Therefore they cannot, except at the start, count on being able to confront the face of destitution with a proper supply of strong and visibly adequate feelings either, for most of the feelings that appear voluntarily have acquired their form and scope from that thin, impoverished, in between life they usually live. A gap between that turbulent destitution and that docile, dwarfed feeling seems inevitable. In order for this gap to be bridged, at least scantily, destitution must also be disarmed and de-dramatized.

I believe that, at least intellectually, I understand the temptation of writing while living on tiptoe, conjuring that high-tension Sunday of involvement to last out the whole week; the incomparable atrocity of destitution seems to cry out for incomparable reactions and descriptions, it's true. Even so, this must be a dream of escape. Soon enough the person who seeks to become one with suffering overworks his emotional capital and is forced to *borrow* feelings: his own feelings from the time when the experience was luxuriantly new or else feelings inscribed in the (since the war) Auschwitzically strained literary conventions of suffering. The latter is more legitimate and perhaps primarily more difficult to see through, but sooner or later, even if the text seems to bleed from its wounds, it often appears clear that the face of suffering has been seen and encountered not by a specific individual but by a curious astral body of feeling.

Upset at no longer being ignited by the same fire he sees burning before his eyes, the reporter at the front finally sets his words on fire—and with that, breaks the contact between feeling and hand. Upset at no longer being upset by the madness of the war, the playwright of suffering appropriates the fiery tongs of expressionism for his own purpose in order to transform the stage once more to a Nazi Golgotha—and thus avoids encountering suffering personally. But the same dream of escape also haunts many Western intellectuals who would never think of writing in this spirit and who have not tried to draw the world's destitution into their writing by more tranquil means either. If you ask them why, they generally answer that they feel only their own impotence and insufficiency: what can they do? They would hardly reply with such surrender if they weren't approaching a dream of a totally unprecedented involvement, otherwise they quite likely would immediately have sat down and done what intellectuals always have done when they felt they were outsiders to something significant: studied the subject.

A term in the Peace Corps or an indignant book from Africa—this has recently become a customary, estimable result when Westerners of tender conscience first awaken to underdeveloped countries. But such actions are unreliable proof of commitment; the chaff isn't sifted from the wheat until later. What is rare, as we know, is not that people venture forth as doctors and social workers but that any of them manage to stay after the great calling has dwindled down to a strenuous and thankless detail job. Nor is it rare that Western writers are shaken by their first meeting with the Third World, but it is rare that any of them at home in the welfare state manage to keep their commitment alive for years, channeled into working habits, reading habits, conversation habits. Very likely, an ideology is required in order to manage this. What is really hard for all the people working for and describing underdeveloped countries seems to be letting their commitment get cool without letting it grow cold.

An area of commitment of the magnitude in question here necessarily attracts to it a great many people prone to bad trips: parasites of feelings, adventure seekers, hysteric cases, little hunters after big subjects, fugitives from our secure Western affluence, romantics of quantity, seekers of sufficiently strong motives for unproportionately strong aggressions, idle experimenters clutching at an engagé straw, egotists of regeneration, people who refuse human contact seeing a chance to love at a distance, Belsen pornographers, exhibitionists of benevolence, and ordinary torture terrorists. Therefore the literary conventions of destitution seem fairly factual, and these kinds of convention are also breaking through more and more forcefully in Europe and America. Expressionist plays of indignation are giving way to feature plays such as *The Investigation* (by Peter Weiss), and travel reports from Asia, in which you seldom quite know who can show off the nakedest wound, the travel writer or Asia, are giving way to series of interviews without comment such as *The Children of Sanchez* (by Oscar Lewis) and *Report from a Chinese Village* (by Jan Myrdal) or to a combination of travel report and lyrical reflections on life or to a combination of collected poems and dossier. The traditional literary forms have been subjected to an increased pressure of facts, and I believe it's characteristic that the strongest accounts of the torture in Algeria have been not those that occurred in emotion-charged novels but those that occurred in fact-charged diaries, the testimony of witnesses, the journals of invalids.

If you venture out into the world with the secure, Western, possession-mad assurance that Europe or America is the world's city, and the remainder its enslaved suburbs, it might suffice to skim the cream off the splendor and wisdom of the Orient hastily, via interpreters, to save at least something of value from the heathens' clutches; how much Eastern poetry, for example, did not pine away in Asiatic obscurity before it was elevated to ornamentation and marginal décor in the works of a Goethe, a Kipling? If such an assurance is lacking, flip the seesaw the other way around: arrogance goes down, the need for knowledge goes up. The more humbly fact-gathering literary conventions send the writers back to the school bench.

Travel accounts grounded in the conception that it's so remarkable that a writer visits China that, without knowing anything about the country, he should impart his personal impressions to Westerners appear just as anachronistic today as the "literary letters" from Paris or New York (written by thoroughbred natives) in the magazine *Encounter*. If the same kind of travel accounts were written instead by Koreans, Malays, Arabs, or Indians and dealt with *Europe* or *America*, the matter would be considerably more interesting. Rather one such travel account on the annual list of translated imports than five new experimental novels from the Common Market. On the other hand, if one writes about the Third World for the domestic market, the person immediately appears less interesting than the subject, and the individualistic literary habits with which we've infested both ourselves and the environment ever since Romanticism can then seem inadequate or misleading.

Is there a possibility of turning aside from this seductively obstructive tradition so that it's possible to see and describe what's happening in the world without swathing it, with every line and gesticulation, in a haze of predominating personality? Is there a possibility of writing about communal questions without replying with that go-getting, emotion-maintaining individualism in the very language and tone of voice? Is there any possibility of holding our ground against that novelty-chasing, fashion-possessed commercialism that reduces art works to commodities and readers to passive consumers? Or is literature in our capitalistic society doomed to wear itself out chasing its tail in the squirrel cage of technological development?

So much for habits. The fastidious reader has certainly marked that I've restricted myself mainly to the sort of habits that let themselves be established without social upheavals and that, consequently, really crucial reforms (i.e., revolutions) have been passed by. But this book is not about the way the world is to get better, either. It's about the way we're to learn to see with new eyes how poorly things are going in the world.

One habit that would eliminate many personal tragedies, if it were initiated, is the habit of regarding the normal human body as so approximate and diversified that even specimens with four fingers, one ear "instead of two," one leg shorter, a very large head, or an arm as short as a hand could be classified among the well-shaped and be permitted to walk around on the streets freely without arousing wonder or gloom. But we can be glad that broadmindedness when it comes to physical deviants has been extended so far that it's accepted for people to have different skin colors and nose shapes without being lynched.

Progressive parents today bring up their children without following the traditional division of sex roles: boys are allowed to cry and stay at home, while girls have to manage by themselves and get prepared for a career, etc. But even before this upbringing has gotten under way, it is sabotaged by friends, newspapers, and teachers, and surely out in the cold world it becomes apparent that the children derive no pleasure from their upbringing, but on the contrary have a rougher time of it, since society is partial to the traditional sex roles. When even a modest habit like this runs up against trouble, you can easily imagine how death-doomed it would be to try to introduce into Western homes a habit that would be opposed to their very fundamentals.

The habit in bringing up children and in family life of prohibiting all talk of ownership when it concerns persons and all talk of individual ownership when it concerns things.

I mean not only talk of ownership but ownership itself, but it's precisely in the talk that the prevailing mentality is clearly divulged. Society's children do not exist, only "my" child and "your" child, with the mouth pursed on the possessive adjectives. Common property exists, but completely predominant are "my" bed, "my" room, "my" playthings, "your" birthday, "your" friends. And "our" possessions, in the sense of the family's possessions, are assigned their value by being played off, in the interest of family egotism, against the possessions of the families next door. Let's imagine that one heroic family manages to prohibit all this thinking of property so that they own neither each other nor the things in the house but just live together and, individually or jointly, use those things that are available in the house. In order for this to succeed, however, the family must live in complete isolation, for as soon as the door is opened, social life streams in, and social life is saturated with thoughts of property, stamped from start to finish by mine and yours, by my advantage and your disadvantage, by my success and your failure, by my affluence and your poverty.

So this habit cannot be established either. I mention it anyhow because I believe that sooner or later it becomes necessary to take the step from property culture to communal culture in a world that is shrinking to one country—and also necessary for us who will be obliged to transform our entire economic system to arrive at that point.

If Jesus Came Back

If Jesus came back in this year of Our Grace he would find that those who profess to believe in him live almost exclusively in the rich quarters of the world's city. He would find that those with the earthly responsibility for the propagation of his teachings and those with power to influence the life of the Christian church are comprised of rich people, of those learned in the Scriptures, of pharisees, and of vendors. He would find that his disciples in these quarters, the shepherds of the flock, had forgotten the social message of the Gospels and for hundreds of years had followed him less than they had followed the centurions, the moneylenders, the rich men, Pontius Pilate. He would find that these his new disciples had used their power over the people to stand his teaching on its head: instead of taking from the rich and giving to the poor they had converted to taking from the poor and giving to the rich, and instead of loving their neighbor and living in the spirit they had converted to using their neighbor and amassing riches upon earth. He would also find that the lambs in the flock seldom protested against this Gospel, for they were no longer poor either. But even in these rich quarters he would find the kind of people who doubted these new teachings, the kind who did not want to amass riches on earth and who still wanted to love their neighbor, and though not all of these were believers but many were atheists, he would be pleased and thank God. He would be pleased and thank God until he realized that these grumblers seldom could make their voices heard and that they usually let false prophets hoodwink them: it is true, they did not amass riches themselves, but neither did they decline those riches that others amassed among the poor in order to give to them, and they tried to love their neighbor, it is true, but they did not visit their neighbor nearby in the quarters of the poor and seldom even the few neglected poor in their own quarter (many had been put away in homes), for they had been persuaded that their neighbor was to be found among the ninety-nine bloated domestic sheep they already had around them.

If Jesus came back he would thus not even be pleased with the grumblers, for he would not detect any differences between their conduct and that of all those who called themselves Christians (or atheists) in the rich people's quarter. Whereas, he would find a difference in character, and true to his teachings, he would pay heed to this difference in character, condemning all false prophets and vendors and taking mercy upon their misguided victims, forgiving them and weeping for them, "for they know not what they do."

If Jesus came back and landed by mistake in these groaning quarters (they were full of crosses), he would probably stow away this judgment as soon as possible and in great haste prophesy the downfall of the New Jerusalem, for he would know that he had come to the wrong place and without delay would have to repair to the poor quarters in the world's city. Only there would he find people whom he could share bread and wine with, recognize as his brothers, and invite to paradise, and he would find them in untold numbers and destitution, poor and outcast, publicans and sinners, sick and maimed, prodigal sons and lost fathers, and he would tell them all that the last shall be the first. On certain streets of this slum of the world's city he would find visitors from the fashionable quarters, mainly vendors and moneylenders, who had realized that the poor can be made even poorer if only a person exerts himself, but also a number of missionaries and social workers, Salvation Army soldiers and working-class ministers, who had realized that their neighbor is to be found not in luxury but in destitution. The former he would drive out, and among the latter he would sift the chaff from the wheat by inviting all to be seated alongside the beggars, juvenile delinquents, and old alcoholics on the bench in the House of the Lord that is now quite empty, for those who had visited the quarters of the poor in order to become saints on earth would decline company like this in the temple and only those who had visited the quarters of the poor to meet their neighbor would gratefully accept.

If Jesus came back and immediately revealed his name, many in the quarters of the rich would be doubtful since he looked like a working man, but the powers-that-be would fire off a cannon salute for the Lord of the universe, arrange a gala dinner at the White House in his honor, announce a formal session of the U.N. disarmament commission, and invite him to a papal procession at St. Peter's Cathedral; even so he would not remain. If Jesus came back and immediately revealed his name, many in the quarters of the poor would be joyfully surprised by the fact that he appeared as one of them, but the powers-that-be and the masses would mock and jeer him, hang a stone tablet with the inscription KING OF THE WEST around his neck, paint his face white, and wind a turban of the Star-Spangled Banner around his head; even so he would remain. He would begin living among the poor, working and starving as they do, and after some years he would no longer be remarkable to them and a stranger but as one of them. In this section of the world's city he would then found a religious revival, first among those who had once read the Gospel and were then never able to visit the Christians' temple, then among those who had once met Christian centurions and vendors and had then never been able to read the Gospel, finally also among those who, without knowing either Christ or Muhammed, knew the rich and the pharisees well enough to seek their neighbor spontaneously among the oppressed of their own kind and kin, and to all these he would say that it was time to decamp and go to the quarters of the rich in order to preach the Gospel there for all those who for hundreds of years had taken Jesus' name in vain.

If Jesus came back walking at the head of the mob of this world's city, the Christians would not strew any palm branches before his feet and no cannon salute would sound; if he began to tell the rich that they should give their possessions to the poor, and that they should stop listening to their clergy, who did not know what the Gospel was, they would mock and jeer him; and if he invested his words with power by having his band of disciples increase a thousandfold and draw closer in menacing multitude, the rich would lose their patience, shoot right into the unarmed multitude, arrest Jesus for being an agitator, have the Pope excommunicate him, and arrest twelve thousand of his closest disciples. Even so the band of disciples would continue to grow.

If Jesus came back and excited men's minds in the world's city, they would have to call a meeting of the U.N. General Assembly, which is located in the quarters of the rich. In the U.N. General Assembly, the Afro-Asian states would speak warmly in favor of this new Jesus whom they would take as their ally, and just as strongly, the Western powers, as specialists on the real Jesus, would turn against this Anti-Christ endangering world peace. The Latin American delegates would not dare vote against the Western powers, and as a matter of principle, the Soviet Union would abstain from voting, no decision could be reached, so the question would have to be referred to the International Court of Justice, which is also located in the quarters of the rich. And the International Court of Justice, by seven votes to six, would sentence Jesus to death. The people of tender conscience in the rich section of the city would dislike the sentence, but they would dislike it in silence. The rioting of the poor around the grounds of the court would be in vain, for one Swedish and one Chilean U.N. battalion were to keep guard over the area day and night up to the time of the execution. Finally Jesus would be strapped down in the electric chair, which is also located in the quarters of the rich. But the current would never be turned on, for at the last moment the World Health Organization within the U.N. would prescribe a psychiatric examination of the doomed man and he could not be declared healthy, wherefore the International Court of Justice would have to change its sentence to life imprisonment. At last the U.N. Security Council, which is also located in the quarters of the rich, would be forced to give notice of an extra session in order to decide upon an appropriate place for Jesus to be confined, and this time the Soviet Union would not inject their veto but in steadfast atheism would give their support to the name suggested by the Western powers: that sparsely populated suburb Greenland. And the Christians would rejoice, for not only would they have got rid of a rebel and insured themselves against an extremely awkward, let alone improbable, resurrection, but above all they would have managed to deprive the poor of a dangerous martyr of the Lumumba or Malcolm X type, and the slum dwellers of the world's city would stand there with a long face, exactly as that time at Golgotha.

Now there is no prevailing agreement on what Jesus actually meant, so a person can conceive of his return in other ways too. Maybe, to the joy (and wonderment) of many ecclesiastical princes, he would find himself very much at home in the rich people's quarter and thank God that so many souls there had invested their talents so well (in the sense of the parable) that they could afford to give alms *annually*.

Maybe he would only be confused.

Maybe no one would recognize him.

But if there exists today a negative image of Jesus among the people in the Third World, it's an image of Jesus as white, as fat, as privileged, lovingly forgiving all those who oppress their neighbor just so long as they go to confession afterward or fill the poor box with coins. And if there exists a positive image of Jesus among the people in these countries, it's an image of Jesus as colored, as hungry, as rebellious, lovingly seeking his neighbor among the last on the earth and seeking his enemies in holy wrath among the first on the earth.

Neither of these images of Jesus is found among those Western color lithographs which are somewhat in demand today. But once in the sixteenth century, in that explosive moment when protest against the domination of the church had not yet been castrated into Protestantism, the farmers of Germany suddenly took it upon themselves to read the Gospel without first having their masters disarm and distort the social significance of the words, and at that moment they saw exactly these images of Jesus.

That's how I see it. If, as a whole, the Western church can be cured of its profound social perversion of many hundred years, it's the Third World and the examples from the Third World that can provide the only remedy: a realization, here and now, of who our neighbor is.

It's Africans and Asians who today must missionary among us, not we among them.

Four Myths

1. *There are democratic countries.*

There are only countries that more or less cleverly keep their dictatorial elements in check. Those countries—primarily the Western industrial ones—that, with angelic arrogance and duplicity, generally call themselves democracies because they have democratic constitutions and a respectable supply of freedoms and rights for their citizens, all have these dictatorial elements to combat, tame, compromise with, or succumb to. Some of them can be disarmed—the nobility and the court formerly, the church in several areas today. But the most important ones cannot be evaded, especially not the new economic nobility—and the new economic nobility is extraordinarily interested in the maintenance of a strong war/defense power, as well as in an intelligence service that effectively keeps track of rebels and Communists. A solvent church working to preserve the status quo is also a good thing, the finance nobility thinks.

The finance nobility, the military power, the intelligence service, and the church all restrict themselves to rigidly hierarchical organizations and possess exceptional opportunities to exercise their power in secret, undisturbed by democratic considerations and public spotlights —thus the designation dictatorial elements. They live as young cuckoos[1] in the nest of the little birds of parliament. High finance, the military, and the intelligence service are also the power factors that play the leading role when market-quaking heads of state are expelled and reactionary dictatorships are restored.

Normally both the military power and the church are presumably kept reasonably in check in the capitalist countries, and the secret police that function within the borders of many West European countries seem unusually lenient and discreet compared with the good-sized staff of professional bloodhounds the Soviet Union traditionally employs to terrorize its citizens. But at regular intervals examples of the kind of terror of which these agencies are capable are also offered on the parliamentary home front when opportunity is presented. The McCarthy persecutions in the U.S.A. and the activity of the O.A.S. generals in France during the Algerian War are worth recalling, as well as the Vatican State's more chronic exercise of power

[1] Besides being famous for its charming song, the cuckoo is infamous for its peculiar habit of laying its eggs in other birds' nests and leaving its young to be hatched and reared by their adopted parents, often at the expense of their adopted siblings.—Trans.

in Italy, an uncommonly striking example of a dictatorship in the midst of democracy. It can be added that in countries that often wage war—consonant with the United States, France, and Germany—the military tends to retain a large part of its power even in peacetime: war veterans populate the administration, military men take over the intelligence service, old Nazi officers occupy leading NATO posts, generals are elected President, and disarmament advocates get their influence cut back.

To see a danger in all this, for democracy as well as for world peace, seems now to be ever so obvious after Hitler. The Fascists in Germany and Italy proved clearly enough what explosive strength the anti-democratic forces possess even in the proudest parliamentarian countries, and with their fortunately poorer resources, Franco and Salazar are proving the same thing today on the Iberian peninsula. If we don't keep the big-business men and the generals in line, our democratic institutions can easily be overthrown too, it is sometimes said with self-critical perceptiveness in the West. Here, however, Western self-criticism generally comes to a halt, which is as understandable as it is regrettable, for the most dismal truth is not that "our democracies" *can* wind up where Spain and Portugal have wound up if we don't pay attention, but that we have in fact already wound up there, in our (old and new) colonial policy. "Down there," in the Southern Hemisphere, we Westerners use in principle the same methods that Hitler used against the German Jews, that the United States has used for a long time against her black people and Indians, and that Salazar uses today against his Portuguese manpower, and we have done it for hundreds of years. It is only the forms that over the years have been made more palatable to parlor society. Invisible agents and harsh agreements instead of visible troops, etc.

This truth in itself ought to be sufficient to put an end

to the myth of the Western industrial countries as democracies. Sufficient and then some.

But myths are hard to kill off and what is most important to emphasize in this connection is perhaps that it's not any special terrorist agencies that are carrying on in the colonies but the same kind of totalitarian elements that sneak around infiltrating the West's increasingly tarnished corridors of democracy. The businessmen, above all, are the same, and if on fertile home ground they need not occupy themselves with the same kind of conspicuous exploitation the destitution in the proletarian countries betrays, they can, however—with the masses' well-being as an unsurpassed protective shield—accomplish a great deal: factory shutdowns and layoffs without appeal, formations of monopolies and cartels, speculation in land values and unfair advertising, depopulation of provinces "unsuitable" for industry, exchange of expensive French manpower for cheap West African manpower, tax exasion and capital flight, production of junk, building obsolescence into capital goods, effective barricade-building against democracy and economic equality within business enterprises, construction of gigantic family empires, control over all leading banks, establishment of politically dubious networks of agreements on private bases inside and outside the West, dirt cheap import of raw materials from the underdeveloped countries, and high-priced export of industrial products to the underdeveloped countries, and so forth.

Individually powerful dictatorial institutions double their power many times over by joining forces. Intimate dealings between church, high finance, and officers' corps occur not only in the Spanish-speaking part of the world but also in West Germany, France, and Italy. By this means a good deal is gained: for themselves the exploiters obtain moral sanction for their activity and thus a pious countenance of defending the fatherland, the church acquires greater resources and an elevated social reputation, the status quo-preserving character of the preaching is guaranteed, the wars acquire a quality of righteousness, and so on. In America, which has no state church, the capitalists have been able to "safeguard" the preaching by financing a great deal of religious activity, in approximately the same way as the bankers of the Pentecostal Movement in Sweden have financed Scandinavia's largest tent religion. Consequently, there doesn't seem to be any great risk that the preachers in the U.S. will suddenly turn the tables of capital theology and say that Jesus was not speaking figuratively at all when he damned the rich but that he was speaking figuratively instead when he maintained that each and every one should invest his talents. More powerful, however, are the more secular mergers between military power and big capital, in particular when the government is along on the sideline. The Pentagon is not only the United States' department of defense and one of the world's largest organizations but also a powerful landowner, both inside and outside the country; thousands of officers are among the top employees. Of the Pentagon's orders for war matériel, a substantial share generally goes to General Dynamics, which in turn has a couple hundred retired officers among its employees. Thus the popularly elected United States Administration will make its decisions, so crucial to world peace, between the pressures of two totalitarian groups both interested in the same thing, increased armaments.

Now there are no countries lacking in dictatorial elements and the reason is simple: democracy is impractical when something has to get done quickly. If a government takes the parliamentary road there will, of necessity, be long drawn-out discussions, delays, publicity, and compromises, and splendid efforts run out into the democratic sand. If instead the government negotiates in silence with the industrialists or the military power, sends out trade delegations from the private sector, has the intelligence service enlarged so that it can expel inconvenient rebel leaders and organize spontaneous rebellions, obviously "without the knowledge of the government," or take the matter into their own hands, not informing the parliament until afterward, then a good deal can be accomplished. Nor is this anything to get disturbed about, since the democratically functioning democracy is a myth. What is something to get disturbed about, on the other hand, is that the power of the totalitarian elements is not acknowledged and articulated in the West but is kept quiet, smoothed over— people don't let on about it. The only thing that is said, upon appeal, about the finance nobility, for example, is that it is placed under democratic control—the young cuckoos have become little birds too. But if this were the case, how would one then explain the fact that freedom of the press seldom or never is used to throw light upon the doings of the finance nobility? That our free press seldom dares to speak out on the power of the instruments of dictatorship? One finds in the reference books of the Western world just as few enlightening words about Morgan, reportedly the world's most powerful finance group, as the Soviet encyclopedia devotes, for example, to Trotsky.

In the U.S.S.R., we know, dictatorship is acknowledged, and since not infrequently its undulating long arms strike out at individuals, the Russians in general, though ill-informed on a good many things, can't be drifting in a state of uncertainty over what kind of society they live in. But on just this crucial point the people of the Western world are hoodwinked, for they are seriously told that the democratic forces once and for all have come out on top. Not the least of what is happening in this age of prosperity ideology is that democratic organizations are being transformed into oligarchies in which the bosses soon have more in common with bosses in other fields, for example commerce and industry, than with the groups of people who elected them. At the same time democratic preparedness among the people is impaired by means of such intrinsically excellent things as personal security and relative prosperity—and the instruments of dictatorship acquire a larger arena. It's possible that democratic preparedness in the West today is *dangerously* impaired. The process of de-democratization seems to be able to proceed without the people noticing it.

Presumably Rosa Luxemburg showed foresight when she turned against the very opposites of dictatorship-democracy—rejecting Lenin's idea of dictatorship as well as Kautsky's idea of democracy—and spoke out for something so offensive to our prudish welfare ears as a union of dictatorship and democracy, a kind of democratic dictatorship, for today she can count on support in both Eastern Europe and Africa. According to the same pattern, the Western powers, though without Rosa Luxemburg's approval, could be called authoritarian democracies or dictatorial democracies. It could be added that the instruments of dictatorship strike a good deal harder in Eastern Europe, but in return they're significantly more reactionary in Western Europe.

Certainly, it's not a democratic wind that is blowing in the world today, and if we're to divide up the countries of the world by means of the democracy-dictatorship pattern, only three types seem clearly recognizable: predominantly bad dictatorships, predominantly good dictatorships, and a number of mixed states where reactionary and progressive tendencies wage an undecided battle. The bad dictatorships are obviously those that work for the worst for the majority of people (Paraguay, Spain), the good dictatorships are those that work for the best for the majority of people (China, Tanzania), and the mixed states are those that have strong democratic institutions as counterbalance against their reactionary instruments of dictatorship (Italy, Mexico) or those that compensate their weak democratic instruments by means of progressive institutions of dictatorship (Czechoslovakia, Egypt). If there is a fourth group of states, it doesn't seem to consist of democracies either but of states that don't function at all (India).

More fruitful grounds of division are conceivable, but if we accept this one it is no longer meaningful to draw the democracy-dictatorship line of distinction *between* different countries but only *within* each individual country. In every country the dictatorial tendencies do battle with the democratic tendencies, and it is the course of events in the Third World in particular that forces us to realize this.

2. *The administrators of commerce and industry play a more and more important part in the welfare state, but the political power lies with government executives and parliament.*

Notoriously shy as they are, the administrators of commerce and industry have invented this myth themselves. They've also been able to spread it effectively, partly by letting the politicians take the public thrashings and keeping themselves personally in the background, partly by buying up and exercising control over a sufficiently large number of mass media and propaganda organs. Not until afterward does it usually come to light what the finance nobility have done.

Sometimes the political power lies with the businessmen, sometimes it lies with the politicians, and sometimes the parties share it (so-called mixed economy). More need not be said, actually, but since examples of the businessmen's political power are not taken up so frequently, I'll gladly seize the opportunity and become specific. The examples below are gathered partially from newspapers which now and then write candidly about business matters (*Der Spiegel, The New Statesman, The New York Times*, etc.), partially from *Finansmakt och storpolitik (Financial Power and Great Power Politics)* by Thomas Rördam,[2] such an ardent friend of free competition that he has taken it upon himself to stigmatize monopoly and abuse of economic power wherever they occur.

At the beginning of World War II a leading American oil concern sold fuel oil to the Japanese navy; the price was half of what the U.S. military power had to pay. However, the concern was not punished for this treasonous deed, which came to the attention of Washington too late; instead it received $100 million in government subsidy after the war for drilling oil in Saudi Arabia. Another American oil concern sold synthetic aviation fuel, which it was licensed to manufacture, to the Japanese without the government knowing it and by this means the air attack against Pearl Harbor was facilitated.

During the Korean War not only one private American shipping concern but also four government-subsidized shipping firms were caught in the act of transporting to Mao's China toluene, lubricating oil, steel plate, and other goods strategic to the war; during the first phase of the war Mao received a couple million tons of fuel oil in this way from the enemy country, the United States.

The German finance nobility made early preparation for World War II, among other ways, by establishing a large number of cartel and patent agreements, primarily with American firms. In the period between the wars, I. G. Farben and Standard Oil (with John Foster Dulles as a

2 From the Swedish edition of *Monopolernes tyranni* (Copenhagen: Det Danske Forlag, 1962). In the Swedish translation (Stockholm: Rabén & Sjögren, 1964), pp. 36 and 107.

legal adviser) entered into a patent agreement "according to which the Americans pledged themselves not to produce synthetic rubber." So long as the U.S. and Great Britain controlled the rubber plantations in Southeast Asia this did not matter so much, but when the Japanese captured these during the war, the Americans were thwarted in their war efforts; for a long time the Nazis were alone in being able to use synthetic rubber in their war industry. In a similar fashion the Allies were impeded at the beginning of the desert war by a cartel agreement on wolfram between Krupp and General Electric that was already drawn up in 1927; by means of this the American raw materials price had been driven to such a high level that no appreciable production of wolfram steel could get under way for the war industry. Not until the U.S. Office of Price Administration forced General Electric to lower its price could the Allies' armour-piercing projectiles be given the same striking power as the German ones, undeniably a divergent aspect of the legend-rustling tug of war between Rommel and Montgomery. The Ruhr trusts had already concluded production agreements with English and French arms factories before 1914, agreements that were renewed or expanded after the Peace of Versailles, and during the period between the wars the international steel, pig iron, and railroad rail cartels were created over the heads of the governments, primarily on German initiative. Close ties of military-industrial friendship were thus established on a private basis long before the war between Germany and the Allies. At the "summit meetings" of international cartels—to which the politicians and news services were obviously not admitted—the foundation was laid for a war machine that the international finance nobility more or less generally hoped would be able to crush the Soviet Union and world communism.

It is still uncertain how many agreements advantageous

to German interests were made additionally advantageous from the side of Western finance just in order to facilitate the defeat of the Soviet Union; at this time the Dulles brothers were already pleading Wall Street's cause. However, it's clear that after Versailles, the finance nobility of the Western powers purposefully paved the way for the Ruhr and that, just as purposefully, the Ruhr paved the way for Hitler. As early as 1924 Fritz Thyssen contributed to the financing of the Nazi Party, and in 1931 he took the initiative in promoting the election fund for Hitler (several million marks, paid partially by the German people in the form of increased coal and steel prices) which, according to the American *German Report*, assured the Nazis' victory at the polls; the president of the Mannesmann concern led the "Aryanization" of large Jewish enterprises; beginning in 1933 the head of the Flick concern was head financier for the SS and the National Socialist Party, plus, together with Krupp, Hitler's principal arms supplier; the Siemens and Klöckner concerns were not passive either, least of all when it came to confiscating foreign businesses during Hitler's war campaign. A remarkable form of international finance collaboration at the same time made it possible for Stinnes, Krupp, Thyssen, and several others to transform their "branches and offices throughout the world to Nazi spy and propaganda centers."

Nor have representatives of the Ruhr been able to keep from boasting about their performance—contrary to the custom in financial circles. Two statements by Thyssen are especially well known: "I paid Hitler" (the title of his memoirs) and "We forced Germany to leave the League of Nations." Von Papen, who had intimate dealings with both Thyssen and Krupp, is responsible for an even more pretentious formulation: "Hitler in power? No, that gentleman is only appointed by us. We're the ones who rule."

The same finance dynasties have prevailed through the

entire twentieth century in the Ruhr, exactly as is the case in France, Sweden, England, etc. Since the war the Ruhr has, as we know, regained its full strength, with the help of American capital particularly. The Marshall Plan and protection against communism are usually mentioned in this connection; less often is it mentioned that U.S. steel magnates benefited by the weakness of defeated Germany and bought their way into the Ruhr in the same manner that Esso and the other oil giants took advantage of England's weakness and bought their way into the Middle East. Germany's moderate corporate tax and (comparatively!) low wage level attracted the Americans, who, despite the Allied ambition to destroy the Ruhr immediately after the war, had as early as 1948 succeeded so well with their "aid" that *The New Statesman* was able to write on October 5 of that year:

> What has been created is nothing less than a large joint stock company, whose stockholders are Americans, and whose directors are Germans.

Today the steel barons are regularly authorized by the Bonn government to negotiate with the government heads of the Great Powers, an example of divided political power. At the same time the Ruhr concerns have their own diplomatic representatives. Krupp has two permanent "ambassadors" in Moscow and exchanges trade commissions with the Eastern bloc—as a first step toward diplomatic ties with West Germany. Investing money in the Soviet is an old German capitalist habit from the twenties, cherished especially in ultra-nationalistic FDP circles, paradoxically enough. Krupp was set free from prison in 1951 on the expressed promise of selling all his steel and coal assets and with the pathetic declaration: "Never again will a single gun be manufactured in my name." Sixteen years later he has relinquished his empire, which does not imply, however, that the concern has acquired a more peaceful orientation; it's considered to be foremost in the world in the mining of titanium, a not especially peaceful metal, and built steel mills, irrigation plants, and nuclear reactors throughout the world, not least in the Third World. In this remarkable rehabilitation Krupp has been assisted by Wall Street especially—also assisting was the publications king Luce (*Time, Life, Fortune,* etc.) on behalf of the English-speaking public—but Axel Wenner-Gren, Krupp's old Swedish cohort from economic invasions into South America between the wars, has also pitched in as much as he could, in the purchase of Bochumer Verein, for example.

Shortly before its downfall, Krupp discovered that Angola has richer untapped ore supplies than perhaps any other country in the world and therefore put up 190 million D-marks in order to extract Angola's iron ore (with added difficulties for Swedish ore as a consequence). The investment is probably being made with the redoubled approval of Salazar and Bonn, but if the Bundestag wanted to make trouble, they would have to do it carefully, for an open repudiation would damage the Ruhr and as a result the entire Federal Republic. Business initiative that ties the politicians' hands behind their backs in this fashion is very common.

Perhaps the most powerful banking firm in Europe is Rothschild Frères in France, with strong interests in the Sahara's oil, Katanga's copper, France's nuclear industry, and South Africa's diamonds. The firm has an English branch, Rothschild & Sons, with which collaboration was recently re-established in order, in a very obvious manner, to facilitate Britain's admission into the Common Market. The Rothschilds are going to build a railroad tunnel under the English Channel. Recently what are usually called "advanced plans" came to the attenton of the public. "Advanced plans" usually imply that big money has already been laid out, and when big money has been laid out this usually influences political decisions. Presumably de Gaulle can ignore Harold Wilson but hardly Rothschild Frères.

Matters seem to stand about the same with the supersonic plane, which also was not written up in the press until the leading airplane manufacturers of the Western world already had invested several billion in the project. Today politicians and scientists are discussing seriously whether the noise damage will perhaps be too severe, whether the money ought to have been used instead to make jet planes safer for traffic, whether the project perhaps ought to be stopped or postponed, etc.—but then the invested billions are already functioning as an extraordinary means of political pressure.

When, as in these cases, the initiative lies with the businessmen, one can often count on a priority politics in "the welfare states" that is just as myopically profitable as it is feebleminded: first the cars are built—then the roads; first the shoulders of the road are filled with runover bodies—then the hospitals are built; first the cities are contaminated—then the purification plants are built; first comes the furniture—then comes the housing; first rockets are sent to the moon—then tractors are sent to underdeveloped countries; first comes everything we don't need— then come the things we need. And what do the impoverished governments do? The impoverished governments ask the manufacturers to turn out still more cars, exhaust fumes, furniture, and airplanes—otherwise there will be no money left for hospitals, roads, housing, and purification plants.

The Korean War meant an enormous boom for the industry of the United States—and, consequently, for that of all Western Europe. The war in Vietnam is less of a paying concern, but there is no doubt of the fact that the war was welcomed by Wall Street. *The New York Times* writes: "The expansion of the war has infused new life into the declining market. The latest reports for Vietnam were the necessary stimulus at just the right time." The *Wall Street Journal* writes: "The financial world is optimistic primarily because of the great war efforts in Vietnam. With confidence people are hoping for a trend toward rising profits during 1966." *Svenska Dagbladet,* a major Swedish daily, writes: "It appears clear that defense expenditures in the future too will have a stimulating effect on the economy during the coming twelve months" (figured from August 1966). Nevertheless, there are dissatisfied people on Wall Street too, especially within the nuclear industry and the chemical industry, for they consider themselves to have been treated unfairly by the Pentagon's policy of commissions. The napalm orders have surely been large, but poisons have been used less diligently, and above all, the nuclear industry has thus far had no pleasure at all from the Vietnam war. Can the nuclear weapons manufacturers hope for a conflict with China? In this situation a government wanting industry to flourish is subject to pressure; enough said.

The difference between this and the prewar period seems to be that the finance nobility in the United States and Western Europe no longer need to conduct their foreign policy by themselves and behind the politicians' backs. In the rampant spirit of the Common Market, capital and government—whether the government is conservative or social democratic seems to make no difference—are more and more often pooling their interests. The young capitalist cuckoo is adopted by his democratic stepparents. As a result it has become more difficult to determine where the initiative and the power lie, but certainly this doesn't mean that the finance nobility have had their political power cut back. The West German lawyer Fritz Bauer writes of the big concerns:

> The monopolies make the decision between war and peace. The civilian population pays. The international conferences, in which the monopolies participate, and their correspondence with one another show a striking similarity to meetings of heads of state and exchanges of international dispatches, and in conformity with states, the monopolies also enter into non-aggression pacts and assign spheres of interest between them.[3]

Within its sphere of interest each large concern can determine the rate of production and prices, which generally implies that the raw materials-rich underdeveloped countries are the ones to suffer. In this way Unilever has long reigned supreme along Africa's west coast, Union Minière in the Congo, Oppenheimer in South Africa, Aramco and British Petroleum in the Middle East, British interests in Malaysia, United Fruit in Central America, Shell and Standard Oil in Mexico, the banking houses of Schröder and Rothschild in Brazil, the Baring Brothers banking house in Argentina—but it doesn't seem to be so awfully different in Western Europe: Agnelli in Italy, Shell and Unilever in England-Holland, the steel barons in West Germany, the Wallenbergs in Sweden.

When the vital interests of the large concerns are threatened, in fact, the governments often benevolently put pressure politicians, agents, troops, or bombers at their disposal (the Suez, Iran, Iraq, Katanga, Guatemala, Cuba, Brazil). However, more frequently it happens that the Western governments prefer to play a more kindhearted role in the world's economic game: they come around later and smooth things over with foreign aid, gifts of grain, family planning, or chest-toned speeches in the

[3] Fritz Bauer, *Monopolernes diktatur* (Copenhagen: Forlaget Fremad, 1948), p. 72.

U.N. after the big businesses and their helpmates have taken care of the unpleasant details, lowered the raw materials prices of the monolithic cultures, gotten a lucrative war started in underdeveloped countries, beaten down a slave strike, burrowed away that shameless share of the profits in Zürich, and used the rest to buy up a piece of a news agency. This more hypocritical way of collaborating with capital is seldom cheaper for the governments, but it's undeniably more pliable than napalm and gunboats, particularly if the sovereign in question wants to live up to the old Western image of the Statesman: that cleverly cruising and democratically struggling commander in a world ruled by harsh economic laws. This is still rather popular. Unfortunately, the intimate communion between political and finance nobility seems to make it harder and harder to hold on to that image for long, and not even President Kennedy was able to keep his financial advisers at far enough range to succeed for more than a few moments—as a speaker—in looking like Benjamin Franklin.

Against this background, it is naturally easiest, or at least most honest, to place the businessmen directly in the government and administration, which in fact happens.

Ernest Oppenheimer is most well known as the creator of the worldwide diamond syndicate—diamonds are plentiful but Oppenheimer has made them rare—but he was not satisfied with the presidency of two of Africa's largest industrial enterprises, De Beers and the Anglo-American Corporation. He also made himself a political career. First as mayor of the diamond city of Kimberley, then as arms financier for the war against the Germans in Southwest Africa (where there are also diamond mines), finally as member of Parliament in the Union of South Africa.

The Jewish banker Robert Pferdmenger, "Aryanized" after 1933 and recently deceased, was a part of the leadership in the Ruhr and was Adenauer's financial adviser.

Later he divided his time between the vice presidency of August Thyssen-Hütte AG and the Bundestag in Bonn.

Ulick J. Alexander was associated with the financial administration in Great Britain during the period 1928–1952, at the same time he held the post of president in Tanganyika Concessions. He also served as a member of the board of Union Minière and Banque Belge.

As soon as de Gaulle came to power in 1958, his old friend Georges Pompidou had to take a leave from the directorship of Rothschild Frères in order to become first councilor, then prime minister. During the Algerian War he pleaded the double cause of his company and the President in negotiations with the FLN, and although at that time (1961) Pompidou wisely left the government, there were voices in the National Assembly asking what the initials RF actually meant, République Française or Rothschild Frères. They have reason to ask this today too, for Pompidou is back as head of the government.

Otherwise it's mainly the Americans who have excelled in double careers of this type. As chiefs of the military command in Berlin, the men who after 1945 were assigned to carry out the sudden counter order from the Allies (read U.S.A.)—don't destroy the Ruhr but build up German industry—represented the corps of officers, Washington, and Wall Street all at the same time. Beginning in 1950 General Lucius D. Clay—German sympathizer and anti-Communist, famous as the man of the airlift—became chairman of the board of Continental Can Corporation and a member of the board of General Motors and the Chase National Bank, among other organizations. His successor, John McCloy—later one of Kennedy's closest advisers and the U.S. disarmament negotiator (of all things)—was related to Adenauer through his wife's side of the family and, as rehabilitator of the Ruhr, represented an American law firm of the same politically influential type as the Dulles brothers' Sullivan & Cromwell, a firm with strong contacts with the Chase National Bank, in its turn an agent for the Standard Oil firm, an old hand at doing business with the Germans. Clay and McCloy helped back Ludwig Erhard. However, neither Clay nor McCloy had direct contact with the American firm that fought primarily for a concentration of power in the Ruhr, the banking group of Dillon, Read & Co., legal representative in the thirties for Fritz Thyssen and holding company in Nazi Germany's war industry. The problem was solved by appointing one of the leading men behind Dillon, Read & Co. as McCloy's economic adviser. Douglas Dillon, the head of the banking firm, was working at this time for the creation of a coal and steel pool in Europe, and the economic-political links came full circle in a manner satisfactory to Wall Street when the same Douglas Dillon eventually became Secretary of the Treasury in Kennedy's cabinet.

President Kennedy was famous for surrounding himself with young progressives, yet not only Dean Rusk and McNamara but also Allen Dulles, John McCloy, and Douglas Dillon were there. Which warmakers and Wall Street nobles surround Lyndon Johnson?

Forgive me that in presenting my examples I speak so much about the United States and West Germany, as well as about monopoly and cartels, but the disproportion is not my own but that of the Western world. Only six of the Western world's fifty largest industrial enterprises are non-American. Our European prosperity is to a great degree dependent upon market conditions in the U.S. (the war industry included). The industrial center of the Common Market and Western Europe is located in the Ruhr. West Germany is Europe's leading NATO power. And at least 90 per cent of the "free" enterprise in the West is dominated by monopolies, cartels, and other arrangements limiting competition.

Lately the need for economic planning and better guarantees against crises has given the governments a hold on the finance nobility. More and more often the finance nobility need the help of the governments. But at the same time the businessmen in the prosperity ideology have got an even better hold on the governments. The increase of production has become the crucial factor in the welfare states, for without increased production there are no wage raises, no social improvements, and no increase in aid to underdeveloped countries. The way in which commerce and industry conduct themselves in order to increase production becomes a secondhand question, so long as they increase it. When the need arises, the finance nobility have unrestrictedly good opportunities to clench their political fists.

3. *The industrial countries are self-supporting, but the underdeveloped countries cannot get along on their own.*

The industrial countries are not self-supporting; they need each other and they need the raw materials and manpower of the underdeveloped countries for their industries. How the underdeveloped countries would get along on their own is uncertain; what we do know is that so far the industrial countries have not allowed them to try standing on their own legs—or to join forces.

God has seen to it that nature's riches have fallen the lot of the United States and the Soviet Union in particular abundance. In fact, the United States and the Soviet Union could very well have been self-supporting. The U.S., however, has committed herself to an industrial production of such gigantic proportions that it is necessary for her to import anyhow. For their steel production, Americans have the world's richest iron supplies at their command, plus great quantities of molybdenum and vanadium. But manganese, chrome, nickel, and tungsten are also needed for good steel, and these metals the U.S. must import. Here Brazil, the Philippines, Bolivia, and earlier Cuba have come into the picture. In addition, the U.S. does not have sufficient reserves of ore with high mineral content, which, on the other hand, Venezuela and Brazil have. Wolfram also strengthens steel, for war purposes among others, and here the United States' own supplies do not suffice either. Portugal, Korea, Bolivia, and Vietnam are better supplied. Oil is another example—remarkably enough, since half of all the world's petroleum is produced in America. But if the Middle East has only a limited share of today's oil production, it's precisely in countries like Saudi Arabia, Iran, and Kuwait that the completely predominant share of the world's oil reserves are available, and the American oil concerns are planning ahead.

The U.S. has indeed committed herself to those underdeveloped countries I mentioned with strong economic and political ties, equipped them with conservative regimes, and corrupted them for the sake of the raw materials. In approximately the same way as the Soviet Union exploited her Eastern European neighbor countries economically after the war and at the same time rummaged about in their leadership, cleaning out elements hostile to the Soviet.

The fact that Europe is even more dependent than the Soviet Union and the United States is less remarkable, for Europe is comparatively poor. There's a great deal of coal in England, Germany, and Poland, iron in France and Sweden, bauxite in Southern Europe, sulfur in Eastern Europe, and so forth, but Europeans must import most of the raw materials for their industry, especially oil. This is one aspect of Eastern Europe's dependence on the Soviet Union and Western Europe's dependence on the United States that is emphasized all too seldom. But here, too, the underdeveloped countries come into the picture. Why was it the Dutch, Portuguese, Spaniards, and British in particular who early in history built ships and ventured out to colonize the world? Had they heard tales of the earth's riches that were not to be discovered on their own territory? They wanted to have these riches and they still want to have them.

But God has made not only North America and Russia rich but also many countries in Asia, Africa, and South America. Later Mammon in Western guise has tried to transport these riches to Europe.

What we call underdeveloped countries today provide the world with half or more of the cumulative production of, among other things, tin, bauxite, diamonds, natural rubber, jute, coffee, tea, cocoa, and rice. The Third World also contains great supplies of gold, copper, uranium, titanium, silver, cotton, tobacco, sugar, and, not least, oil. But who has so far had the most pleasure from the bauxite in Guiana and Surinam, from the rubber in Indonesia and Malaysia, from the oil in the Arab world, from the tin in Malaysia and Bolivia, from the gold and diamonds in South Africa, from the copper in the Congo and Chile, from the fruit in Central America? Not the population of these countries, to say the least.

One important difference seems to be this: while the West, by means of industrialization, has *made itself* dependent upon the rest of the world, the underdeveloped countries have *been made* dependent upon the West, generally against their will. The economy in the majority of Latin American states has been structured by Wall Street and Washington so that, for example, they cannot produce anything but those raw materials America wants and, consequently, cannot take the step out of the monolithic culture stagnation either. Chile, Venezuela, and Guatemala all have the natural prerequisites to create a richly varied industry, but the American concerns have forced them to concentrate their production on one or a couple of raw products such as copper and oil; the industrial products they have to buy from the U.S. instead for high prices. Countries that are restricted to one-sided raw materials production become, as we know, especially subjected to the fluctuations of the world market price and the pricing policies of the monopolies. Seldom or never do they have the chance to set their own prices.

The underdeveloped countries have become free, it is said. But Brazil, which became free in the year 1830 and is one of the richest countries in the world in raw materials, after 130 years of "independence" has not achieved greater economic (and political) independence than the French-governed Ivory Coast has after six years. Brazil is helplessly fettered by American and West European capital—which immediately gets aid from Washington if a Brazilian ruler gets it into his head to nationalize the electric power or the oil. There is a risk that Africa's nations have an equally long road to travel to freedom. Today they are just as free as beggars are in contrast to passing millionaires.

The West does too little today for the underdeveloped countries, it is also said. But judging by trade activities, the trouble seems to be instead that the West does too *much* for the underdeveloped countries. We help them hand and foot.

How do the industrial countries go about constraining the underdeveloped countries? They make use of tariffs, import quotas, and duties, for example, in order primarily to protect their own industrial products from foreign competition. Tariffs are traditionally set high for finished products and low for raw products, whereby the underdeveloped countries have particular difficulty exporting what they principally need to export, namely industrial products. Only their price-dumped raw materials export is "favored." In no sense can the Indian economist Jagdish Bhagwati be accused of being unfriendly toward the West, but when he gets into the world's disadvantageous, not to say devastating, terms of trade for the underdeveloped countries, he cannot restrain himself from criticizing. The West Germans oppose India's sewing machine export by means of a harsh quota system, and the Swedes oppose India's carpet export by means of high tariffs; then they smooth it over with shipments of powdered milk.

For that matter, the industrial countries don't really need to inflict damages at all, for the underdeveloped countries did not enter into the "world market" until it was given final shape suitable to those states that created it. Since the poor countries find themselves in an inferior position from the outset, it's often sufficient for the industrial countries to treat them as they treat each other: give loans at high rates of interest, invest in export in order to improve the balance of payment, and stock up on commodities. In Sweden lately the state has jostled the Swedish export industry in order to compensate for the increased import, and the result was not long in coming: during the first half of 1966 Swedish export to underdeveloped countries rose by 15 per cent, the import from underdeveloped countries hardly increased at all. A good way to bring down the imports from underdeveloped countries is also to establish agricultural protectionist trade blocs as well as to produce synthetic raw material surrogates. First we force the underdeveloped countries into one-sided production of raw materials; then we do everything we can to make ourselves non-dependent upon the raw material in question—whereupon the price falls to the catastrophe level. Recently the head of the World Bank sounded the alarm and expressed the opinion that the industrial countries (he meant the Western countries) must review their whole purpose "in relation to the developing countries." Since 1961 the "pure" aid to underdeveloped countries has stagnated at $6 billion a year and tends, in other words, to fall in proportion to the national products. At the same time, the aid to underdeveloped countries seldom goes to the most needy countries but to countries in which the Western countries have economic interests, military bases, or the like. (During the period 1957-1959, American aid—which lately, in conformity with that of the Russians, has been cut down—went to India, South Korea, Pakistan, South Vietnam, Mexico, Argentina, Colombia, Brazil, Israel, Morocco, Tunisia, Libya, and Egypt in the order mentioned.) What has increased, moreover, is private investment in underdeveloped countries: the interest rates have been raised, export has gained ground at the expense of import, the debts of the underdeveloped countries have risen, and the terms of trade persist. As a matter of fact, foreign aid—which we always make such a fuss over to avoid talking about exploitation—makes up only a small part of the economic activity with (or in) the underdeveloped countries. And all the while everybody talks of the necessity for multilateral initiative it is on the bilateral level that the increases take place.

For the present the only way for the underdeveloped countries to get better terms of trade seems to be to establish close ties with a certain industrial country or to associate themselves with either the European or the American bloc. The French commonwealth countries, for example, have been awarded favorable terms of trade that several of their neighboring countries can only dream about, and the EEC has abolished the excise on tea at least. As we know, the price these underdeveloped countries pay for their benefits is having their political independence decreased (for example in the U.N.). But at the same time the Third World as a whole pays a considerably higher price, for every country or group of countries that establishes separate agreements with the industrial countries in this way also drives a nail into the coffin of Pan-Africanism, Pan-

Arabism, Pan-Americanism, or the idea of an Asian community.

In both Eastern and Western Europe, people have realized in recent years that in order to ensure their continued prosperity, they must join together in the area of trade policy. When the same idea is presented by Nasser or Boumedienne, by a Mexican or by an Indonesian, however, it is maintained in European quarters that this is sheer fantasy and romanticism, an escape from local problems. Perhaps the proletarian countries are in fact romantic when they dream of their own federations and alliances, of their own merchant marines and world banks, but if so it is not because the idea of unity would be impractical or unrealizable. It is because the industrial countries find it so repugnant and dangerous that they are prepared to do all they can in order to deter its realization. If the underdeveloped countries join together in blocs, these blocs can also become power factors within world trade; if instead they remain splintered and divided up, the industrial countries can continue to dominate them. In today's Africa, the dominance of the whites is not decreasing; it's increasing instead.

The French economic geographer Pierre George sees the Balkanization, the splintering of small nations antagonistic among themselves, as the greatest threat the Third World has to face today. A look at the map suggests what is in question here. So long as the Frenchmen were on the scene, French West Africa was permitted to encompass a very large area. Today the same French West Africa is split up into more than ten different states, all, moreover, associated with France to such a high degree that they have become inaccessible to Pan-African invitations. The Congo has become two and nearly became three; Nigeria seems to be taking the same road; Rhodesia has already taken the same road, and in the South, one little province after another is proclaimed a "free" state. Like Central America, the Middle East has long been a crazy quilt, and the prospects for unity efforts in the home territory of the oil have not exactly brightened through the birth of Israel. In Asia, West Europeans, Russians, Japanese, and Americans have struggled for nearly a century to dismember mighty China, and today the Americans seem to want to keep it up. In India the British cleverly added fuel to the animosity between Hindus and Muslims that finally resulted in the formation of the state of Pakistan, which in turn is also divided. The Americans' division of Colombia, by means of which Panama was freed for the building of the canal, can also be named, as well as the dismemberment of the Dutch East Indies into Malaysia, Singapore, Indonesia, and half of New Guinea. Brazil, India, and China are the only underdeveloped countries that have remained large despite all the assaults, but of them, China is alone in keeping foreign influence in check. For the time being.

At strategic places the geographic dismemberment is matched by political dismemberment. Nasser knows what the idea of Pan-Arabic union is worth in money (oil); so the U.S., England, and France see to it that enemies of Nasser and friends of the oil concerns have their say in the management. They also supply all the countries with arms with which they can shoot at each other. What is remarkable in this is not that the powerful industrial countries have succeeded but that, despite everything, Nasser has so far managed to hold his job. In order to get kicked off the throne for sure in an underdeveloped country rich in raw materials, it is enough, from what we have seen, either to threaten nationalizations or else to work for alliances of underdeveloped countries, and Nasser has done both of these. In return, the circle of his allies has been decimated (Ben Bella, Kassem, Nkrumah, etc.), and exactly as was the case with Castro in Latin America, Nasser has been isolated.

Obviously many other factors enter in—the cold war

and the disintegration of tribes in Africa—but the battle for raw materials often seems to be the deciding factor, and in this battle the old divide-and-rule technique of colonialism has once again become a guiding star of trade policy. The experts now seem to be agreed that the world's supply of raw materials is going to suffice; it's the distribution of the resources that's the big problem, and here there are no supranational bodies that can intervene. The only rule that carries weight is that the mightiest gets the most, and this is a rule that de-colonization has not managed to budge. On the contrary, de-colonization seems to have opened the door for a freer flow of capital from north to south.

Finally it should be pointed out that in this area too the Soviet Union is subject to a more 'lenient verdict by the world's proletariat than the Western powers are. The Soviet expects no guarantees against nationalizations and radical reforms from the underdeveloped countries with which they establish economic contacts. And when the Russians come, the government of the underdeveloped country knows that these Russians represent the Soviet Union and therefore act with political responsibility. When the underdeveloped countries deal with the businessmen and trade delegates of the Western powers, they don't always know to what extent they're dealing with the country in question or to what extent with a young cuckoo without political responsibility.

But even the Russians are cheapskates when it comes to world market prices, and for the present, even the Russians seem to prefer wooing the underdeveloped countries into their own federations and blocs rather than encouraging federations and blocs in the countries themselves. Consequently, we may never have the opportunity to see whether the underdeveloped countries together can break free, at least not in this century. What has happened in

China and North Korea, however, demonstrates clearly enough that the conception of the underdeveloped countries' inability to get along without Western help is a Western myth.

4. *A balance of power prevails between East and West.*

If a balance of power prevailed between East and West—and now I'm counting China in the Eastern bloc—China would not only be a member of the U.N. Security Council but at the same time she would kick one or two of the Western powers out of the U.N. Security Council; the U.S. would be forced to withdraw a couple thousand of the military bases that today encircle the Soviet Union and China from all directions, and the Eastern side would have to establish its own network of bases in Mexico, Canada, Alaska, and the West Indies; China would annex Formosa and at the same time transform the Bahamas or Glasgow and its environs into a Chinese crown colony; together the Eastern countries would take over control of the World Bank, appropriate for themselves half of the influence in the U.N. special agencies, arrange in South Africa a coup d'état hostile to the West, reinstate Goulart, Jagan, and Arbenz, and establish communist regimes in Indonesia and Sweden; the oil concessions in Iran and Libya would be transferred to Soviet possession, and China would have control over raw materials production in the Philippines and in Burma; in return for the Western powers' taking over a million infantry troops of the Eastern countries, West Germany would be disarmed, France's nuclear weapons would be scrapped, a certain portion of the United States' nuclear weapons arsenal would be taken over by the Chinese, and the Russians' national product would be doubled, all at the same time.

There is no balance of power prevailing between East

and West, in other words, and there never has been one. What the side of the West, with the United States in the forefront, has been striving for throughout the postwar period has been not to create or secure a balance between the world blocs, but to *avoid* such a balance at any price. Every time the Soviet Union has made an advance, people in Western quarters have talked about the necessity of stopping this advance in the interest of the balance of power and of world peace, but what they've been safe-guarding at that moment has been only their own upper hand in the matter—which in a very real sense has in fact constituted and constitutes a threat to world peace.

When the history of the Western news agencies is writ-ten, I wonder whether the period 1945–1962—from Hiro-shima to the Cuban Crisis—won't be counted among the agencies' most brilliant epochs in terms of influence, for during this period they managed to fool not only the West-ern public but also the majority of politicians and experts in the West into believing that the Soviet Union—severely damaged by the war and throughout this entire period weaker—constituted the major threat to world peace and represented the one imperialistic power before all others. At the same time the news agencies managed to present the U.S., flourishing and incessantly warring, as the big helper and guarantor of peace, the sole hope of the war-weary world. (The Third World, however, viewed it dif-ferently.) They even managed to arouse a sense of destiny: it was only a matter of time before the U.S.S.R. would have passed up the U.S., soon the whole world would be in the clutches of communism—and the Russian atom bomb and Sputnik I were taken as "proof." The high point of this journalistically brilliant epoch was reached in 1962, when by virtue of her inferiority, the Soviet Union was forced to withdraw her missile base in Cuba without getting any compensations at all (not even the removal of the *Amer-*

ican base in Cuba). World opinion was persuaded instead that by virtue of their firmness, Kennedy and the U.S. had got their Russian equals to realize that world peace must be safeguarded and the balance of power preserved (the American missile bases around the Soviet Union included). That is not to say that the Western agencies have been slacking off since 1962. When it comes to depicting weak China as the primary threat to the United States and world peace, they've really put their hearts into their work.

Sensible people now raise the objection that it never was a case of any all-inclusive balance of *power* between East and West but only of a limited balance of *terror* in the field of nuclear weapons. Since 1949 the U.S. has not been able to atom-bomb the Soviet Union without being atombombed back herself, and with this realization, the parties have concluded armed peace. Indeed, in this sense a person can speak with certainty of a balance between East and West—so long as he remembers what a superior arsenal of weapons and above all what a superior system of bases the U.S. has on hand. In an atomic war the U.S.S.R. would be able to inflict great damage upon the U.S., but in a few minutes the U.S. would be able to lay waste to the entire, powerful Soviet Union, for she has every direction available to her. But what is crucial is that terrorist thinking has more or less imperceptibly been extended to concern a balance of power on a large scale and in all central areas. It is in this spirit that, ever since the war and up to the present day, people keep speaking of "East and West," of "The Iron Curtain," and of "the two blocs," as if the power were equally divided between them.

Now my wish is not that a real balance of power be established between East and West but instead that all of this Western East-West thinking be junked—to the benefit of the Third World. Besides, if, in improbable fellowship, the Russians and Chinese seriously started carrying out the program of equalization I have sketched above, much blood would flow and a good many more tons of the under-developed countries' raw materials would be thrown away on meaningless space races and shows of prestige. But, unfortunately, this wish for the long run must be brushed aside in the short run for an opposite wish—for the lack of balance is so great today that a major conflict can very well come out of it. For every escalation that is carried out in Indochina while the Russians keep silent, this threat seems to press closer. The fact is, it is thinkable—and unfortunately many have already thought of it—that the Soviet Union, aware of her inferiority, will not *dare* to counterattack if the United States starts bombing China's nuclear industries. Above all, it is thinkable that American strategists believe and are betting that the Russians—in deeper and deeper conflict with China and seemingly more and more anxious to save their own skins—will not intervene and that hence the U.S. can "calmly" attack China. Alongside the unregulated battle over the world's raw materials supplies, the superior power of the United States in the game between blocs is perhaps the most serious threat today to our continued existence.

In other words, you don't have to be a sympathizer of the cold war, you don't even have to be a Socialist today in order to wish the Eastern side greater successes than the Western side. It's quite sufficient that you dislike world war.

Meetings

1.

Some years ago on the train from Berlin to Prague I met two Jordanians who were studying in East Germany.

"What do you think of East Germany?" they asked.

I answered exactly what I'd just felt about it. "Dismal and shut in."

They were astounded. To them East Germany was bright and attractive, an industrialized socialistic state that —unlike extravagant West Germany—worked for peace as well as decent living conditions for the majority of the citizens.

"But many people have a very hard time in East Germany."

"Hard? Why, it's a rich country!"

"You should see Jordan," said the other one.

I tried to qualify my statement. "I was thinking mainly of East Berlin. I've only passed through the rest. There's a kind of gloom that hits you immediately in East Berlin . . . haven't you felt it?"

"No," said one.

"You must have been there on a Sunday," said the other.

They must be Communists, I thought, nodding my head convinced. Why, I had *seen* with my own eyes how gloomy East Berlin was. Still, when the Jordanians talked about East Berlin it seemed as if they had experienced the city as they described it—with their own feelings and not just as they'd been taught.

This was peculiar.

"Are you Communists?"

"We are Socialists."

It got quiet a moment.

"Aren't you a Socialist?"

"I am . . . generally radical (they smiled). . . . I distrust fixed ideological systems. . . ."

"But surely you vote for one party?"

"Yes, for the Social Democrats."

We went on to talk about Israel.

The Jordanians believed the Arab states ought to solve the Jewish problem together in exactly the same way as the Western powers, for their part, solved it after World War II: by evacuating most of the Jews to a different part of the world. Possibly Australia.

"A couple of million. The rest could stay where they are."

"Or go home to West Germany."

They weren't only Communists: they were fanatical anti-Semites too. I began to feel uncomfortable.

"But Israel is the homeland of the Jews," I said carefully.

At that point they raised their voices.

"It's *our* country. The Arabs have lived there for eight hundred years."

"The Israelis and English drove us away."

One of them was born in the western part of Jerusalem, the other in Nazareth. They didn't want to live in exile all their lives.

"Have you ever been outside Europe?" asked the one from Jerusalem.

"Unfortunately not. But it would be interesting to go to Asia."

They looked at each other. "Interesting" was definitely the wrong word. The one from Nazareth sighed. The other said something in Arabic. I started getting worked up.

"Do you really believe you can get rid of the Israelis?"

One drew his hand across his throat like a knife and smiled.

"It's not only the capitalists who have weapons!" the other one shouted.

It seemed as though I'd landed among Arab extremists.

"Do you know what the Jews do outside our refugee camps?" shouted the one from Nazareth again.

For a moment I thought he planned to cut my throat too. The other smiled and smoothed it over. "My friend is so involved in politics he can never leave his rifle at home. Ack-ck-ck-ck-ck-ck-kkkk—"

The friend smiled in spite of himself.

"You wouldn't understand," he said.

"At any rate, I don't understand why it has to be done with violence," I said.

Now both of them looked at me as if I were some strange animal. "Are you a pacifist?"

I didn't know what to answer. Apparently no matter how obvious my remarks were, they became astonished. Again they questioned: "Are you against violence?"

"Obviously, I'm against violence."

They looked at me and then at each other.

"You mean, there are actually Europeans who are against violence . . ." said the one from Nazareth.

"I'm a Swede," I heard myself say.

It grew quiet again. We were approaching the Czech border. Maybe they didn't know what *"Schwede"* meant. The one from Nazareth took out a book.

"Politics, politics, politics," said the more cheerful of the two and again drew his hand across his throat like a knife, smiling. I got up my courage.

"Is your friend studying politics here in East Germany?"

Instead of answering, the Jordanians started speaking to each other in Arabic. The one, in particular, laughed convulsively while looking in my direction now and then. I thought they were making jokes at my expense.

"My friend is going to be—ha, ha, ha—the greatest engineer in Jordan. The Krupp (he was almost choking with laughter) of the Arab world!"

The Krupp of the Arab world smiled a little. The cheerful one aimed an imaginary gun at him. "Ack-ck-ck-ck-ck-kkk."

"Are you studying to be an engineer too?" I asked.

"Sociology and economics." Aikonnomigs ent socziolzhi. "And you?"

"I'm mainly involved with literature."

"Literature?"

"Yes, poetry mostly."

"I love poetry! Brecht—"

"Yeh, Brecht is really good."

Now they started talking Arabic again. We passed the Czech border. I didn't understand anything. It sounded as if they mentioned Brecht. Our passports were stamped. I felt left out.

"Is there much poetry in Jordan?" I tried.

"*Jawohl*."

"Modern poetry, I mean?"

"You mean poetry written today?"

That would have to do. I nodded.

"*Nicht so viel*."

The one with the book looked up. "More politics."

It got dark. You couldn't see Czechoslovakia. In the mirroring window only myself and the Jordanians were visible. The one from Jerusalem began to doze, the other went back to his book. Why doesn't anybody ever ask you about Sweden when you're traveling? I took out an issue of *Bonniers Litterära Magasin*. A good hour went by. Suddenly the one with the book (the engineer) leaned toward me. He was almost whispering.

"There's one thing I'd like to ask you about."

"Yes?"

"What's your religion?"

"Religion?"

"Yes."

"No special religion."

He wasn't satisfied.

"I mean, which religious . . . which church do you belong to? Which church?"

"No church at all. I am . . . an agnostic. Or a private mystic."

He still wasn't satisfied, tried to start a new sentence, gave up, and woke up his friend. They talked together awhile, the friend nodded understandingly and turned toward me.

"My friend wants to know what your religion is."

"But I'm—"

"In your country, that is. In your culture."

"Oh, I see! Christianity."

"Catholicism?"

"No, Protestantism. Evangelical Christianity."

Now they were satisfied.

"We're Muslims."

"Mohammedans?"

"No, Muşlims."

"Religiously active Muslims?"

They looked at each other. Neither understood.

"We are Muslims."

"Are you Socialists and Muslims both?"

"Of course."

I mustn't think in Swedish terms all the time, I told myself. You have to understand them from their own point of view.

"How can the two go together?"

The one from Jerusalem laughed. "Islam and Socialism go together just like Christianity and Capitalism, ack-ck-ck-ck-ck-kkkk—"

"But then Marx talks about the opium of the people—"

"The Russians are stupid."

They took out round loaves of bread, a knife, and a sausage. The one from Nazareth sliced with hazardous gestures. I went into the dining car. When I came back they were talking mostly Arabic. Just before Prague we exchanged addresses.

"You don't understand what we're saying?"

"Not a word."

When I think back I realize that didn't happen so long ago as I'd now like to believe. Half a year later, anyhow, I got a postcard—it must have been from the cheerful one

222

from Jerusalem. He thought it had been interesting, he wrote, to meet an intellectual from Western Europe.

2.
In the 1530's the great Spanish conquistador Pizarro invited to his camp in Caxamarca the great Inca chieftain Atahualpa. Atahualpa came in a golden throne with thousands of Indians in his retinue and got a royal reception. Throughout the preceding night the hosts had prepared for the visit, partly by praying to God and partly by sharpening their swords, and now they offered their guests a magnificent exhibition of Spanish horsemanship in honor of the chieftain, whereupon the Spanish chaplain gave a lecture on the infallibility of the Pope and the suzerainty of the Spanish monarchy over America. Then the Spaniards attacked, massacring most of Atahualpa's men and taking the chieftain himself to prison. In captivity, Atahualpa was treated like a king, attended by the women of his harem and permitted to learn to play chess. In order to purchase his freedom he had all that his kingdom owned in the way of art treasures of gold and silver—primarily golden vessels and ornaments—conveyed to Caxamarca, and after two months of uninterrupted deliveries, the whole camp was resplendent with beauty and riches. When the great chieftain now made ready to depart, he was first allowed to see Pizarro melt down his kingdom's irreplaceable treasures to ingots; thereafter Pizarro accused Atahualpa of treason, had him strangled, and broke camp to conquer the rest of the Inca kingdom.

Christian civilization opposed to primitive paganry.

3.
In the year 1954 India ordered two steel mills from Europe. One of them was built in Rourkela by a group of West

German concerns, and the other was built farther inland by technicians from the Soviet Union. On both sides the work took nearly five years, and the race between West Germans and Russians was followed with great interest in the Indian newspapers the whole time. The West Germans won, curiously enough by a single day; in return, the long-range production capacity of the Russian steel mill, which was equally large, was twice as great as that of the West Germans.

But it wasn't only the technical side of the question that interested the Indians. Nearly a thousand foreign technicians were required for the job and since these were to live in India for several years, proper emigrant villages had to be built up, and many social and economic problems had to be solved. For the Russians the entire project was organized from the start as a propaganda item, intended primarily to win the hearts of the Indians, and only secondly their money. Surely the West Germans could have regarded their steel mill construction in the same fashion—that is, if it had been handled from the start at a responsible level of government—but it was the steel barons of the Ruhr who were in charge of the building now, and completely different forms of responsibility were decisive for them: responsibility to the stockholders (the project had to make money) and responsibility to the executives (personnel turnover, which complicated the work, had to be prevented by means of privileges).

The first thing the West Germans did upon arriving in Rourkela was get rid of the local liquor prohibition, both for themselves and for the rest of the population. On their side, the Russians had strict orders to respect the Indian alcohol legislation and never drank vodka in sight of the populace.

The Germans built a hospital in which only Germans

could be accepted as patients. The Russians built a communal hospital for Indians and Russians.

The Germans built a clubhouse, bar, swimming pool, and movie house, and these public places of entertainment were also reserved for West German citizens. The Russians also built a clubhouse, but guests and hosts met there in accord with Khrushchev's propaganda motto: "Russians and Indians are brothers." Since the Russians were not allowed to drink vodka on these occasions, the fraternization must have demanded personal sacrifices.

The Germans hired Indian girls as housekeepers and as leisure time companions, the latter to such a degree that the rumor of immoral practices forced the Indian government to conduct an investigation; the fact that the servant girls received wages far higher than those of even highly qualified Indian labor also stirred up bad blood in Rourkela and its environs. The Russians were shrewd enough not to hire any servants at all.

Both Germans and Russians helped the Indians with credit for the construction of the steel mills, and even on this part of the front of the intra-European propaganda war, the Russians won easily. The Ruhr concerns demanded 6.5 per cent in interest, the Soviet Union only 2.5 per cent.

This instructive meeting between East and West, with the Third World watching from orchestra seats, was described by *Der Spiegel* on March 30, 1960.

4.

When village inhabitants who have no weapons or only occasional rifles resist a military force using napalm, a few pathetic shots are heard first, then the napalm rains burning down over the village, where the houses or huts are set on fire, and soon the whole village is burning and the great majority of its inhabitants and livestock are killed in the flames. But when the fire begins to die down and the soldiers not wounded venture to come closer (on healthy legs) to the no-longer-existing village, it often happens—since napalm bombs seldom kill everybody—that somebody comes to welcome them or stands waiting for them out in the front yard of his former house, a surviving villager with a peculiar appearance. The B.B.C.'s war correspondent in Korea described such a meeting:

> In front of us a curious figure was standing a little crouched, legs straddled, arms held out from his sides. He had no eyes, and the whole of his body, nearly all of which was visible through tatters of burnt rags, was covered with a hard black crust speckled with yellow pus. . . . He had to stand because he was no longer covered with a skin, but with a crust-like crackling which broke easily. . . .[1]

5.

Thirteen years after the end of the war, the military armistice commission is still working, without results, in Panmunjom, Korea. Nobody can complain that the committee hasn't been active: over seven hundred meetings have been held thus far, making a good average of one a week since 1953. But very little seems to happen except that for several hours the parties exchange accusations and then part. The peace isn't concluded yet, both parties have broken the armistice agreement (which prohibits rearmament), and the uniting of the country after general elections seems just as far off as ever. It is hardly any more difficult to understand which of the parties does not want to have general elections than it was in the case of Vietnam. In Korea, too, there is a good dictatorship in the north and a

[1] Reported by René Cutforth in the Manchester *Guardian*, March 1, 1952. Cited by David Horowitz in *The Free World Colossus* (London: MacGibbon & Kee, 1965), p. 136.

bad dictatorship in the south, and the good dictatorship's men would probably win the majority of votes even in the south—and "communism" would triumph. Nor does the status quo seem to have any appeal for the Americans worth mentioning, for the border between north and south was once drawn so unfavorably that the wolfram mines along the thirty-eighth parallel wound up mainly on the side of the North.

The parties meet in a barracks that is situated half in North Korea, half in South Korea. Through the northern entrance come the Chinese and North Koreans; through the southern one come mostly Americans and South Koreans. Generally, Chinese and Americans, the chief antagonists of the Korean War, seem to lead the negotiations. Outside the barracks North Korean soldiers march through precision drills in Hitler style—at least that's the way it was when a Swedish journalist was last there on a visit—and on their side the South Koreans (with "foreign aid" money?) have built a pagoda-like structure which, in the still surviving spirit of Syngman Rhee, they call "Freedom House." Here, in the demilitarized zone, stand the delegates' cars too: Volga and Zim in the north, Ford and Chevrolet in the south.

In this there is little to wonder at: armistice commissions often get stuck in the quagmire between East and West. What is remarkable is the U.N.'s role in the Korean connection. When the Chinese walk into the barracks they represent only themselves; when the Americans walk into the barracks they represent the U.N. Given the choice at the start of the war between appearing as a supranational body and appearing as the U.S.A.'s lackey, the U.N. "chose" to appear as the U.S.A.'s lackey, and sixteen years later, nothing seems to have changed in this respect. It's the U.N. who come from the south side and get out of their Fords and Chevrolets; it's the U.N. who pass "Freedom House" and open negotiations with their "enemies" from the communist world; it's the U.N. who, in American uniform, blow cigar smoke into the eyes of the Chinese delegates and whine that the fact that the U.S. has begun rearming in South Korea in exchange for South Korean troops helping the Americans in Vietnam in no way implies any breach of the armistice agreement.

During the Korean War sixteen U.N. nations fought on the side of South Korea, and of these, six are still represented in the commission. All walk through the southern entrance, and the majority of them are guaranteed U.S. sympathizers or sellouts to the U.S.: Great Britain, the Philippines, Turkey, and New Zealand. On the other hand, the two countries of the opposite side have nothing to gain from the U.N.: they belong to an international pariah, a kind of political leper colony that cannot even be sure of counting on the support of the ever more haggling Soviet Union. Seventeen years after the establishment of the People's Republic, China, the world's largest country and moreover one of its few decent countries, is still excluded from the U.N., while some of the world's least decent countries—among others, South Africa, Portugal, and the United States, chronic U.N. Charter breakers—exert power and influence there. The fact that North Korea is excluded from the U.N. is less remarkable—so is South Korea, as well as both of the combatant states in Germany and Vietnam. But it should be noted that West Germany, South Korea, and South Vietnam have been selected to some ten of the U.N.'s special agencies, while North Korea, North Vietnam, and East Germany are excluded even from these.

The more that is gradually divulged about the course of events of the Korean War, the greater appears the obscurity of the U.N.'s position on the side of the West, and the more that is gradually divulged about the first ten years of the U.N., the more clearly the long-standing, crushing dominance of the U.S. within the organization stands out. The election of Taiwan to the U.N. Security Council and the voting in the fifties on China's membership in the U.N. bear witness to this belief. Not until the year 1961 did the Afro-Asian bloc begin to threaten the United States' assembled predominance of votes, and that time the victory had to be purchased at the Africans' price: electing Mauretania and Outer Mongolia as new members. In 1965 the U.S. had a somewhat easier time of it, and once more in 1968 the United States can count on the majority to follow her line, with the help of Ghana among others; however, the margins have dwindled. But in Korea nothing has been changed since the beginning of the fifties: here the pitch of the U.N. is still identical with the pitch of the U.S.

If a person wants to believe that a balance of power prevails in the world and that the U.N. is the supranational, neutral guarantee for this balance of power, he is wise not to think about this meeting between East and West that is under way week after week, year after year, in Panmunjom.

6.

One night on TV I saw the Senegal National Ballet Troupe, another night I saw a dance revue from Luxemburg. The difference was great.

I don't know how genuinely Senegalese the African ballet was—maybe it was ground down to suit the European audience. Anyway, the dance from Luxemburg was easy to recognize from American musical films: a large number of girls in matching net stockings and tinselly little dresses jumped around in a line, curved out into fan formations, and throughout their ranks made movements which, scarcely notable in themselves, were intended to create an effect by being executed by everyone at exactly the same

229

time or with a certain calculated delay. Expensive scenery in the background and big, orchestrated hit tunes. The dancers in the Senegal Ballet were fewer, the scenery simpler, and the orchestra generally reduced to a couple of drums. The costumes varied, and when any of them stood in line clapping their hands or flinging their legs out, the coordination in the line was always bad; for that matter, even though the dancers were rather few, it never happened that they all did the same thing at the same time. In each dance different events occurred on the stage, and synchronized effects were rare. Most of them seemed to do what they wanted.

When somebody leaned forward in the Luxemburg group the others also leaned forward in the same fashion and at the same moment or else a tenth of a second later so that it looked as if the line "billowed." When somebody leaned forward in the Senegal Troupe, a couple leaned forward in a different direction, while another group reeled with their arms in the air, and between these unordered groups—you can hardly talk about lines—it happened that one man and one woman danced as a couple, while a third person, perhaps a rejected suitor, did repeated somersaults in a corner, seemingly outside the action. According to European concepts the Senegal Ballet seemed on the whole poorly "coordinated." One dance that had to do with a wedding celebration began with the wedding guests rocking back and forth or clapping hands, while the drums worked themselves up to a more and more frenetic tempo; then one of the guests sprang forward and danced individually, and after he or she had danced awhile somebody else came out instead. Then if there was somebody who could kick up his heels behind him or turn handsprings, he got to do that, but when the others had tired of his tricks, they came stamping forward and started dancing in front of him so that the audience could no longer see what he was doing. Seldom then did the acrobat with-draw but was caught up into the others' joy of the dance and started dancing around with them, no longer in the center of activity but apparently glad even so. After a while you couldn't see who he was in the crowd.

Now individual contributions were not lacking in the Luxemburg ensemble either. In certain numbers there was a totally dominating star, but then it was not a ques-tion of a dancer but of a songstress who, indeed, tried help-fully now and then, in the rest between each verse, to dance like the others but who mainly stood still singing a hit tune, while the dancing behind and around her went on as before, faithful to that basic principle that seems to be shared in the West by gymnastics exhibitions, water bal-lets, and different kinds of expensive shows as well as by military parades throughout the world: mass effect. On a revue stage it is possible to give the illusion of an avenue with fluttering treetops, for example, but it goes without saying that five thousand housewife-gymnasts with out-stretched arms at the Stadium can achieve a more powerful effect of an avenue.

The basic principle for the Senegal Ballet's dance was something else. Perhaps you could call it a common joy of the dance. The dances were set up collectively—the ac-tion in them generally required everybody's cooperation—but no military or gymnastic discipline seemed to occur, in any case not visibly. Instead the allowances for individ-ual deviations and improvisations were substantially large throughout, and the purpose of having these free reins, which sometimes seemed to lead to pure chaos, must have been to encourage just this joy of the dance. Certainly it is not possible to *create* a joy of dance by means of just any kind of arrangement, but if there's a potential dance pleasure, it can be coaxed in this way to burst into full bloom, which in fact happened and happens. When they dance, the Senegalese Troupe radiate a joy that is just as contagious as that which Miriam Makeba generates when she sings and Eusebio rouses when he plays soccer.

When U.N. Day is celebrated and the weather is clear, it sometimes happens that a number of pilots are assigned the task of writing the word PEACE in the sky with the help of their airplanes. In order for this to succeed each pilot has to concentrate his attention 100 per cent on looking, in his sheet-metal armor, not like an airplane but like one-fifth of a stem of a letter of the alphabet. The least deviation from the course jeopardizes the peace and uncharitably reveals that there's a human being sitting amid the letters of the alphabet. The girls in the dance revue from Luxemburg seemed to function in the same, depersonalized way, as cogs in a piece of machinery. They didn't lack faces, but they were obviously selected and shaped up to resemble one another as much as possible: the same height, the same build, the same dress, the same make-up, the same hairdo, the same way of showing their matching white teeth so that an effect of mass smiling could result. In the Senegal Ballet both tall and short, scrawny and muscular, bald-headed and long-haired, gaudily dressed and naked entered in, and nobody made a movement in exactly the same way as any of the others, any more than uniform smiles or laughter occurred. Each one smiled or laughed in his own way. The division of sexes was unclear too. In the one dance from Luxemburg in which men also took part, all the girls had green dresses and all the men peppermint-striped jackets and straw hats; the sexes were mingled in the middle, generally to dance in couples, but as soon as the dancers drew back, gentlemen's and ladies' sides were formed immediately; the men also had their own "masculine" routine while the girls danced in a "feminine," mincing way. In the Senegalese dances in which not all of the female participants had the upper part of the body bare, it was a good deal more difficult to tell the sexes apart. The costumes were seldom uniforms of sex; gentlemen's and ladies' sides seldom occurred—the sexes were mingled, rather; not even the routine offered a sure guide. A muscular, acrobatic dancer with short-clipped hair could turn out to be a woman; when you had picked out the male partner of a dancing couple it eventually turned out that the "female" partner was a man too.

The Senegal Ballet was able to indulge in all these freedoms without for a moment jeopardizing the impression of mutal cooperation and collective participation. No one, on account of his passivity, appeared to wind up outside the group spirit or be reduced to a walk-on; no one managed for more than a moment to "steal" the dance from the group by a star solo act, either, for soon enough the star was always eclipsed by the group's pleasure in the dancing or else a new star turned up. With his own personality, his own style, his own deviations, everyone was *a part of it*.

Seen in terms of psychology of cultures, perhaps it should rather have seemed the other way around, at least on a superficial comparison. It's not in Senegal or Africa, of course, but in the West, that, traditionally, great weight is placed on such things as private initiative, private ownership, individual success, personal salvation, investment for personal gain, idol worship, esthetic originality, psychological self-realization—in short on different forms of individualism. Such ideals are certainly not lacking in Africa, particularly not after European colonization set in, but the deciding factor for the pattern of culture seems generally to be the opposite ideal: the idea of the large family, *Ujamaa*, and in connection with this, such things as communal effort, collective ownership, shared responsibility, emphasis on collective kinds of art such as dance and music, emphasis on a greater group togetherness from the start (by the uniting of relatives or by polygamy) than the union between two people—one man and one woman, one I and one thou—that is established in the West to engender the "core of democracy." Tom Mboya writes in one passage:

> Most African tribes have a communal approach to life. A person is an individual only to the extent that he is a member of a clan, a community, or a family.[2]

It is, in other words, in a cultural milieu strongly emphasizing collective values that the dance of the Senegal Ballet, seemingly devoid of collective discipline, has come about. But is there really a contradiction here? On the contrary, isn't it true that the person who is accustomed to living and working in a group from the outset also has the easiest time playing out his individuality and unique personal style within the framework of the collective dance?

The conventions that have been developed in the West for a number of collective activities—for gymnastics exhibitions and mass meetings, for cocktail parties and committee meetings—are in many cases admittedly unimaginative and impersonal. Often the emphasis on discipline and uniformity seems so strong that every attempt at improvisation and personal expression is nipped in the bud. Whatever kinds of people have created such collective monstrosities as the German committee meeting, Swedish group gymnastics, or the American cocktail party, it cannot possibly be a question of any socially gifted human beings. Probably it's successful individualists who are behind it, lone prestige wolves who have grown up in stuffy little families and accustomed themselves from the start to having their own room, their own things, their own money, oriented early to becoming go-getters, making a personal contribution, making a name for themselves and having a career, at worst at the expense of close bystanders. At least it ought to be true, for just such social cripples —they might be businessmen, scholars, white-collar offi-

[2] *Freedom and After*, p. 166.

cials, or writers like myself—seem to be doomed, in the presence of every form of collective community that transcends the marital twosome, to react with panic-stricken bewilderment, if you will, with pessimism. I can't develop my personality here, it's a matter of playing a role here, subordinating myself to a collective ritual as pliantly as possible—in other words, the self, with its rough edges, has to be left at home; if I have the power to direct the collective myself, then I'll see to it that the ritual gets so formalistic that no individual surprises need be feared, that a plastic-coated cocktail conversation replaces personal conversation, and that all forms of communal joy in dance are killed and clogged up with a kind of precision pleasure for leg-flapping robots. The idea that individual expression and group sharing do not exclude but necessarily entail each other doesn't seem to be able to penetrate such mechanized heads, for this would imply that they were forced to play on equal terms with their own accessible self—and not with that depersonalized fish-in-the-water personality that dread of society and bad habit have led them to develop, sometimes to committee-mad perfection.

Now even in the West there are people who have grown up in big families or who find it natural for other reasons to make their way into groups in order to realize themselves (and not in order to run away from themselves). But when they try at their place of employment and in organizations to institute a bit of big-family life, they often buckle under at the task in that depersonalized, veneer community, for most of the people who surround them seem to be hopelessly habituated to bringing only a tenth of their personality with them to the job or the association—the rest is left at home in their two-room apartment—and being suddenly personally exposed and confronted disturbs them. On the whole there doesn't seem to be much that the socially talented people can do in our latitudes—other than personally bring a teeming *Ujamaa* into the world or plunge themselves into a life of free-for-all private parties. In Africa these homeless souls, if the image fits, would find what they're looking for more easily in work teams, in associations, in dance groups. The Senegal Ballet's way of dancing, like a big family on a picnic, already suggests what an enormous amount, in social terms, Africa has to teach America and her old governess and Caligula, Europe.

Or is this drawing a bit too bold and far-reaching conclusions from the accidental encounter between a European revue and an African ballet on a TV set? I'll take that risk.

7.

Japanese meet Americans.

On August 9, 1945, some days after the first encounter of the Japanese people with nuclear power, President Truman furnished the following justification for the bombing of Hiroshima and Nagasaki:

> ... in order to shorten the agony of the war, in order to save the lives of thousands and thousands of young Americans.[3]

8.

In *The Wretched of the Earth* Frantz Fanon tells of a thirty-year-old French police inspector who visited the writer at his psychiatric reception room during the war in Algeria. The inspector is nervous, smokes five packs of cigarettes a day, and wants to be cured of what he calls his "fits of madness."

> Can you give me an explanation for this, doctor: as soon as someone goes against me I want to hit him. Even outside

[3] From a radio speech on August 9, 1945, reported in *The New York Times*, August 10, 1945, p. 12.

my job, I feel I want to settle the fellows who get in my way. . . .[4]

In his home, not least, he is often seized with rage and rashly strikes his children. When on one such occasion his wife protests, he strikes her too and ties her to a chair. The symptoms have appeared in connection with "the troubles," and have been made more severe by the fact of his serving as examining officer. "Sometimes I torture people for ten hours at a stretch . . ." "What happens to you when you are torturing?"

> . . . it's very tiring . . . It's true we take it in turns, but the question is to know when to let the next chap have a go. . . . Our problem is as follows: are you able to make this fellow talk? It's a question of personal success. You see, you're competing with the others. In the end your fists are ruined. So you call in the Senegalese. But either they hit too hard and destroy the creature or else they don't hit hard enough and it's no good. In fact, you have to be intelligent to make a success of that sort of work. You have to know when to lay it on and when to lay it off. You have to have a flair for it.[5]

One problem in the treatment consists of the fact that it has to take place while the man still is "working full-time." His superiors refuse to give him time off, at any rate so long as he cannot produce a doctor's certificate of his illness, and the inspector himself refuses to let Fanon write out such a certificate. "The weaknesses of such a procedure may easily be imagined."

Another difficulty arises. Fanon was not an Algerian, but as a colored man in Martinique, he was, from birth, just as familiar with the French colonial empire as any Algerian; indeed, after medical studies in France he moved to North Africa, first as a psychiatrist in the Algerian city of Blida and during his last years (he died of leukemia in

[4] Fanon, *op. cit.*, p. 217.
[5] *Ibid.*, p. 218.

1961) as a doctor in Tunisia. From the outset he participated actively in the Algerian liberation movement. In other words, it was to a political resistor that the white police inspector came to be cured, but Fanon was in fact accustomed to this; pursuant to his duty as a doctor he accepted all kinds of patients. What was special about this meeting between enemies in the midst of the war was that the police inspector came with a request which must be designated as remarkable against the background of the facts cited here. Fanon reproduces his request in the following way:

> As he could not see his way to stopping torturing people (that made nonsense to him for in that case he would have to resign) he asked me without beating about the bush to help him to go on torturing Algerian patriots without any prickings of conscience, without any behaviour problems and with complete equanimity.[6]

That was eight meetings. But not one of them was any confrontation, at least not on equal ground. Instead of being confronted on the same level and face to face, the Westerners still chose to be above, to disguise themselves, to disregard their counterpart, or, with violence, to keep him oppressed.

How long is this going to be able to continue without the world blowing up in midair? Will America and Europe spin their gyrating prosperity faster and faster, soon impoverishing the entire world, even until they are restrained by violence?

This much seems to be certain: the meeting between rich and poor, between exploiters and exploited, seems to force us who are rich to review painfully, to review a dizzying lot of what we have long cherished and taken for granted.

[6] *Ibid.,* p. 219.

Leftover Notes

There are humane and inhumane forms of oppression; there are just and unjust wars; there are dictatorships that want the best for the people and there are dictatorships that don't want the best for the people, but freedom, peace, democracy?

Serfdom didn't end in the nineteenth century. It was only transferred from Europe to the colonies.

Colonialism did not end by the very fact that the colonies got the right to vote in the U.N. It was only transferred from the map to the account books.

Ordered out of China, missionaries moved their base to Japan.

The welfare state is populated today by technologists and economists who say that the administrative problems in our modern civilization have grown so complicated and difficult to survey that they must be taken in charge by specialists, otherwise development cannot advance. The welfare state is populated today by technologists of novels and data programmers of poetry who say that the esthetic problems in our modern culture have grown so complicated that they must be taken in charge by specialists, otherwise the development of art cannot advance.

What the welfare administrators are hiding is the simple fact that our development implies the other peoples' death. What are the writers hiding?

If simplification is one of the foremost weapons of revolutionary thinking, complication is one of the foremost weapons of conservative thinking.

"The situation in the underdeveloped countries is actually extraordinarily complex."

"It's not so simple as you think."

"To give an opinion on economics you have to be an expert."

We're not living in an evil world. We're living at best in an evil part of the world.

Buddha said in the scriptures:

> Do not believe what you have heard. Do not believe in traditions because they have been inherited through many generations. Do not believe in something because it is talked about and many others believe in it. Do not believe that that to which you are bound by habit is truth. Do not believe in something because of the authority of your teachers and forefathers. Believe only after carefully observing and analyzing that which corresponds with reason and promotes the good of everyone—and live accordingly.

The geographical dividing line in the world no longer runs

between East and West but between North and South. Between the Soviet and the rest of Asia, between Europe and Africa, between North America and South America: it is here the new cold war is being waged and the new iron curtain is being drawn down.

Since 1958 world trade prices for the underdeveloped countries' raw materials have dropped by an average of 7 per cent, while world trade prices for the industrial countries' raw materials (including wheat) have risen by 10 per cent.

If you will not admit to the difference between good and bad dictatorships, between just and unjust forms of violence, and nevertheless want to make a contribution to benefit mankind, you ought to join Amnesty International and fight just as wholeheartedly for the freedom of the prisoners who are enemies of the government in Guinea as for the freedom of the prisoners who are enemies of the government in South Africa. What does it matter that you're sticking your head in the sand when it happens in the name of freedom!

Pacifism is about to drive the world to destruction.

In Johannesburg, Sara Lidman once heard a Boer wife say something very honest:

> One thing that foreigners never understand about our native problem. Why, it's not because they're of a lower race that we can't put up with them but because they're of a lower social class. Those people who run around with black big shots on the Continent, dancers and musicians—they think that South Africa is full of that kind and that we whites who live here don't have any judgment at all. I said to one of those Negrophiles who collects darkies like Meissen porcelain, do you think I have anything against a washed, good-looking African with some education? It's just that there aren't any in Africa. Would you dream of associating with a common worker, I said to him. No, I

knew it. So I told him that any worker at all in Europe is pure middle class in comparison with our natives, who are dirty ragamuffins without the slightest notion of higher values. I don't have any racial prejudices, but I keep to the social class where I'm at home.[1]

It takes a good deal of entering into the spirit of what is alien to us, but on the crucial point we need not enter into this spirit at all, for they're all there in our own history: the undernourished Red Cross children in the mines of Manchester liberalism, the dirty niggers in Paris' Age of Enlightenment, the backward Indians on Czarist Russian property, the untouchable castes in Renaissance Spain, and the retarded mestizos in today's South Italy. The workers.

Maybe it's the same story with socialism as with Christianity, that it takes poverty and the battle against poverty in order to be able to live a somewhat unperverted life? The degeneration comes later. At any rate, that's the way they seem to see the matter in the proletarian countries when they say:

Socialism yes, only no Russian ideologists.
Christianity maybe, only no European missionaries.

Aid to underdeveloped countries, Europe's Marshall Plan to the Third World.

Seeing the world as one country and seeing the world as pluralistic is not a contradiction. Not until multiplicity is seen at close range does it cease to appear foreshortened. See the class society of the world as an enlarged Brazil or India and the incongruities strike your eye just as powerfully as the basic, catastrophically growing injustice enchaining it all.

Perhaps there is no hope. We just hope anyhow.

[1] *Jag och min son* (*I and My Son*), pp. 88–89.

Index

England, 12, 13, 34, 38, 50, 82, 91, 102, 106, 194, 196, 200, 202, 205, 211
Erhard, Ludwig, 203
Erlander, Tage, 103, 105
Eskimos, 13
Ethiopia, 71, 111, 119, 121, 122, 128, 129, 130, 131, 132, 134, 136
Europe, 21, 30, 35, 37, 38, 45, 62–63, 68, 70, 71, 72, 74, 75, 78, 81, 82, 83, 88, 89, 90, 97, 106, 113, 115, 118, 141, 146, 157, 164, 165, 172, 186, 191, 198, 199, 200, 203, 205, 207, 210, 238, 239, 241
European Economic Community, 209

Fanon, Frantz, 49, 50, 62–63, 67, 72, 83, 85, 236–38
Ferdinand the Catholic, 14, 47
Finland, 97
Formosa, 59, 116, 213, 229
France, 12, 34, 35, 36, 81, 82, 186, 187, 188, 196, 205, 210, 211, 213
Franco, Francisco, 187
Franklin, Benjamin, 34–35, 201
Frisch, Hartvig, 12, 35
Fuentes, Carlos, 58

Gagarin, Yuri, 78
Gandhi, Indira, 51
Gandhi, Mohandas, 21, 26, 62
Geez, 129
Genghis Khan, 161
George, Pierre, 210
George III, 69

Germany, 42, 68, 75, 81, 103, 106, 110, 183, 187, 188, 195, 196, 200, 203, 205, 208, 213, 217
Ghana, 57, 108, 229
Goethe, J. W., 162, 172
Gold Coast, 37, 115
Gothenburg, 11
Goulart, João, 213
Gray, Dorian, 33–40, 71
Greece, 106
Greenland, 182
Grousset, René, 91
Guatemala, 116, 140, 200, 206
Guiana, 82
Guinea, 111, 206, 241
Gutenberg, Johannes, 14

Hägglöf, Gunnar, 103
Hammarskjöld, Dag, 147
Heidelberg Man, 9, 15
Herodotus, 11
Hinduism, 15, 57, 96
Hitler, Adolf, 46, 85, 187, 195
Ho Chi Minh, 71
Holland, 9, 13, 200
Hong Kong, 14
Humphrey, Hubert, 104

Incas, 14
India, 3, 10, 13, 14, 20, 38, 50–52, 61, 87, 110, 112, 114, 115, 139, 192, 208, 209, 211, 223–24, 242
Indians (American), 37, 74
Indochina, 82, 115, 216
Indonesia, 7, 13, 44, 115, 139, 206, 211, 213
Interarmco, 44–46, 140

International Court of Justice, 72, 159, 181
International Development Association, 159
International Finance Corporation, 159
International Monetary Fund, 159
Iran (Persia), 38, 39, 45, 92, 116, 143, 200, 205, 213
Iraq, 10, 56, 140, 200
Israel, 209, 218, 219
Italy, 106, 110, 130, 187, 188, 192, 200
Ivory Coast, 207

Jagan, Cheddi, 213
Jakarta, 24
Japan, 13, 59, 75, 76, 106, 112, 115, 160, 193, 239
Java Man, 9, 15
Javits, Jacob, 104
Jesus Christ, 12, 56, 61, 128, 148, 177–83, 189
Johnson, Lyndon, 203
Jordan, 217, 218

Kassem, General, 140, 211
Kautsky, Karl, 191
Kennedy, John F., 201, 202, 203, 215
Kenya, 45, 55, 116, 120, 134
Khrushchev, Nikita, 225
Kim Il Sung, 71
King, Martin Luther, Jr., 26
Kipling, Rudyard, 172
Klemmer, William, 13
Koran, 136
Korea, 59

Korean War, 35, 44, 48, 59, 140, 193, 198, 226–28
Krupp, Josef, 195, 196–97
Kuwait, 39, 205
Kyrklund, Willy, 20, 92–93, 94

Lao-tse, 10
Latin America, 6, 14, 15, 37, 68, 72, 75, 79, 81, 104, 114, 206, 241
Lenin, V. I., 191
Leopold II, 14, 143
Lewis, Oscar, 172
Liberia, 111, 116
Libya, 209, 213
Lichtenstein, 45, 46
Lidman, Sara, 241
Lindqvist, Sven, 61
Liverpool, 41
Livingstone, David, 157
London, 19
Louis XIV, 58
Lumumba, Patrice, 34, 182
Lundberg, Erik, 107
Lundqvist, Artur, 2, 3, 4
Luxembourg, 229–34
Luxemburg, Rosa, 191

Madagascar, 140
Madras, 4
Makeba, Miriam, 232
Malaysia, 71, 110, 115, 200, 206, 211
Malcolm X, 59–60, 182
Mao Tse-tung, 71, 193
Marshall Plan, 196
Marx, Karl, 74, 84, 155, 222
Marxism, 68, 74, 88
Mau Mau, 134
Mauretania, 229

DATE DUE

Demco, Inc. 38-293

D0971333

Murder on the Hoof

Also by Kathryn O'Sullivan

Foal Play

Murder on the Hoof

Kathryn O'Sullivan

Minotaur Books

A THOMAS DUNNE BOOK
NEW YORK

This is a work of fiction. All of the characters, organizations, and events portrayed in this novel are either products of the author's imagination or are used fictitiously.

A THOMAS DUNNE BOOK FOR MINOTAUR BOOKS.
An imprint of St. Martin's Publishing Group.

MURDER ON THE HOOF. Copyright © 2014 by Kathryn O'Sullivan. All rights reserved. Printed in the United States of America. For information, address St. Martin's Press, 175 Fifth Avenue, New York, N.Y. 10010.

www.thomasdunnebooks.com
www.minotaurbooks.com

Library of Congress Cataloging-in-Publication Data

O'Sullivan, Kathryn.
  Murder on the hoof : a mystery / Kathryn O'Sullivan.—
1st ed.
      p. cm.
  "A Thomas Dunne Book."
  ISBN 978-1-250-04946-9 (hardcover)
  ISBN 978-1-4668-5048-4 (e-book)
  1. Women firefighters—Fiction. 2. Fire chiefs—North Carolina—Fiction. 3. Sheriffs—North Carolina—Fiction.
4. Murder—Investigation—Fiction. 5. Corolla (N.C.)—Fiction. 6. Outer Banks (N.C.)—Fiction. 7. Mystery fiction. I. Title.
  PS3615.S66M87 2014
  813'.6—dc23

                                    2014008155

Minotaur books may be purchased for educational, business, or promotional use. For information on bulk purchases, please contact Macmillan Corporate and Premium Sales Department at 1-800-221-7945, extension 5442, or write specialmarkets@macmillan.com.

First Edition: May 2014

10 9 8 7 6 5 4 3 2 1

For all those working tirelessly to protect
Corolla's wild horses

Acknowledgments

As always, I couldn't have written this book without the support and love of numerous people. Thanks to my husband for patiently critiquing this book, cooking me meals to keep me writing, accompanying me on signing and conference trips, and showing his love each and every day; to my father for his helpful feedback and support; to my mother for her enthusiasm and reconnaissance missions; to the rest of my family and childhood friends for attending signings and library events; and to my colleagues at Northern Virginia Community College for encouraging me every step of the way and surprising me at signings.

A very special thanks and deepest gratitude to the amazing team at St. Martin's Press: my insightful and kind editor, Toni Kirkpatrick, and her assistant, Jennifer Letwack; my hardworking and considerate publicist, Justin Velella; my new publicist, Shailyn Tavella; and my eagle-eyed copy editor, Carol Edwards.

Sincere thanks to my agent, Eleanor Wood, for not only believing in the book, but also in me, and for her wonderful title contribution.

Thanks to Andy Mueller for his beautiful photography of Corolla's Whalehead Club in Historic Corolla that graces the cover, and to David Rotstein, Executive Art Director at St. Martin's Press, for reaching out to him.

Sincere thanks to all at the Corolla Wild Horse Fund who are dedicated to protecting the beautiful wild horses depicted in this book. May every reader be inspired to support their work with a donation at www.corollawildhorses.com.

Fond thanks to the independent bookstore owners, bloggers, and librarians for hosting me for events, inviting me back for future visits, for carrying my work, and for your love and support of writers everywhere.

Thanks to my playwright friends who have known me from the beginning; my mystery and romance writer friends who have welcomed me into their ranks with encouragement, humor, and support; and my friends in the Web community who have cheered every accomplishment along the way.

Finally, a heartfelt thank-you to the men and women of Corolla Fire and Rescue who inspired me to begin this series and who are more skilled, noble, diverse, and humble than any characters I could write.

Murder on the Hoof

Chapter 1

Fire chief Colleen McCabe scrutinized the sea of battered bodies scattered on the beach like shells after high tide. Nearly a dozen of Corolla's citizens were slumped in the sand. Firefighters and EMTs rushed about the scene, performing first aid on the injured, who groaned in pain and clutched damaged limbs. Other victims lay eerily motionless in the hot morning sun. Sparky, Colleen's Border collie, paced—one ear up and head cocked—as the rescue team called out vital signs, stabilized neck injuries, and carried individuals to nearby ambulances.

The wounded were familiar to Colleen, active members of the Corolla community, which added to the disturbing nature of the scene. Nellie Byrd, the popular owner of Nell's Gift Shop and Rentals, slouched at the foot of a dune, clutching her thigh and wincing as Kenny Ward, one of Colleen's firefighters, carefully examined her ankle.

"A duck and a flea," Kenny said softly to Nellie.

Nellie blinked at Kenny, dazed.

"Come on, Nell. Twenty-three. A duck and a flea," he said again, prompting her.

"Thee and me," she responded with a weak smile.

Kenny was reminding Nellie of their mutual love of the Whalehead Station's Bingo Night, and Colleen nodded in approval at his ability to establish rapport and keep Nellie calm. Satisfied that Nellie was in good hands, Colleen focused on the rest of her team. One of her men tended to Rita Riddle, a woman in her late fifties and owner of Great Escapes clothing store. Rita sat unusually still as her head and right eye were carefully wrapped with gauze. Other rescuers efficiently applied pressure to wounds, examined victims for concussions, and wrapped those in shock in reflective blankets to keep their body temperature steady and protect them from the sizzling August heat.

Colleen eyed the growing crowd of onlookers. There were now almost two dozen people in bathing suits, shorts, and sun hats gathered at the scene's perimeter, pointing, whispering, and recording with cell phones. Much to her annoyance, one bystander was tossing popcorn in the air, attracting a flock of squawking seagulls. Colleen was thankful Bill Dorman, her best friend and the Currituck County sheriff, was there to keep the vacationers at a safe distance and informed about the details of the unfolding event. Bill could command a crowd with a single word and a stern expression.

The ocean breeze shifted and carried a gust of humid air and a loud wail over the area. Myrtle Crepe, Colleen's crabby retired third-grade teacher and head of the Lighthouse Wild Horse Preservation Society, writhed in the sand, with blood oozing from an ugly gash on her forehead. Myrtle gasped, her face the picture of agony, then panted rapidly, moaned once more, and collapsed in a woozy heap.

Colleen watched with apprehension as chubby Bobby Crepe, one of her firefighters in training, crouched next to his mother and attempted to take her pulse. Remaining objective and professional while performing medical treatment on family members was often difficult.

"How's it going?" Bill asked.

Just then, Myrtle yelped, yanked her wrist away from her son, and bolted upright. "You're doing it wrong, Little Bobby. Don't use your thumb!" she barked, all signs of wooziness gone.

"Are you breaking character?" Bobby asked with a tisk and shake of his head.

Myrtle clenched her mouth shut and flumped back in the sand with a resigned huff. Bobby suppressed a grin and took his mother's wrist again.

"Maybe it wasn't a good idea having Bobby practice on Myrtle," Colleen said.

"You wanted him to experience the worst-case scenario," Bill said with a wink.

She checked the time and signaled Jimmy Bartlett, her well-respected veteran captain.

Jimmy blew a short blast on his whistle. "Okay, everyone, that's the end of the training exercise," he called out.

One by one, the wounded citizens rose, smiling and shaking

hands with the firefighters and EMTs who had been working on them. The crowd of vacationers clapped and whistled, prompting some of the role players to take a bow. Sparky barked and ran among the "injured," curiously sniffing the fake bloody wounds. The seagulls screamed at the dispersing crowd and flew away down the beach.

Colleen had had her doubts when it had first been suggested, but Myrtle and her fellow community theater actors had done a fine job playing victims for her firefighter and EMT training session. She had been particularly impressed with the makeup skills of Rich Bailey, the eldest son and funeral director at Bailey and Sons Funeral Services. Rich had created remarkably convincing latex gashes, derma wax broken noses, and oozing contusions. In the past, Colleen had had her team use a moulage kit to craft injuries, but their work was amateurish at best compared to Rich's. *I guess there's nothing like the makeup skills of a professional mortician,* she thought. Rich's expert makeup techniques, combined with the unpredictability of working with strangers, had proved a more realistic and valuable experience for her team than working on one another.

Nellie removed the bandage from her ankle and waved happily to her nephew, Adam Jones, who was standing nearby, recording the entire exercise. Adam had recently graduated from film school and had been in town for the last month helping Doc Wales, the local equine veterinarian, rewrite *Wild and Free,* a play about the history of the Corolla Spanish mustangs, for the community theater's and Lighthouse Wild Horse Preservation Society's upcoming fund-raising production. Nellie had convinced Adam to film the training to help Colleen and her team.

Lane Walker, a handsome gray-haired member of the theater group with a Casanova reputation, straightened his shirt and strode toward Adam. "Would you like an interview, young man?" he asked. It wasn't so much a question as an authoritative offer.

"Sure," Adam said, and focused the camera on Lane.

Colleen marveled at how actors seemed to truly enjoy being in the spotlight. She had always been more of a behind-the-scenes person. Yes, as fire chief she was often the focus of attention and could turn on the charm for public events and press conferences, but her natural inclination was one of introversion. If born into a wealthy family, Colleen was certain she would have led a life of lazy solitude, reading books, gardening, and perhaps even learning to play the piano. But she had grown up with hardworking, ambitious parents who had instilled those values in their daughter. When she took more than a day off of work, she felt downright slothful.

Colleen listened to Lane regale Adam about a character he had played on *Red Alert,* a 1970s cop television show, as well as his detailed preparation for today's role as accident victim.

"Look at him," said Myrtle in a disapproving voice as she joined Colleen and Bill. "Always the scene stealer."

Lane's experience in Hollywood was clearly trumping Myrtle's acting experience in college.

"Lane's certainly popular," Colleen said, knowing the comment would provoke Myrtle.

"Hmpf. That's because he flirts with anything in a skirt. Makes me utterly uncomfortable."

"If Lane's been troubling you, Myrtle, just say the word and I'll talk to him," Bill teased.

"Oh!" Myrtle exclaimed, not appreciating Bill's joke. "Men," she added, and marched off toward Nellie.

"What was that about?" Bill asked, genuinely surprised.

"I suspect it has something to do with the play production," Colleen guessed. "You know Myrtle hates it when anyone challenges her authority. And Lane has professional acting chops, something Myrtle lacks."

The remaining actors joined Lane to listen to his interview. Among them were Sam Riddle, a retired businessman turned Food Lion employee; his wife, Rita; and Fawn Harkins, a recent college graduate and, at twenty-one years old, the youngest member of the acting troupe.

Several EMTs crowded around Fawn, offering to help carry her over the sand to show off their strength. Colleen watched with concern as one by one her men hoisted a giggling Fawn into the air. The young woman was a natural beauty with a pretty smile, dimpled cheeks, sun-kissed skin, long tresses, and a curvy figure that moved unencumbered beneath her flowing tie-dyed dress. Colleen didn't begrudge Fawn the attention; she was a vibrant young woman with obvious assets. It was how Fawn had become a source of tension at the station that concerned her.

Fawn was the girlfriend of Chip Reed, one of Colleen's EMTs. About a month ago at a family and friends station picnic, Chip had caught Fawn flirting with the other men. Colleen had had to step in before it came to blows and had ordered everyone to leave the dramatics to the community theater group. Anything that interfered with her guys working as a team was not only unwelcome; it was dangerous. She was glad Chip was delayed returning to town from visiting a sick relative. He wouldn't have liked seeing his girlfriend feeling the biceps and quads of his fellow EMTs and firefighters.

"That girl's trouble," Bill said, observing Fawn.

"You have no idea." Colleen's phone buzzed, alerting her to a message. "Not again."

Bill squinted at her quizzically.

She glanced at the text: CONFIRMING ARRIVAL OF CAST/ CREW OF *REMEMBERING ALWAYS*. LOOKING FORWARD TO MEETING YOU.—W.E.

"It's Wendy Everett, the production manager from Zeon Pictures," Colleen said, rolling her eyes and returning her phone to her pocket. "I'm getting a dozen texts from her a day."

"You can't blame her for wanting to make sure everything is in order. We're not L.A. types."

"We're not island bumpkins, either," she said with indignation.

"It's not every day we get studio folks in town. People are excited. You have to admit it's good for business."

She shook her head. Between the theater group and film company, Corolla was being overrun by actors, and the movie was all anyone had been talking about for weeks. "I heard the lead actress—what's her name?"

"Hayley Thorpe," Bill offered.

"That's it. She's a soap star, I think. . . . Heard she's a handful."

"Perhaps we should reserve judgment about Ms. Thorpe until she gets here," he said with a firmness that surprised her.

"Great. All the guys at the firehouse are swooning. Now you, too?"

"Don't worry," he said, amused. "I'm not the swooning type."

"We'll see," she said with skepticism.

Bill chuckled.

Colleen spotted Rich Bailey closing his makeup kit. "Hey, Rich," she called out. "Good job today."

"It's always nice working on the living," he said. "Let me know if I can help again."

"Will do."

Bill put on his sunglasses. "Unless you need me, I'll be heading back to the office."

Colleen surveyed the scene. Her men had packed up the last of the equipment and were lingering to chat with the actors and a handful of curious vacationers. "Looks like we're good," she said, and whistled for Sparky. The dog spotted her and came running. "We still on for dinner?"

"You bet," Bill said with a nod, and moved to go.

"You Chief McCabe?" asked an approaching man with a burned beer belly wearing plaid swim trunks and flip-flops.

"Yes."

"You all done with your training stuff?"

"We are."

The beer-bellied man raised his brows. "Then someone oughta tell that lady over there on the dune before she cooks herself," he said, and gestured to an area beyond where they had been practicing.

Colleen squinted in the direction of the dune. "Thank you," she replied, puzzled.

"No problem," the man said with a wave, and lumbered off toward Lighthouse Drive.

"Wonder who it could be," Bill said, joining her as she trudged through the sand with Sparky at her side.

"A Method actor," she said with a shake of the head.

They marched to the foot of the dune, rounded the corner, and discovered Doris Jenkins unconscious in the sand. Doris was a plump, curvaceous woman in her sixties and an actor with the community theater group. Sparky lowered his head, cautiously approached the woman, and sniffed her leg.

"Sparky, heel," Colleen commanded. The dog whimpered but obediently retreated. She squatted next to the woman and nudged her shoulder. "Doris?" Nothing. She scanned Doris's face. Despite the rising temperature and humidity, Doris's coloring was pale. Colleen tilted her head close to Doris's mouth. The woman wasn't breathing.

Damn. She grabbed Doris's wrist and confirmed her fear: no pulse. She shifted her position, wiped the saliva from Doris's mouth with the bottom of her shirt, and started CPR. "Get Jimmy on the phone."

"Already on it," Bill said, hitting speed dial.

"Tell him to get the guys back out here," she said while rhythmically pressing on Doris's chest.

"Jimmy? Bill here," he said into the phone as he moved away toward the beach. "Chief McCabe needs the rescue guys north of the training area ASAP."

"And Bill?" she called over her shoulder. "Tell him this isn't an exercise."

He disappeared around the dune to help Colleen's men find their location.

Colleen scrutinized the woman's unresponsive face as she performed CPR. After multiple attempts at revival, she reluctantly stopped her rescue efforts and noted the time on her watch. It was no use. Doris was dead; she had been for some time. Colleen wiped sweat from her forehead and upper lip, stood, and kicked the sand in frustration.

Jimmy and Bobby soon arrived with the stretcher. Thirty yards down the beach, children played happily in the waves as Colleen's men gently placed Doris's body into the body bag for transportation to the morgue. She heard the zip of the body bag behind her. Jimmy and Bobby lifted the stretcher.

"You did great today, Bobby," she said, noticing his pensive expression as he passed. "Don't let this get you down."

"Thanks, Chief," he said, dejected.

Jimmy nodded to her and they vanished around the dune.

Sparky moaned, wanting to follow. "Okay," she said, patting the dog's rump. "Go to the station." And with that, the dog took off to accompany her men the short distance to the firehouse.

She gazed up the beach with sadness. She couldn't help feeling partially responsible for Doris's death. She shouldn't have allowed someone of her years to spend so much time in the heat.

Older adults had a more difficult time regulating body temperature. Doris had died right under her nose, with an entire team of EMTs nearby. She rubbed her temples, trying to push away the mounting headache and feelings of guilt.

"You okay?" Bill asked.

Colleen shrugged. No, she wasn't okay. She was angry. Angry that somehow she might have contributed to Doris's death.

"You can't beat yourself up about this."

"After everything that happened last month with Max Cascio, I thought we had had enough death for one summer."

The two watched in silence as the ocean pushed toward land, then withdrew again. Life had returned to normal in the weeks since the arrest of Max Cascio, nephew of Antonio "Pinky" Salvatore, one of Corolla's most successful developers. The federal agents were gone, the horses had been returned to the sanctuary, Myrtle's house restoration was under way, Bobby had begun firefighter training, and Myrtle and Nellie were busy with the Lighthouse Wild Horse Preservation Society and the upcoming theater production. Colleen and Pinky were even forging a new friendship—what type of friendship it was, she still wasn't entirely sure of yet—but things had changed between them after Pinky had donated a house intended for demolition to the station for a Burn-to-Learn drill.

She and Bill had also grown closer since Max's arrest—but not as close as she had hoped. They had shared movie nights and dinners and had even arranged to take off work for a day trip down to Ocracoke, at the southern end of the Outer Banks, to hear Ocracoke's native musicians at the Deepwater Creek Theater and Music Hall, but Colleen couldn't help feeling that there was something preventing their relationship from deepening. Still, she was happy they seemed to be moving away from a purely platonic one. She stole a look at him. As if sensing her gaze, he turned and smiled.

"I'd better head back," she said. She couldn't spend all day staring at the ocean. "I've got a lot to talk about with my team."

They marched through the sand to the short boardwalk at Dolphin Street that intersected with and linked the beach to Lighthouse Drive, where Bill's SUV was parked on the shoulder of the road.

"I'll check on Marvin," he said, and opened his door. "It's not going to be easy for him without Doris."

"I don't envy you," she said with sincerity. She had always found it difficult to be around the grieving. "Mind if we take a rain check on dinner? I could be a while at the station."

"Not at all. Call me if you need anything."

Colleen gave Bill a short wave as he pulled onto Lighthouse Drive. She took a deep breath and then headed along Dolphin Street to the firehouse to check on her team.

Chapter 2

"You couldn't put out a match on a windy day!" came an angry voice from inside the Whalehead fire station.

"Please, I have more time parking the engine than you have on the job" was the sarcastic retort.

Colleen's brow furrowed as she left the road and jogged across the parking lot toward the voices.

"Hose puller!" Chip yelled, jerking on Kenny's shirt as she entered the empty bay.

"Nozzle jockey," Kenny grunted, expertly breaking free of Chip's grasp and putting him in a headlock.

Sparky circled and barked at the two wrestling men.

"Enough!" Colleen said.

All in the room, including Sparky, jumped. Kenny released Chip and shuffled back a few feet with his head down.

"Did you see that?" Chip said, rubbing his neck and pointing at Kenny.

"I did indeed, Mr. Reed," she said, trying to keep her cool. "I also saw that you started it. Care to explain why?"

"As a matter of fact—"

"And please don't tell me it's about your girlfriend. I believe I've already made myself perfectly clear about not bringing your personal life to work."

The rest of the men stole glances at one another and smirked. She deduced from their reaction that the fight had indeed been about Fawn. Colleen hadn't had any trouble with Chip until he had started dating the girl several weeks ago. Now trouble was all she got from him—and Fawn was always the reason. He gaped at her, mouth open but silent.

"You're *on* the job; now get *into* the job," she said sternly. "That goes for all of you," she added, turning to address the rest. "We'll have a meeting about the training soon. Until then, I suggest you make yourselves useful."

The men dispersed, moving to do equipment checks, clean the engines, and in general make themselves scarce.

"Kenny, I'd like to speak with you," she said on her way up the stairs to her second-floor office.

"Woowee!" came a response from below.

Colleen stopped mid-step.

"What a babe," someone else remarked, followed by a low whistle.

She swung around, ready to lay into her men, and discovered them intently watching two women and a man approaching from the parking lot. She descended the stairs and observed the strangers as they strode away from a Lincoln SUV with tinted windows and headed across the asphalt. The group was led by a cute twentysomething woman with a bob haircut, tailored clothes, and a phone to her ear. Behind her followed an equally tailored young man. The third member of the party was an attractive woman, perhaps in her early forties, wearing Jackie Kennedy Onassis–style sunglasses, a flowing pale pink blouse, red capri pants, and matching sling-back pumps. The woman screamed glamour, and it suddenly dawned on Colleen who she was.

"Now that's a kitty I could rescue," she heard one of her team say. Colleen observed the men in her peripheral vision and caught a few checking the freshness of their breath and straightening their hair.

"Where can I find Chief McCabe?" asked the cute woman with the bob as she and her companions entered the shade of the station's garage.

"You must be Wendy," Colleen said, crossing the room and shaking Wendy's hand.

"I'm Jason," said the young man, shaking her hand. "I'm Ms. Thorpe's assistant."

"Nice to meet you."

"And, as I'm sure you know already, this is Hayley Thorpe," Jason said, stepping back and with a sweep of the arm gesturing toward Hayley in a way someone might do when introducing royalty.

Hayley Thorpe removed her sunglasses. Much to Colleen's amazement, she heard a collective sigh from her men.

"Lovely to meet you," Hayley said, extending a dainty, perfectly manicured hand.

Colleen took Hayley's hand in hers and was suddenly aware of how rough her own skin must feel against the satiny soft skin of Ms. Thorpe's palm. She released her grip and unconsciously placed her hands behind her back.

"I wasn't expecting you, Ms. Thorpe," Colleen said, glaring pointedly at Wendy. Wendy smiled back, unfazed.

"Please, call me Hayley," the actress said with a purr.

"Hayley insisted we come unannounced," Wendy explained. "She wanted to see the station and your world as it normally is." The young woman punctuated her remark with a quick once-over of Colleen's appearance.

"Yes, well," Colleen stammered, suddenly feeling self-conscious about her attire. "We had a training exercise on the beach this morning. Everyone's a little tuckered out."

"Oh, I don't know," Hayley said, luxuriously strolling toward the men. "All I see are handsome faces."

She watched in wonder as Hayley introduced herself to the men one by one, made little comments to each that only he could hear, and graciously allowed them to take pictures with her on their cell phones. Jason beamed and Wendy checked a text message. They had clearly witnessed Hayley in action many times before. Hayley finished introducing herself to the last firefighter, then turned, spotted Sparky, and, to top off her charm offensive, rubbed the Border collie behind the ear. When Sparky moaned with pleasure, Colleen could swear some of the men did, too. By the time Hayley was done making her rounds, her men were smitten fans. It was going to be tough, if not impossible, to get her team to focus at the debriefing today.

Wendy read a message on her phone. "The house is ready," the production manager said to Hayley.

"It was lovely meeting all of you," Hayley said. The men stammered feeble responses. "You have quite the crew, Chief McCabe. You're a lucky woman."

The guys grinned.

"Yes, well, they're a great team to work with," she said, not sure how to respond, since she preferred not to think of her men in the way Hayley clearly did.

"I look forward to shadowing you," Hayley said.

Colleen furrowed her brows.

"We'd best be going if we're going to meet your friend," Jason said, taking Hayley's arm and guiding her from the station's bay.

"Bye," the star said, and swiveled on her heels.

"Bye," the men replied in dreamy unison.

Colleen hurried after Hayley, Wendy, and Jason. "Excuse me, Ms. Thorpe," she called out. "What do you mean by 'shadowing' me?"

Hayley raised an eyebrow at Wendy and Jason.

"I thought I'd texted you," Wendy said to Colleen. "Hayley's going to shadow you at work during her stay when she's not filming—to help her with her character."

"What exactly do you mean by 'shadow'?" Colleen asked.

"She'll follow you around while you do your job," Jason said matter-of-factly.

"Don't worry," Hayley said with a pat on Colleen's arm. "I'll be as quiet as a mouse. You and your men won't even know I'm here." And with that, the three retreated to their vehicle.

Like hell my men won't know you're here, she thought. She watched as the Lincoln SUV disappeared up Lighthouse Drive. As if the summer hadn't been eventful enough, now she was going to be followed around by a famous actress. She didn't know how, but she was going to have to discourage this. There was no way she and her men could do their jobs while being distracted by the beautiful and charming Hayley Thorpe.

She heard the click of Sparky's nails behind her. "You weren't any help," she said as he reached her side. Sparky squinted at her, and she could swear he was smiling.

Just then, Jimmy and Bobby pulled in.

"You're back early. Is everything okay?" she asked.

"Turns out the ME had staff in Duck. We were able to transfer custody of Doris's body there," Jimmy said. "What are you doing out here?"

Colleen realized how strange she must appear, standing in the middle of the lot and staring blankly off into the distance. "You just missed Hayley Thorpe," she said, as if that were a perfectly logical explanation.

"Hayley Thorpe? Constance Hope from *Passages in Time*? She was here? I love her," Bobby gushed.

Jimmy smiled in agreement. Great, Colleen thought. Hayley Thorpe's conquest was complete.

"She took pictures with everyone. I'm sure some of the guys will . . ." Her voice trailed off. Bobby was already out of the vehicle, half waddling, half jogging to the station to hear all about the celebrity visitor. It was the fastest she had seen Bobby move—ever. Despite weeks of training, Bobby had managed to lose only ten pounds. Perhaps I should have a picture of Hayley Thorpe at each end of the relay drills to motivate him, she thought.

Jimmy grinned. "Looks like Bobby's a fan."

"You think?" she asked sarcastically.

He raised his brow in surprise. "You're not?"

"She seems like a perfectly nice person, but I just found out she's going to be following me around on the job—something to do with the film she's doing."

"You mean like Take Your Soap Star to Work Day?" he asked with a chuckle.

"Yes," she said, not finding it the least bit amusing. "Only it won't be for a day. A day, I could handle."

"I don't see the big deal."

"Oh really?" She gestured to the interior of the station, where Bobby was now surrounded by the rest of the men, who were enthusiastically showing off their cell phone pictures.

"I see what you mean," he said, now fully appreciating the impact the celebrity's presence would have on their work.

"I'll have to make it clear to Hayley and the film people that her presence is too much of a distraction."

"That's going to sound like you're jealous."

She shot Jimmy a look.

"Not that I think you are," he quickly added. "But to people who don't know you, it could look like one woman being petty about another."

Colleen bit the inside of her mouth. As much as she hated to admit it, her dependable captain had a point. To someone from the outside, she might appear to be a queen bee feeling threatened by another queen bee buzzing around her hive. But she was neither a queen bee nor someone who had ever had problems with women who were. And she didn't want to stir up trouble with the Chamber of Commerce or Currituck County by seeming difficult.

"I need a man to make the request," she said, thinking aloud.

"That might work," Jimmy said, and stroked his handlebar mustache. "But it would have to be the right man."

"How do you mean?"

"Someone with authority or power. And with a woman like Hayley Thorpe, it wouldn't hurt if he was good-looking."

She considered what he was proposing. Where could she find a handsome man with authority to charm Hayley out of following her around on the job? Her phone buzzed to life. She pulled it from her pocket, checked the number, and grinned.

"I may have just the guy for the job," she said, and hit the AN-SWER button. "Hello, Pinky," she said, winking at Jimmy.

Jimmy raised his brows in surprise.

"I was calling to find out if we're still meeting about the donated property," Pinky said, referring to the house he had donated to the station.

"Absolutely," she said cheerfully. "I'll be there in a few."

"Looking forward to it. Until then, ciao."

"Ciao," she said, and hung up.

"'Ciao,'" Jimmy said, imitating her.

She playfully swatted at his arm. "Pinky will be the perfect distraction for our Ms. Thorpe."

He eyed her, unconvinced. "How do you figure?"

"Think about it. He's owns a third of the properties in Corolla— probably even the house Hayley's staying in—he's not bad-looking, and he's charming in his own way."

Jimmy gawked at her. "Wow. Never thought I'd see the day when Colleen McCabe would call Antonio Salvatore charming."

"Do you have someone better in mind?" she asked, folding her arms.

"I thought maybe you'd ask—" he began, then stopped. "Oh, it doesn't matter. Why am I even getting involved in this?" he said, and headed toward the station.

"Tell the guys I'll be back within the hour. We need to meet about today's exercise," she called after him.

Jimmy waved over his shoulder.

"Sparky, come," she called, walking to her SUV. She swung open the door, hopped in after Sparky, started the engine, and drove up Whalehead Drive.

Chapter 3

Colleen's concern about having Hayley Thorpe looking over
her shoulder lessened as she made her way toward the house
where she was to meet Pinky. Hayley obviously had a healthy appreciation for men. Pinky would be just the ticket to distract her.
Not only was he one of the wealthiest citizens in Corolla but Colleen knew firsthand how he liked to wine and dine a lady. Pinky
would keep the actress so busy that she would soon forget about
shadowing the local fire chief. Once she convinced Pinky to
introduce himself to Hayley and maybe invite her for a cruise
down Currituck Sound on his boat, she was certain she could
return her station to a normal routine—or as normal a routine as
possible with a film crew in town.

She drove north on Route 12. As she approached the Sheriff's
Department, she decided to fill Bill in briefly on the arrival of

the film company and see how he had made out with Marvin, the deceased Doris's husband. She drove into the Sheriff's Department's lot, found a space, parked, and went inside with Sparky. The cool air-conditioning refreshed her spirit as she made her way down the hall to Bill's office. She found the door ajar. Sparky barged in.

"Hey," she said, knocking on the door and stepping into the office.

Bill looked up from his desk. "Hey," he responded unenthusiastically.

She sat in the chair in front of Bill's desk. She had known him long enough to know something was troubling him. "Everything okay?" she asked, motioning for Sparky to sit at her feet.

"I saw Marvin Jenkins."

"I take it from the look on your face that he's not doing well with the news of Doris's death."

"No," he said. "But not in the way you'd think." He left his desk and peered out the window. "He was actually quite angry."

"It's not the first time you've encountered that reaction," she said, trying to console him.

Bill turned to her. "He was angry about Doris's participation with the theater group."

"Oh."

This was not good. She, too, had been uneasy about Doris's involvement. What if Marvin decided to get difficult and launch an inquiry into why she had let Doris participate in the exercise, given her advanced years? Like all the participants, Doris had signed a liability waiver, and Colleen was certain that she and her men were without fault, but any inquiry was usually a source of concern until it was resolved.

"Did he say if he was going to lodge a complaint?" she asked, figuring she'd better start preparing for it now.

"A complaint?" he asked, bewildered. "About being in the play?"

Now it was Colleen's turn to be confused. "The play? What about it?"

Bill leaned against the desk. "Apparently, the amount of time Doris has been spending at rehearsals has been a source of conflict. Marvin said he'd tried to get Doris to quit but that she'd refused, even said she'd get a divorce before she'd leave the play."

"That's dedication," Colleen said, amazed. Bill's silence put her on alert again. "Is there something else?"

"It's hard for me to believe doing a play or your training exercise would make him that angry. He kicked the wall. Nearly broke his foot."

"Sounds about right."

"How so?"

"I had a roommate in college who was a theater major. Her boyfriend was a real pain, always calling our room, asking where she was and then slamming the phone down when I told him she was at the theater. For her senior thesis, she was acting in a show. He tried to sabotage her by buying her tickets to a Broadway play for the same night and insisting she skip her final performance or he'd break up with her."

"What did she do?"

"Missed her show. And never acted again, as far as I know," she said. "She used to say, 'Theater is a jealous lover,' but it was clearly her boyfriend who was the jealous one. Sounds like Marvin felt the same way."

"Still," Bill said. "His reaction . . . Doris's reaction . . . they seem extreme."

"You've obviously never lived with an actress."

He smiled halfheartedly but said nothing. Her eyes narrowed. *He doesn't believe me*, she thought. She knew Bill's skepticism was part of his nature and what made him a good sheriff, but she hated when he turned it on her.

Bill's cell phone vibrated with an incoming text message. He checked his phone, then flipped it over on his desk. "I hate to change the subject, but I have an appointment. Was there something you needed?"

Distracted by the news about Marvin, she had almost forgotten why she had sought him out. "It can wait," she said, figuring he would find out soon enough about the film company's arrival. "You've clearly got enough going on right now, and I should be on my way."

"Are you sure?" he asked, but he was already moving toward the door to usher her out.

"Yeah." She rose and tapped Sparky's rump for him to follow. "I'll give you a call later."

They exited the cool building that housed the Sheriff's Department and headed out into the sweltering heat of the parking lot. She dashed to the SUV, which, fortunately, she had parked in the shade, slid in behind Sparky, started the engine, and cranked up the air-conditioning. As she was about to pull out, she was surprised to see a Lincoln SUV with tinted windows pull in. It was the same SUV that had chauffeured Hayley Thorpe into her world. Seconds later, Hayley alighted from the backseat of the vehicle. Colleen watched with curiosity as the woman paused in front of the building's front door, checked her lipstick, and then entered. Poor Bill, she thought, Hayley's going to shadow him, too. He will most certainly tell her no. And once Bill denies Hayley's request, it will be easier for me to do the same.

She glanced at the Lincoln, noticed Wendy and Jason talking in the front seat, and wondered why they hadn't gone inside. Colleen had been under the impression that a woman like Hayley wouldn't travel without an entourage. She twisted in her seat and strained to see Bill's office window through the branches of pine trees next to the building. The window was empty for a moment and then she caught a glimpse of Bill. She couldn't be sure, but she thought he appeared uncomfortable. She debated going in and rescuing him, but the desire soon disappeared and was swiftly replaced by one of wanting to punch him.

Hayley Thorpe, famous soap actress, came into view next to Bill and, as if she had done it a thousand times before, kissed him on the cheek. When he returned a quick kiss to Hayley's cheek, Colleen's heart leaped into her throat and then sank to her stomach. A second later, the two moved away from the window and out of sight.

Colleen blinked. She felt her cheeks get hot, her ears burn, and her legs weaken. Even though she was seated, it was as if a hurricane-force wind had blown her off her feet. Why had the celebrity kissed Bill? Why hadn't Bill acted surprised when she did? And why had he kissed her back? Had Bill known Hayley was coming to see him? Had Hayley been the reason he had rushed her from the office? She took a deep breath. Don't blow this up, she told herself. Hadn't she already seen the woman's effect on the guys at the station? That's merely how Hayley behaves with men. Flirting was part of the woman's DNA. But flirting was *not* part of Bill's DNA. Many times, Colleen had wished it was. There was obviously more to the interaction between Hayley and Bill.

She resisted the urge to go back inside and demand answers. She knew she'd only look foolish and possibly embarrass Bill. She needed to gather additional information before she said anything to him. But how could she find out what was going on without seeming to be nosy? She peered out the windshield and discovered the answer sitting right in front of her: Wendy and Jason. Of course, Colleen thought, they'll know why Hayley is meeting with Bill. She put her SUV into gear, pulled alongside the Lincoln, and rolled down her window.

The Lincoln's driver's side window rolled down. "Hey!" Wendy said cheerfully.

"Hey!" Colleen replied, trying to match Wendy's perky greeting. "I saw Ms. Thorpe is checking out the Sheriff's Department. Doing more research for her movie?"

"Oh, no," Jason said. "Apparently, she and the sheriff go way back. She wants to talk to him about a security issue. Funny how Hayley has a friend even here, isn't it?"

"Yes . . . funny," Colleen said, forgetting all about trying to be perky.

"You want me to tell her you were asking for her?" Wendy asked, ready to text a message.

"No!" Colleen said. Wendy and Jason looked at her, surprised. "It's really nothing. It can wait. I'd hate to disturb her when she's clearly got more important things on her mind."

"Okay, then," Wendy said, untroubled.

"See you later," Colleen said, and pulled away.

She zoomed down Route 12 with the window open, not really aware of where she was heading. The ocean air whipped her hair around her neck and across her face. Sparky squeezed closer, wanting to catch some of the wind for himself. She peeked at the speedometer. If she didn't slow down, she or someone else might get hurt. She needed to find a quiet place where she could think and clear her mind. She steered off of Ocean Trail and onto the grounds of the Currituck Heritage Park.

She slowed the vehicle to a crawl, wound her way along the quaint road, passed the Whalehead Club Historic House Museum, and parked in a small private lot near the water. She always found the grounds peaceful—especially now in the late afternoon, when most vacationers had abandoned the beach and other visitor spots and were home showering and planning for the evening's activities. She and Sparky left the SUV and strolled the short distance to the arched bridge that overlooked Currituck Sound.

Colleen stopped at the top of the bridge, leaned against the railing, and gazed across the sound. Sparky sat next to her and tilted his head heavenward to catch a whiff of the brackish air. She listened to the water lapping at the coastline, closed her eyes, breathed in deeply, and tried to calm her mind. Envy was not part of her makeup, and yet, now that she was alone with nobody but herself to account to, she had to admit that that was exactly what she was feeling. She was jealous of Hayley Thorpe . . . and not because of her beauty and charisma—although that certainly wasn't helping matters—but because of the woman's obvious past relationship with Bill. She had always known that he must have had girlfriends before meeting her, but she and Bill had never discussed their old romances. Until now, it was only in theory that she had understood this. With Hayley in town, theory had become reality.

She wondered why Bill hadn't told her about his association with the actress. After all, Hayley wasn't just any girl next door from back home. She was world-famous, with legions of adoring fans. Colleen had never watched soaps, but she remembered seeing friends in college huddled around the television in the student lounge each afternoon as she left for track practice. Many had grown up watching *As the World Turns, Passages in Time,* and *All My Children,* among others, with their mothers or grandmothers and would often discuss the characters as if they were real people. To her, they had been beautiful faces on the cover of tabloids and supermarket magazines. For weeks, everyone in Corolla had been talking about Hayley's arrival. Why hadn't Bill mentioned he knew her? He had had plenty of opportunity. Why hide it? Could he have feelings for Hayley? She pushed the question from her mind. Don't go there, she told herself. Nothing good can come of thinking like that.

"Colleen? Is that you?" came a familiar voice.

"Hi, Nellie," she said, and forced a smile as the woman climbed the bridge and joined her.

Sparky trotted to greet Nellie, tail wagging, and leaned against the older woman in a gesture of affection.

"So, did your crew find working with us useful today?" Nellie asked, bracing herself against the dog's weight.

"I think so. I haven't actually met with them yet."

"Oh?"

"You're wondering why I'm here," Colleen said, reading Nellie's mind. "I needed to clear my head. A lot has happened since this morning."

"Yes, poor Doris. I can't help wondering if she didn't have one of her attacks."

"How do you mean?"

"Doris has always taken naps, at least since I've known her. She said it ran in her family. She'd be talking to you one minute and then the next—bam—she'd be sleeping."

"Sounds like narcolepsy."

"That's what she said it was," Nellie said.

"You think she fell asleep on the beach?"

"She must have. But I've never known her not to wake up after a few minutes. I guess the heat got to her."

Colleen racked her brain, trying to recall what she had learned in her training about narcolepsy. She remembered reading about the sleepiness that Nellie had described and how it was often accompanied by muscle weakness brought on by intense emotion. Perhaps Doris had experienced some type of sudden loss of muscle tone and strength—possibly even paralysis—and, given her age and the heat, her body shut down before she was able to recover and wake up. Any detail Nellie could provide might help with her report and decision about whether or not to use the actors for future exercises.

"Tell me. Did Doris have any triggers that seemed to bring on her attacks? Anything that you can think of that might have happened at the training exercise?"

Nellie pursed her lips, thinking. "No," she said. "The only thing that consistently brought on attacks was fighting with Marvin."

"Which, I understand, she was doing a lot of lately."

"You heard about that? I guess I shouldn't be surprised. Fawn's in the show and dates Chip. I suppose he told you."

"Actually, I heard it from Bill. Bill said that when he broke the news of Doris's death to Marvin, he became quite angry. Apparently, Marvin wasn't too happy about Doris being in the play."

"Oh," Nellie said. "Well, I think I know why that—"

"What are you two talking about?" asked Myrtle, interrupting as she climbed the bridge.

"I was telling Colleen about Doris's condition," Nellie said.

"What a bunch of bunk."

"You don't believe Doris suffered from narcolepsy?" Colleen asked, not surprised by Myrtle's reaction but wanting to know her reason.

"In a word, no. She used it as an excuse to get out of rehearsal. Now she's gone and left me with a role to fill."

"I hardly think Doris died to get out of playing a role," Colleen said, scolding Myrtle for her coldness.

"Perhaps not," Myrtle said, only slightly admonished, "but I'm still an actor short."

"I could do Doris's role," Nellie said.

Myrtle wrinkled her nose. "You're not an actor, Nell. You're a hoofer. You're good at tap dancing and moving the boat cutouts."

"Lane doesn't feel that way," Nellie said, defiantly raising her chin. "I bet he'd let me do Doris's role."

Colleen watched with amusement as Myrtle clenched her fists into balls and her cheeks darkened from light pink to crimson. Even in the small Corolla theater company, there were power struggles.

"Since when is Lane Walker in charge of this production?" Myrtle huffed. "What does he know about the horses? Not that much, I tell you."

"Maybe not," Nellie said. "But he knows a lot more than you do about acting. And I'm going to go ask him." Nellie marched down the bridge toward the Whalehead Club, and Sparky followed.

"Sparky, no," Colleen called, and the dog halted.

"Nellie Byrd, you'd better not flirt with that Lothario to get that role," Myrtle yelled, chasing after her.

Colleen was amazed by how rapidly Nellie crossed the short distance to the Whalehead Club. Myrtle stormed behind her, struggling to catch up, and pursued Nellie inside. Colleen's phone rang and she checked the number. Pinky. Damn. She had forgotten all about meeting him at the house. The last thing she wanted to do was get on Pinky's bad side, after he had been so generous about donating the property.

"I'm sorry, Pinky," she said after hitting the phone's ANSWER button. "Something came up. I should have called."

"I was worried, Chief McCabe. It's not like you to be late."

The genuine concern in his voice doubled her feelings of guilt. Since Max Cascio's arrest for drug trafficking and the murders of a local art teacher and a fisherman, Pinky had been doing everything in his power to make up for the havoc that his visiting nephew had left in his wake. Pinky had generously donated supplies to the school's art program and money to the station's S.E.A.L.S. Ocean Safety Mini Camp for kids. He had even stopped setting fire to debris, saving Colleen numerous trips to his office trailer.

"I'm really sorry," she said, walking back with Sparky toward her SUV. "I'd still like to meet with you about the arrangements, if you're available."

"Over dinner?"

"Tonight?" she asked, panicked.

"I'm afraid I have plans tonight, but tomorrow is free. How about then?"

She covered the phone with her hand and groaned. While she and Pinky had come a long way in the last few weeks, she wasn't sure if she was ready for dinner with him. But how could she turn him down when he was being so understanding about having been stood up? Plus, she still needed to persuade him to distract Hayley Thorpe not only from shadowing her but from hanging around Bill.

"Dinner tomorrow sounds fine," she said, resigned to her fate.

"Why don't we make it eight," he suggested. "In case something else comes up."

Pinky was teasing, but he was also making a point about not wanting to be stood up again. She was going to have to play by his rules. "Eight it is," she said, reaching her SUV. "See you then."

Colleen and Sparky made their way out of the Currituck Heritage Park and toward the station. Her personal concerns would have to be put on the back burner. They had already interfered enough for one day, and there wasn't anything she could do to resolve them at this point anyway. As she passed Monteray Plaza and turned into the Whalehead community, she actually found herself looking forward to the debriefing. It would be a welcome distraction.

The meeting with her team about the events of the morning went better than she had expected. Even the animosity Chip had felt toward Kenny about flirting with Fawn had temporarily disappeared in the wake of Doris's death and Hayley Thorpe's arrival. They had had a moment of silence for Doris, and Colleen had reassured her team that there was nothing any of them could have done to save her. All were in agreement that the actors had been a helpful addition to the training exercise and encouraged Colleen, despite what had happened with Doris, to use them again. She had told them she'd think about it. After dismissing her team, returning phone calls and e-mails, and going through orders for new equipment, Colleen was ready to head home. She clicked the light off on her desk, stretched, and descended the corrugated-metal stairs.

"Night, Jimmy," she said, and patted him on the shoulder as she passed him in the recreation room.

"Hey," he called after her. "I forgot to ask. How'd things work out with Salvatore?"

"I never made it out to see the house, so we're meeting tomorrow night," she said, wanting to get out of the room before Jimmy had an opportunity to interrogate her.

Sensing she was hiding something, he was up from the sofa and by her side before she had a chance to get out the door. "You meeting him at night? You mean like after hours?" he asked, grinning as he walked backward in front of her across the parking lot.

"Yes," she said, rolling her eyes.

"Bill know about this?"

Colleen came to a halt. "Bill? What does he have to do with anything?" she snapped.

Jimmy threw up his hands in surprise. "Nothing, apparently," he said. "It's just that, well, some of the guys still think Salvatore had something to do with what happened with his nephew."

"Pinky's been cleared. Ask Bill. He'll tell you," she said, annoyed that after everything that had happened and all of Pinky's efforts, some community members continued to believe Pinky was part of the Mafia.

"Hey, I'm on your side," he said. "Just thought you should know what some of the guys might think about you being in tight with Salvatore."

"Which is why you're not going to tell them. I'm meeting Mr. Salvatore to go over the details of the house demo. That's all."

"Does he know that?" Jimmy asked with a raised brow.

Colleen swatted at him. She didn't want to think about what Pinky might or might not want from their dinner meeting. "Have you seen Sparky?" she asked, changing the subject and searching for the dog.

Jimmy nodded toward the side of the station, where Sparky was sleeping in a ditch he had dug under the picnic bench. Colleen gave a short whistle. The Border collie raised his head, yawned, crawled from under the table, and trotted to her.

"You ready to go home?" Sparky wagged his tail. "Call if anything comes up," she said to Jimmy.

"You, too," he said with a wink, and scurried away before she could really hit him.

She grinned. As annoying as Jimmy could be, she was deeply grateful for his concern. She thought of him as more like a brother than a colleague and knew that no matter what, he always had her back. It was a relief knowing she could leave the station in his hands. She didn't know what she'd do if anything ever happened to him. She watched him disappear inside before heading home.

Chapter 4

Nothing like discovering a dead senior citizen on the beach, breaking up a fight at the station, catching your best friend and would-be boyfriend kissing a celebrity soap star, witnessing dramatics between old friends Nellie and Myrtle, and arranging a dinner date with a real estate developer who some suspect is a mobster to exhaust oneself, Colleen thought as she parked in front of her house and cut the engine. It felt like days since she had been home. She couldn't wait to change out of her clothes, take a hot shower, and relax with a nice glass of red wine. She'd even allow Smokey to sit on her lap if the cranky cat so chose.

She and Sparky exited the vehicle. The dog raced up the steps, stared at the doorknob and then back at Colleen. Sparky had obviously had a long day, too, skipping his usual evening search for the rabbit that lived in the yard in preference for a meal and his bed. He pawed at the front door. "All right, all right, I'm coming," she said, climbing the stairs and inserting the key into the lock. As soon as the door was open a crack, he forced his way in. Normally, she'd stop such behavior; but tonight, she couldn't blame him. It had been a long day.

She kicked off her shoes in the foyer, clicked on a light and the television in the living room, and crossed back through the foyer to the kitchen. Smokey stretched from her nap atop the dining room table and yawned. "Get down," Colleen reprimanded, and pointed to the ground. The cat let out a sleepy cry of protest and jumped to the floor. No matter how many times she shooed Smokey from the table or scolded her for being on it, the cat persisted in treating the table like her bed. Colleen removed the cloth, dropped it in a ball on the floor near the kitchen entrance, pulled a fresh one from the baker's rack, and spread it over the table. There was nothing appetizing about cat fur in one's food.

Smokey rubbed against her calves as she retrieved and cracked open a can of Fancy Feast ocean whitefish and tuna. Sparky sniffed the air and whined. "This isn't for you," she said to Sparky, and set the dish in front of the cat. "Come on," she said, and the dog followed her to a corner, where she filled his bowl with Beneful beef stew. The sounds of feline and canine slurping filled the air. Colleen's stomach growled. Guess I'd better feed myself, she thought. She tugged open the refrigerator door and scanned its contents: a gallon of milk, two slices of cold pizza, a container of expired vanilla yogurt, and an unopened block of cheddar cheese. She glanced at Smokey's and Sparky's bowls, half-contemplating whether or not the pet food was a better option, and then shook her head. Cold pepperoni pizza it is, she decided, grabbing the plate with the pizza slices, a glass, and a bottle of wine from Currituck County's Sanctuary Vineyards, and then headed into the living room. The shower could wait until after she ate.

She flumped onto the sofa and mindlessly watched cable news. Her thoughts drifted to the day's events. Notwithstanding Doris's tragic death, the training exercise with the addition of the actors had gone well. Even though there was tension in the house between Chip and Kenny over Fawn, she was pleased with her team and how they had worked together. Business at the station was fine.

It was her personal life that was bothering her. But why? Nothing had changed between Bill and her—not really. So what if he'd had a relationship with Hayley? It didn't mean he was interested in her now. In fact, she and Bill had grown closer since early July. So why was she feeling so uneasy? Smokey joined her on the sofa and began her postdinner bath. Sparky entered a moment later and lay on the rug in the center of the room. She envied how secure and content they both were. It was her feelings of insecurity, her lack of confidence and uncertainty about her standing with Bill, and, yes, her self-consciousness about her looks that were bothering her. She poured herself another glass of wine and padded into the hall bathroom for a reality check.

She flipped on the light, leaned close to the mirror, and scanned her reflection. She looked tired, but, all things considered, she wasn't entirely unattractive. She had been blessed with her mother's beautiful ivory skin and her father's steel blue eyes. She had never liked the freckles that dotted the bridge of her nose, but others found them "cute." Her medium brown hair was thick and wavy and framed her face nicely, especially with the ends lightened from the summer sun. On the rare occasions when she had worn makeup and dressed in more than jeans and a T-shirt, some had even remarked that she was pretty. Still, she had never received the reaction from men that Hayley had today . . . and she didn't want to, at least not in her professional life. In fact, in the beginning of her career she had worked hard to downplay her looks. She hadn't wanted to be seen as anything other than a fellow firefighter. *Being a firefighter isn't a beauty contest; all people care about is that we help them.* She growled at her reflection. *Stop scrutinizing your face like an insecure thirteen-year-old. You're fine. You've always been fine. Nothing's changed.* She clicked off the light in disgust and climbed the stairs. She hated herself for thinking like this. It was stupid.

After two glasses of wine and a hot shower, she felt more like herself again. She changed into a pair of comfortable shorts and a T-shirt, opened the bedroom window, settled into bed, and listened to the water from the sound gently lapping at her pier. Soon her eyelids grew heavy and she drifted into a peaceful sleep.

The serenity was short-lived. At 2:30, Colleen tossed in the bed, uncomfortable and hot. She threw the comforter back and flipped the pillow, hoping that the cool underside would help soothe her back to sleep. She woke again at 3:34 and flipped the pillow again. At 4:10, she felt dehydrated, got a drink of water from the bathroom sink, and attempted to lull herself back to sleep by counting backward from one thousand. Finally, at 5:15, she knew it was useless. There was no point in tossing in bed for another hour or so. She might as well get up and start her day.

She changed into athletic gear and her favorite running shoes and groggily descended the stairs. A long early-morning run always helped clear her head. She padded into the kitchen to get a drink of water before leaving. Smokey lifted her head from where she had settled onto the clean tablecloth, blinked, and then drew a paw tight over her face to get more shut-eye. Glad someone's able to sleep around here, Colleen thought. She chugged a tall glass of water, then grabbed her keys and Sparky's leash. At the sound of the jingling keys, Sparky appeared in the foyer, yawned, and stretched first his front and then his back legs. Colleen had stretched upstairs, but she gave a final pull on her quads before opening the door and heading out.

They started off on Lakeview Court, a quiet road that wound through her neighborhood. The sky was lightening, but it was still relatively dark, with about twenty minutes before the sun peeked over the horizon. Birds sang their early-morning melodies and a chipmunk scurried across the road. She turned onto Bluewater Court and then onto Ponton Lane. Back in high school, she had often taken midnight runs and loved the feeling of having the world all to herself. While on these runs, she would occasionally see someone heading out in the dark for a work shift, and it would remind her that there were two worlds—one inhabited by the day dwellers and the other by the night dwellers—and that she was a mere visitor in the night one. Never had she imagined then that she would become a resident of the lightless world when she began doing evening shifts at the firehouse.

She had always found those shifts disorienting and had had trouble sleeping due to the anticipation of a potential call. She didn't think she'd ever get used to night rotations. She approached Route 12, stopped to leash Sparky, and then the two made a right onto Ocean Trail.

As she fell into a steady pace, her mind drifted to the events of yesterday. Nothing that had happened at work was anything more stressful than she had experienced before. Even the arrival of the film crew, while unusual, wasn't something that should be causing her insomnia. It was her uncertainty about Bill's feelings for Hayley and that alone that had kept her up. It was at times like this that she missed having a girlfriend to talk to. Back in high school and college, she had had teammates with whom to share "boy trouble," but, as people do over the years, Colleen had lost touch with a number of her high school and college buddies. That's why it had been nice when she and Bill had become friends.

Colleen and Bill had first met through their jobs. She had been surprised by how quickly she began to feel comfortable around him. While she had always had many gal friends, she had tended to be a bit more reserved when it came to guys. Men had tended to fall into two camps: those whom she thought of in strictly platonic terms and those whom she thought of only romantically. Bill was the first man she'd thought of as both a friend and would-be boyfriend. Despite occasional disagreements, they respected and trusted each other, and he had become the first person she went to when needing to discuss professional or personal troubles. She had never imagined anything or anyone threatening their relationship. But if Bill and Hayley still had feelings for each other, then, Colleen knew from experience, there wouldn't or shouldn't be any room for her. Three was always a crowd.

She left Ocean Trail and ran onto Persimmon Street and then left onto Corolla Village Road. She slowed her pace as she passed the historic Corolla Chapel, the site of many beautiful weddings; the Lighthouse Wild Horse Preservation Society with its official wild horse tours; Island Bookstore, a favorite stop for book lovers; and the Corolla Schoolhouse, a historic two-room schoolhouse recently reopened as a charter school. It was no mystery why Old Corolla Village was popular with visitors. She left the schoolhouse behind as she approached the Currituck Beach Lighthouse. She gazed heavenward at the lighthouse, marveling at the attractiveness of the unpainted brick structure, before jogging onto the Currituck Heritage Park grounds.

Once in the park, she unleashed Sparky and the two happily made their way around the basin, past the boathouse, the wildlife education center, and over the historic bridge. The rising sun washed the sky in salmon-orange rays, and she admired how brilliantly the yellow Whalehead Club Historic House Museum gleamed in the light, a definite jewel in Corolla's crown. Originally built by nature lover and conservationist Edward Knight and his wife as a vacation getaway in the 1920s, the five-story, 21,000-square-foot structure had at various points in time been used as a World War II Coast Guard receiving station, a summer boarding school for boys in the late 1950s and early 1960s, and a rocket-fuel research facility in the mid- to late 1960s. After subsequent unsuccessful attempts at resort development, it was abandoned and left to deteriorate. She was pleased that Curri- tuck County had eventually purchased and restored the property in the 1990s. In 2002, the building had been fully returned to its original splendor and the doors were opened to visitors.

They approached the building, ready to make the turnaround and head home. Inky, a black tomcat who frequented the park and Old Corolla Village, appeared from behind the Whalehead Club and strutted across the lawn. Sparky cocked his head at the sight of the cat and, before she could grab his collar, took off af- ter it. She grunted in frustration and sprinted after him.

Inky spotted the dog, scurried to a propped-open door at the side of the Whalehead Club, and darted inside. The dog tracked the cat into the building, hot on the trail. Please don't let Sparky damage the antique furniture or artifacts, she prayed. She heard barking and quickly entered the house. What unfolded next in- side the Whalehead Club would change the course of events in Corolla for the remainder of the summer.

"Betty Botter bought a bit of bitter butter," Colleen heard a chorus of voices say as she made her way through the pink-tiled kitchen and the Tiffany-designed dining room, searching for Sparky. She paused a moment, puzzled, and listened to a second round of tongue-twister recitations: "Freshly fried flying fish. Freshly fried flying fish." Now Colleen understood what she was hearing. The theater group was having an early-morning rehearsal. Actors, she thought with a shake of the head. She hoped Sparky was with them.

She slowed and carefully made her way from the stunning

dining room into the main foyer and down the hall toward where the voices were clearly enunciating in unison. As she traveled the length of the structure, the voices grew louder. She couldn't help but admire the Art Nouveau architecture and furniture and was relieved that none of the furniture seemed to have been disturbed. She reached an area at the end of the building sectioned off by a temporary curtain. "She sells seashells by the seashore," the chorus chanted. This was clearly where the theater group was rehearsing. She took a deep breath and pulled back the makeshift curtain.

Members of the theater troupe were assembled in a circle in the middle of the library, their lips pursed in exaggerated pouts. She wondered what they were up to and then, a second later, watched with surprise as the actors blew air through their lips, resulting in a loud raspberry sound. Her eyes widened at the sight of almost a dozen of Corolla's finest citizens making what she considered fools of themselves. Colleen decided she'd better get out of there before they tried to rope her into participating in their theater games. She discovered Sparky observing the group from underneath the magnificent one-of-a-kind Steinway sketch-design piano near the window. Inky perched above him on the piano. Colleen couldn't imagine that the museum's curator or tour guides would approve.

Myrtle appeared at Colleen's side. "Look at that foolishness," she said with disgust, indicating her fellow actors.

Not wanting to get into a discussion about the merits of vocal warm-ups and desirous of returning home, she ignored Myrtle's comment and made an effort to get Sparky's attention with a snap of her fingers. Sparky cocked his head, squinted his eyes in a content expression, and proceeded to ignore her. Bad dog, she thought, and tiptoed across the room to retrieve the canine.

"Okay, everyone," Lane Walker said, entering from a second entrance with Nellie under his arm. "I've got an announcement to make." The room fell silent. "Nellie here has agreed to take Doris's role in the play."

A murmur of surprised congratulations rippled over the group. Nellie beamed, and Colleen saw something she had never seen in her before: triumphant pride.

"Just one minute!" Myrtle exclaimed.

"I know some of you may think it a little soon to recast, given dear Doris's passing yesterday morning, but we don't have much time before we open and, as the saying goes, my show must go on." Lane patted Nellie on the shoulder and she nearly skipped with delight to the stage area.

The group dispersed and took their places. The actors strolled to an area in front of the fireplace that was serving as the temporary stage until the production was ready to move outside to the veranda for the performances. Nellie's nephew, Adam, and veterinarian Doc Wales worked on the script at a table on the opposite side of the room, near the antique grandmother clock. Sam Riddle positioned a set piece near the entrance to the sunroom, and Sam's wife, Rita, stitched costumes at a card table in the corner. Colleen wondered if it had been a wise idea to allow the group to use the library for rehearsals. I bet the curator will be happy when they move outside, she thought.

"*Your* show?" Myrtle said, stomping toward Lane. "Since when did it become *your* show?"

Let the drama begin, Colleen thought, taking Sparky by the collar and guiding him toward the exit.

Lane sighed dramatically. "What is it now, Myrtle?"

"You said it was your show. Who put you in charge?"

"I don't believe I said that. But if I did, it was merely a slip of the tongue."

"A Freudian one," Myrtle said under her breath.

"Of course, it's *our* show," he said, gesturing to the others in the room with irritation. "Now if there's nothing further, I believe everyone is waiting."

All eyes fell on Myrtle. Colleen ducked her head, trying her best to be invisible in her retreat.

"Very well," Myrtle said with a huff, then moved sulkily to the area in front of the fireplace and took her place.

"Okay, everyone, let's take it from when the horses are loaded off of the ships," Adam said.

So that's whose directing the show, Colleen thought. Up until that moment, it had been hard for her to tell. She felt empathy for Nellie's nephew. He certainly had his hands full with this group.

"Start the storm, Sam," Adam ordered, and there was a loud rumble of thunder.

Sparky howled and Colleen jumped at the realistic sound effect. Inky leaped from the piano, hitting some of the keys, and took off into another room. Colleen spotted Sam shaking a sheet of metal—the source of the thunder rumble—and smiled wryly. This might not be a bad production after all, she thought.

"Until we're performing outdoors, try toning down the thunder," Adam instructed Sam, and the retiree gave the director a salute.

Colleen paused for a moment to watch what would happen next. The actors standing in the makeshift wings began making whooshing and moaning windlike sounds. Sparky wailed.

"Okay, we'll go," she whispered to the dog, and moved to leave, not wanting to interfere with the rehearsal.

Suddenly, a high-pitched scream filled the air. They might need to tone that down, she thought as she pulled the curtain back and left the library. But then came the slam of a door and a second scream, the one that made her peek back around the drape in time to see Fawn Harkins race into the room, arms flailing and tears streaming down her cheeks.

"Hold!" Adam yelled, as if anyone needed to be told to stop what they were doing. "Is everything okay?" he asked.

"I—I—I—" Fawn stuttered between sobs.

Lane strode to Fawn and put his hand on the young woman's shoulder. "Now, Fawn dear, we mustn't overact. I know we talked about the storm scene being frightening, but this isn't a horror film. You know," he said, turning to the group, "this reminds me of when I did a little picture called *Hall of Horrors* back in 1979. We had this scene where—"

"Ri—Ri—Ri—" Fawn stammered.

"Would you shut your big trap," Myrtle said to Lane. "I think she's trying to tell us something."

"Hold on one minute," he said.

Colleen crossed the room. "I think Myrtle's right," she said, approaching the woman, whose cheeks were flushed pink. "Fawn?" she said in a soft voice. "Do you know who I am?"

The young woman stuttered, "Chief—Chief."

"That's right. Chief McCabe." She was relieved the girl seemed aware of her surroundings.

Fawn's eyes and nose were red from crying. Colleen was struck by the difference in her appearance. The giggly demeanor from yesterday morning was certainly gone now. She wondered if the actress's emotions always ran to such extremes. No wonder Chip was having a hard time with her. Fawn's sobbing became choppy and her breathing short.

"Okay, Fawn, listen to me," she said. "I want you to take a deep breath. Do you think you can do that?"

Fawn sobbed and sucked in short bursts of air. If she didn't get the girl breathing normally, Colleen was afraid the free-spirited performer would pass out from lack of oxygen.

"How about if we do it together. Does that sound good?"

Fawn nodded.

Colleen gave her a reassuring smile. "Ready?"

Fawn nodded again.

"Good. Now take a deep breath in. . . ."

Colleen breathed in and was surprised to find the entire cast taking a deep breath with her. This group has obviously spent way too much time together, she thought.

"That's it. Now hold it . . . and breathe out," she coached. Fawn and the rest of those in the room did as instructed. "Feeling better?"

Fawn indicated yes and sniffled.

"Care to tell us what has you so upset?" The young actress's eyes welled with tears and her breathing quickened. "Remember. Breathe," Colleen instructed.

Fawn gulped in air, paused dramatically, and declared, "Rich is dead!"

The room gasped.

"Oh dear!" Nellie said, and clutched her heart.

"Rich Bailey?" Colleen asked, turning to Nellie, since Fawn was back to sobbing uncontrollably. Nellie nodded.

"He's doing our makeup and lighting," Myrtle added in a worried tone.

"Where is Rich?" Colleen asked Fawn.

Everyone in the room watched Fawn's arm slowly rise and then her finger point to a pair of glass doors in the hall. Sparky sniffed and scratched at the doors, causing one to creak open slightly and a foot to slide out. Fawn let out another wail and bolted at full speed from the room.

Doc Wales rose and crossed toward the doors. "That's the elevator, but nobody can use it."

"You'd better let me," Colleen said. "Sparky, heel," she ordered. The dog backed away. She could feel everyone at her back and sense the tension mount as she reached for one of the handles. She slowly opened a door, revealing Rich Bailey slumped at the bottom of what looked more like an enormous dumbwaiter than an elevator. He was limp, like a Raggedy Andy doll, and his head hung down and to the right.

"First Doris and now Rich," Rita said, shaking her head.

"I wonder why the elevator's up here," Doc Wales said.

"Maybe it's the ghost," Sam offered.

"This play is cursed," added another.

This play isn't cursed, Colleen thought. Someone murdered Rich. She didn't need a medical examiner's report to tell her the marks on Rich's neck had been caused by some type of rope or belt. Just yesterday morning, she had congratulated Rich on his nice makeup work for the training exercise. Now he was dead in the Whalehead Club's dumbwaiter. Rich was one of the most honorable people she knew in Corolla. Why would someone want him dead?

"What should we do?" Nellie asked.

"Call Sheriff Dorman," she replied, using the bottom of her shirt to close the door gently, protecting the others from having to see poor Rich in this state. "Nobody touch anything or go anywhere. I'm sure the sheriff will want to talk to each of you."

The room was still. It was the quietest Colleen had heard the thespians since she had entered the building.

"And," she added, scanning the worried faces, "someone needs to find Fawn."

Chapter 5

"Did somebody mention the Scottish play?" Adam asked in an accusatory tone.

"I think Lane did," Myrtle said, pointing a finger at the debonair actor.

"Don't be ridiculous. I'd never do such a thing," Lane said, genuinely insulted.

"I don't remember hearing anyone say it," Nellie said, trying to recall what had been said during the last few weeks of rehearsals.

"Well, someone must have mentioned the Bard's play," Rita chimed in from her sewing table.

"Maybe it was you and your peacock feathers," Sam said to his wife.

"Or you and your whistling," she retorted.

"Told you they shouldn't let that black cat come around here," Lane said.

"Leave poor Inky out of this," Myrtle told him.

"For the love of God," Doc Wales interjected. "This is all a bunch of ridiculous superstition. A play doesn't become cursed because of black cats or whistling or the fact you mention *Mac*—"

"No!" cried the group of thespians before he could finish.

"Quiet!" Bill boomed.

The room fell suddenly silent. In all the years Colleen had known Bill, she had never heard him shout so loudly. Even though she wasn't feeling particularly friendly toward him, given the Hayley secret he had been keeping from her, she was empathetic. He must be at his wits' end with this group and their superstitions. It all seemed a bit silly to her, but she remembered how grave her college roommate had been when she had told Colleen about theater superstitions. Peacock feathers should never be brought onstage or used as a costume element, since they represented the "evil eye." Whistling in the theater was bad luck because, in the early days of theater, a whistle was a stagehand's way of signaling the lowering of a sandbag and was certain to result in an accident. Three candles onstage meant the person nearest the shortest candle would be the next to marry . . . or die. And the worst of them all: Uttering the name of Shakespeare's play *Macbeth* in a rehearsal or theater hall was an invitation to certain disaster. Since the discovery of Rich's body in the elevator, the actors had been busy blaming one another for violating these traditions and cursing the show.

"Isn't anyone here the least bit concerned about what happened to Rich?" Bill asked, frowning with disappointment at the entire troupe.

The group members lowered their heads in shame. Nice going, Colleen thought.

"Uh, Chief?" Chip said, sticking his head into the room.

"What is it?" She hoped he had found his girlfriend, the runaway actress.

"I've got Fawn outside. But she won't come in."

"For crying out loud," Bill said, now at the end of his patience. "Tell her to stay put. I'll be out in a minute."

"Okay, but . . ."

"Is there something else?" Colleen asked.

Chip stole a look at Bill. The others in the room were now staring at the young firefighter with curiosity.

"With all due respect, Sheriff, Fawn would prefer speaking with the chief."

Colleen glanced at Bill. She knew how much he hated her involvement in his cases.

"You mind speaking to Fawn with me?" he asked.

"Not at all," she said, and moved with him toward the exit. Chip scratched the back of his neck and shuffled his feet. "Something wrong?" she asked.

Chip looked at Bill over her shoulder, then approached. "Fawn wants to speak with just you," he whispered in her ear.

"Why?"

It wasn't like Colleen knew the young woman all that well. In fact, this morning's breathing exercise with the rest of the actors was the most interaction she had had with the girl.

"She says you have a good aura," he said, blushing slightly at having to tell his boss about her aura.

"I'm sure Bill's aura is fine," she replied, resisting the urge to roll her eyes.

"That may be so, but Fawn believes in that mystical stuff. She doesn't want to speak to anyone else. I can't change her mind."

Bill was going to hate this. She patted Chip on the shoulder and turned to Bill.

"What is it?" he asked, not having heard the whispered conversation.

"Fawn wants to speak with just me. Apparently, I have a good aura."

He stared at her a beat. "Are you serious?"

She shrugged.

"For Pete's sake," he said, and ran his hands through his hair.

Colleen lowered her voice. "Fawn's a bit . . . emotional. We might not get anything out of her if you push it."

Bill glanced over at Chip, weighing his options. "Fine," he said. "But I want you to tell me everything she says. No secrets."

Resisting the urge to say something smart about keeping secrets, she followed Chip from the room. Bill could question the rest of the actors on his own.

She trailed Chip down the hall and passed the carved wooden staircase. She noted the swooping nature-inspired architectural features and found it disquieting that Rich had been murdered in such an ugly way in such a gorgeous house. She was thankful that her EMTs and Rodney Warren, Bill's steadfast deputy, had arrived swiftly and sans sirens. They had been able to photograph and document evidence and remove the body before the park began to see visitors. She was relieved that the transfer of

Rich's body had been done with quiet dignity and not under the glare of the local media or the watchful eyes of curious sightseers with video-recording cell phones. They walked out the front door to the porch, where Fawn sat nervously swaying in one of the rockers that lined the sound-facing veranda.

"Chief McCabe's here," Chip said, kneeling next to Fawn and grabbing the rocker to stop it from moving.

She gazed into his eyes, caressed his cheek, and then rubbed her nose on his. "Thanks, Chipmunk."

Chip's cheeks flushed red. "Not in front of my boss," he whispered.

Colleen suppressed a chuckle. The guys at the station would have a field day if they knew about Fawn's nickname for him.

"Why don't you tell the chief what you saw when you found Rich," he said, prompting her.

"I don't want to think about that," Fawn said, and moped.

Colleen sat in a rocker next to the frightened actress. "You said you'd speak with me. I'm here."

Fawn cocked her head and studied her a moment. "May I hug you?"

Chip groaned, mortified.

In all her years of helping people, nobody had ever asked to hug her. "Okay," she said, uncertain how she could say no to this unusual request.

Fawn gently wrapped her arms around Colleen in a hug that barely touched her skin. Colleen wondered what strange ritual she was being subjected to and awkwardly patted the girl's back. She had done a lot of things in service to others, but this had to be the most bizarre. Several seconds passed and then Fawn sat back. Colleen tugged at her shirt, unsure of what to do next.

"You have a nice aura," Fawn said. "Pink. By nature, you're loving and giving. The way you calmed me down earlier proves how sensitive you are to the needs of others."

"Yes, well . . . thank you," Colleen said, trying to maintain a poker face. Under normal circumstances, she would have found it difficult not to laugh at her aura assessment, but she needed to find out everything Fawn knew in order to catch the person who had murdered Rich.

"You're also strong-willed and disciplined and expect high standards from others," Fawn added.

"You got all of that from my aura?" Colleen asked, genuinely amazed at the girl's accuracy.

"That . . . and Chip."

Chip's face flushed red. "Honey . . . Chief, I—" he stammered.

"Relax," Colleen said to him. "So, Fawn, given my understanding pink nature, why not tell me everything you can remember about finding Rich?"

"I don't like those types of images in my consciousness."

"None of us does. But you may know something that will help me catch the person who did this before he or she does it to someone else."

"You think it could have been a woman?" Fawn asked, wide-eyed.

"I don't know. But one thing I've learned is that people, male or female, are capable of almost anything given the right circumstances."

"You couldn't murder anyone."

"We're not talking about me," Colleen said, uncomfortable with how much focus she was getting, especially in front of one of her guys. "Tell me about how you discovered Rich in the elevator."

Fawn glanced at Chip.

"You gotta, honey. Then I'll take you home. She's free to go after this, right?"

"Of course," Colleen said. If Bill needed to follow up with any questions after she had relayed what she had learned, he could do that himself. Maybe the actress would even read his aura.

Fawn closed her eyes, put her hands out in front of her, and began humming softly while her fingers undulated like the tentacles of a jellyfish. *What in the world is this girl up to?* Colleen wondered.

The actress began speaking in a soft, dreamlike voice with her eyes closed. "I was finishing my prerehearsal yoga and working on my character walk in the hall. I could hear the others doing vocal warm-ups, speaking all together, like distant chanting from a faraway shore."

Get to when you found Rich, Colleen wanted to scream, but she just smiled pleasantly.

"I realized I had forgotten my rehearsal scarf." Fawn opened her eyes and said in her regular voice, "I play the wind in the play and use a scarf to create the effect," and then closed them again. "I went in search of a piece of fabric or clothing that I could use. I thought there must be something in the closet that would do. I didn't know it was the elevator. Then I saw a foot, a hand, and then . . ." The actress shuddered and her eyes popped open.

Chip squeezed Fawn's hand.

"Did you notice anything out of place, other than Rich in the elevator?" Colleen asked.

Fawn squinted, as if trying to recall something.

"Tell her everything," Chip instructed.

"It doesn't make any sense."

"What doesn't?" Colleen asked, trying not to lose her patience.

"For some reason, when I think about Rich, I see a blue-green color."

"So?" Colleen said.

"It's impossible for him to have an aura. Only the living have auras."

"Maybe it's not his aura that you're seeing."

"But if it's not his aura . . . whose?" Fawn's eyes widened. "You think it's the killer's?"

"Is blue-green the color of a killer's aura?" Colleen asked, unsure how any of this would help the investigation.

"No," the actress said with a frown.

Colleen was no closer to figuring out what had had happened to Rich than before. She spotted early-morning visitors taking a walk near the water on the park's self-guided trail. The visitors waved at them and she gave a short wave back.

"Can I take Fawn home now?" Chip asked.

She nodded. "Thank you for your help. I'm sure Sheriff Dorman will be in touch if he needs anything further."

The couple descended the veranda stairs. "You will figure out who did that horrible thing to Rich."

"I hope so," she said.

"You will. Pink individuals hate injustice. You won't have it any other way." And with that, Fawn made her way across the lawn with Chip and disappeared around the corner.

What Fawn had said about her was true, but that was no guarantee she'd be able to flush out the killer. Still, in some odd way it gave her confidence that she would. Next you'll start believing in horoscopes, she thought. The notion that her aura could somehow predict her ability to solve this crime was preposterous. She headed inside to tell Bill what she had learned from Fawn—minus the information about her pink aura.

She entered the Whalehead Club and closed the front door. She saw movement at the top of the stairs. Was that Sparky? She had left him with Bill while she talked to Fawn, but with everything that was going on, she wouldn't have been surprised if the dog had slipped away. She heard a door creak overhead and peered up the staircase. She listened down the hall and heard Bill still questioning actors. She looked into the adjoining dining room and down the back hall to be sure she wasn't being watched, then squeezed past a sign at the bottom of the stairs that read STAFF ONLY and quickly climbed the steps to the second floor.

At the top of the steps, she contemplated which way she should go. She crept down the narrow hall and peeked into a room. Unlike the areas that were open to the public, this room was sparsely furnished and had a lonely feel despite the cheerful robin's egg blue paint on the walls. It reminded her of times when she had moved into a new apartment. The room was missing the furniture and personal touches that made a place feel like a home. Something darted to her left and she tiptoed in that direction.

She reached the end of the hall and entered a lovely room directly above the library. An Art Nouveau bed was covered in a floral comforter and atop the bed lay a pair of women's riding breeches. Given the meticulous display of items in the room, Colleen suspected that she was in the bedroom of the former mistress of the house, Mrs. Knight. She could hear the sound of Bill questioning someone in the room below, crossed to a vent near the far wall, and listened. She was surprised by how clearly she could hear the conversation. It was as if she were in the library with them.

"So you were the first person to arrive this morning?" Bill asked.

"That's right," a male voice replied.

She pushed on the vent lever in an attempt to open the slats so that she could see the person Bill was speaking to, but the vent wouldn't budge. She lay on the cork floor and put her ear to the opening.

"And you didn't notice anything out of the ordinary?" Bill continued.

"Not really. It was pretty quiet," the man responded.

The voice didn't sound familiar. Since she knew all the members of the theater group, she wondered whom Bill could be speaking to and then it occurred to her that it could be Nellie's nephew, Adam. It would make sense that he had been the first to arrive at rehearsal. He was the show's director.

"If you can think of anything, even if it seems trivial, please don't hesitate to contact me," she heard Bill say, but her attention was now drawn to the curtains hanging before the window a few feet away.

She lay, cheek to the floor, studying the teal drapery. The lily pad pattern sewn into the material reflected beautiful craftsmanship. She slowly rose, her eyes scanning the fabric from floor to ceiling. One of the panels seemed to be more loosely tied than the other. What if Fawn did have psychic or mystical abilities? What if the blue-green color she saw wasn't the dead Rich's aura, but a vision or clue to the murder weapon? Despite the absurdity of the idea, she inched toward the curtain to get a better look at the tasseled rope tiebacks.

Suddenly, Inky bolted from behind the curtain and ran from the room, claws digging into the floor as he took off down the hall. Her heart raced and she took a deep breath. Clearly, she hadn't had enough sleep last night. She resumed her inspection of the tiebacks and curtains. The rope on the left had a light layer of dust and the folds in the panel appeared well set, as if the curtain had been hanging there for some time. She scanned the other panel and her brows furrowed. The right tieback lacked the left's dust, the wrinkles in the drape revealed that it had been recently disturbed, and the tassel was missing fringe. Was this the rope that had been used to kill Rich?

"Can I help you?" came a voice from behind her.

She whipped around and discovered Kyle Prescott, a wiry museum intern who led the ghost tours of the Whalehead Club, observing her from the doorway.

"Sorry," she said, embarrassed at having been caught snooping. "I know I shouldn't be in here."

"If you're looking for Sparky, he's down in the kitchen."

"I hope he hasn't caused you any trouble."

"He's fine," Kyle said. "Was there something else I could do for you?"

"This curtain," she said, indicating the right-hand panel. "Have you or one of the staff adjusted it recently?"

Kyle crossed to the window and donned glasses to inspect the drape. "No, but I can ask my boss when she gets in," he said, and reached to rearrange the curtain.

"Don't," she blurted out.

He froze.

"I'm sorry. It's just that . . . well, I'd like to get Bill up here if you don't mind."

Kyle glanced at the rope, puzzled for a moment, and then his eyes widened in understanding. "I'll be right back," he said, and hurried from the room.

Moments later, he returned with Bill.

"Kyle says you want to see me."

She stepped aside and gestured to the right curtain panel. "I can't be sure, but I think that rope might be what was used to kill Rich."

Kyle gulped and his hand went to his own throat.

Bill inspected the rope. "You got a clean plastic bag anywhere?" he asked the intern over his shoulder.

"I'm sure I can find one," Kyle said, and disappeared.

Bill sighed and shook his head.

"What is it?" she asked.

"There were fibers this color on the collar of Rich's shirt."

A heavy silence settled over the room. The murderer had likely been standing on this very spot when he or she had removed the rope from the curtains, used it to strangle Rich, and then returned it to its original location. Whoever murdered Rich must have known about this room.

"The killer is one of our own," she uttered.

"Let's not get ahead of ourselves," Bill warned.

"Found one," Kyle said, appearing in the doorway with a Ziploc bag.

"Why don't you stay right there," Bill said. Despite his admonition not to jump to conclusions, she could tell by his tone that he was considering the likelihood of Kyle as a suspect. "You'll need to close the Whalehead Club today," he said. It was an order, not a request. "And I'll want to speak to you later about who has access to this area. That's all."

Kyle stole an uneasy glance around the room and retreated down the hall.

"You think one of the staff killed Rich?" she asked.

"I have no idea." He carefully collected the rope into the plastic bag and zipped it closed. "What made you notice the curtains anyway?"

"Fawn said something about seeing a blue-green aura, so when I—"

"Hold on," he said, interrupting her. "A blue-green what?"

"Fawn has some rather unusual notions—crystals, horoscopes, auras, that kinda thing. I don't understand it any more than you, but she said she saw a blue-green color and thought it was some-one's aura."

"What does an aura have to do with your being up here or someone strangling Rich with this rope?"

"I thought I saw Sparky up here and wanted to get him before he got into trouble. Turns out it was only Inky hiding. As for how the aura is connected to the rope . . . all I know is that when I saw the curtains, something told me that the fabric was the same color Fawn had seen."

"I'm still not sure I understand, but I'll have the guys get up here to dust for fingerprints. Did Fawn share anything else?"

"Only that she was doing her warm-up ritual, went to look for something to use as a costume in what she thought was a closet, and discovered Rich inside the elevator."

"Nobody I spoke with saw anything, either, but I heard a lot of complaints about the production."

I'm sure you did, she thought. "So you don't suspect anyone in the theater troupe?" He didn't respond. "Or do you?"

"There's something going on with that group, but I'm not sure it has anything to do with Rich's death. I got a sense people are keeping secrets."

The image of Bill kissing Hayley at the police station flashed through her mind. "You don't keep secrets," she said. "They keep you."

"What?" he asked, confused.

"Nothing," she said. "Well, if you don't need me, I should be getting home. I'm overdue at work."

"You want a ride?" he asked, following her from the room and down the stairs.

"Don't you need to stay here or get that processed for evidence?"

"You're on the way, and Rodney's downstairs."

They reached the bottom of the stairs, slipped past the sign, and found Sparky asleep on the kitchen floor. "Come on, boy," she said.

"Is something wrong?" Bill asked.

"Why?"

"You got quiet all of a sudden."

Yes, something's wrong. Your ex is in town and you still haven't told me. Why is that? But she couldn't say that. Not if she didn't want to come across as insecure and possessive.

"A ride would be great," she said, and the two of them and the dog exited the building, heading toward Bill's pickup.

The ride home would be the first time they had been alone without the possibility of interruption since she had discovered Bill's past relationship with Hayley. She hoped they wouldn't get into a discussion about the film crew. She knew herself well enough to know she might have a hard time hiding her feelings. She wasn't exactly known for her poker face.

Chapter 6

"If you're searching for a friend without faults, you will be without a friend forever." This was the Irish saying her mother often quoted to her whenever a childhood pal had done something Colleen didn't like, and it was the one running through her head now as Bill drove her home. Why was she feeling so disappointed in him? What had he really done, after all? Not told her about an old girlfriend? So what? She hadn't told Bill about her loves. He might have a perfectly good reason for not revealing his past liaison with the celebrity. Maybe it hadn't been a pleasant breakup—not that it was any of her business. Besides, it wasn't like she and Bill had a commitment of any sort. This thinking was rational and helped ease some of her uncertainty, but she still felt the urge to withdraw.

"Everything okay?" he asked.

She took a second to respond. She had been so wrapped up in

her ruminations that she hadn't realized they had been driving in silence. "Yeah," she said.

A Volvo station wagon pulled in front of them on Route 12 and Bill was forced to slow down. An awkward silence followed as they crept along behind the other vehicle.

"Interviewing the actors was interesting," he said, trying to make conversation.

"I'm sure."

The Volvo exited into the Monteray Plaza parking lot and they picked up speed.

"Did you know Lane has been married three times? Told me he's still in love with each and every one of them."

She found it interesting that he was bringing up the topic of love. "You think that's possible? A man loving more than one woman at the same time?" she asked.

"I guess some guys tell themselves it is. I got the sense there's some history with those actors."

"Showmances," she said as Bill turned onto her road.

"What?"

"Romances that last the duration of a show. New show, new showmance."

"I should have gone into theater," he joked.

The forgiving attitude toward Bill that she had had moments before disappeared in a flash. He slowed in front of her house and she jerked on the door handle before the vehicle had come to a complete stop.

"Hey," he said as she leapt from the SUV and let Sparky out from the back.

She forced herself to make eye contact.

"Maybe we could get together after you're off today. Catch up," he said.

"I have plans," she replied. Even as the words came out of her mouth, she knew she was saying them to punish him.

"Oh," he said, surprised but not put off. "If it won't be too late, we could get coffee."

"I don't know when I'll be home. Maybe another time."

She closed the door, gave Bill a curt wave, marched up the porch steps with Sparky, and disappeared inside. His car idled in the driveway. A moment later, he drove away. She exhaled deeply. Sparky cocked his head at her.

"Was that as awkward for you as it was for me?" she asked her canine companion, and rubbed his ears. He moaned softly with happiness. She could always count on the dog's unconditional love when she was feeling out of sorts. It was time she got to work. She took off up the stairs for a quick shower and change of clothes.

She felt better after a shower and a bite to eat, and it didn't hurt that she had planted in Bill's mind a seed of curiosity—or maybe jealousy—about whom she would be with that night. A voice in the back of her head told her that he hadn't deserved the comment, but she couldn't help it—she felt better. Maybe because it gave her the illusion that she was somewhat in control. Of course, there was no such thing as control when it came to affairs of the heart. Wasn't that, after all, what many great novels, songs, and plays were about? The fact that we can't control whom we love or when? Still, as she drove through the Whalehead community to the firehouse, she allowed herself the deception that she had regained some command of her heart. There would be plenty of time to face reality later.

"Hey," Jimmy said as she entered the station with Sparky. "Nice of you two to join us."

"Funny," she said, knowing he was teasing. "Everyone here okay?"

"Homicide calls are never easy. Chip's taking it pretty hard."

"Fawn was understandably upset at finding the body. Has Chip returned from dropping her off?" she asked, searching the hallway.

"He's out back, exercising."

Colleen left Jimmy and Sparky in the dayroom. She needed to talk to Chip and make sure he was fit to be on duty. It wouldn't do to have him agitated if a call came into the station. She found him in the back of the building, where they ran practice drills. He had stripped off his T-shirt and was swinging from the bar, doing pull-ups. His tan skin glistened with sweat. A tattoo of a fawn seemed to leap on his left shoulder blade with every repetition. Things must be getting pretty serious between those two, she thought. Chip grunted as he hoisted himself up. He had clearly been at this for a while.

"Hey," she said as she approached.

He finished a final pull-up, dropped to the ground, and grabbed his T-shirt. "Hey," he said, and wiped the sweat away from his face.

"How's Fawn?"

"Better now that she's at home."

"And you?"

Chip shrugged.

"You want the day off?" she asked, wondering if it wouldn't be better for him to be with his girlfriend.

"No, I'm fine," he said, and slipped his T-shirt back on.

"Look at me." He did as instructed. "I need to know that you're really okay. I can't have you on duty if your mind is somewhere else."

He stretched his right shoulder and punched the air in frustration. "I wish Fawn would quit that play."

"Because of Doris and Rich dying?"

"Yeah, but even before that she'd been telling me about how much those people pick at one another. She's a sensitive person, you know?"

"Theater people can be a bit intense at times."

"Fawn says that when Myrtle and Lane go at it, Nellie gets in the middle, which irritates Adam because he thinks that undermines his job as director, which Sam agrees with, but then Rita defends Nellie, which leads to Rita and Sam getting into it, and then Doc Wales threatens to quit because he thinks everyone is crazy and forgetting about the horses and the reason they're doing the play, and it goes on and on like that . . . every week."

"That is a lot of drama." Her mind reeled from all the gossip that had gushed from Chip.

"You think that's how all actors are?" he asked, a worried expression on his face.

She didn't want to influence Chip's feelings about Fawn's involvement with the production, so she chose her words carefully. "I think sometimes the wrong personalities can end up together."

She wondered what other information Chip had about the group. Maybe he could give her some insight into Marvin's dislike for them. "I understand Marvin didn't like it that Doris was in the show."

"I can see why."

"Did Fawn ever say anything to you about them having difficulty?"

"Not that I can remember."

"She mention anyone ever having a beef with Rich?"

"No," Chip said. "In fact, Rich is the only one Fawn said everyone in the group liked. Whenever they had to put something to a vote, they'd let Rich be the tiebreaker. She said he'd weigh all sides, do research, whatever, and come up with the best decision."

"He was a decent guy," Colleen said, saddened anew at the loss of Rich and Doris.

The back door to the station opened and Jimmy emerged holding a small white box and beaming from ear to ear. She was amused by his expression and curious as to what could be the source of his glee.

"A package arrived for you," he said, handing her the box.

"Really?" she said, genuinely surprised. "I wonder what it could be."

Jimmy tried to hold it in, but a giggle escaped from his lips.

"What's with you?" Chip asked.

"You'll see," Jimmy said, and pointed to the box.

She examined the subject of Jimmy's obvious amusement. It was just a white box. What was the big deal? Then she noticed the small sticker holding the lid closed. It read *Island Blooms.* Oh no, she thought, and looked sheepishly up at Jimmy, who was grinning like the Cheshire cat.

"Aren't you going to open it?" he asked.

"No, that's okay."

"Who's it from?" Chip asked.

"Yeah," Jimmy said. "Who it's from?"

Colleen's eyes narrowed to slits. Jimmy knew exactly who had sent it and what it contained. Anyone who had ever gone to a prom or wedding knew.

"Looks like a corsage box," Chip said, stating the obvious.

"Yes, I believe it is," Jimmy agreed.

The longer she put it off, the worse it would get with Jimmy. Better to get it over with before others from the station wandered out to discover what the fuss was about. She tore the sticker seal and lifted the lid. A pink freesia surrounded by baby's breath perched delicately atop pale green tissue paper. The flower's citrus fragrance floated into the air.

"Hey, it *is* a corsage," Chip declared, delighted that he had been correct.

"There's a note," Jimmy said, grabbing for a small white card tucked under the baby's breath.

She swatted his hand away and took the card. "Looking forward to tonight, A.S." it read. She slipped the note into her pocket. What the heck did Pinky think was going to happen tonight?

"Looks like your date is going to be fancy," Jimmy said.

"Date? What date?" Chip asked, now more interested than before.

"There's no date," she said. "Why don't you go inside? I'd like to talk to Jimmy alone."

Chip smirked. "Sure, Chief," he said, and hurried inside the station. It would be only a matter of minutes before the entire house knew about her nondate date.

"You could have left this on my desk," she said after Chip was gone.

"What? And miss seeing that look on your face?"

This is what comes from missing meetings with Pinky Salvatore, she thought. You end up with a pink corsage.

"You know you're gonna have to dress up," he said.

"What are you talking about?"

"Salvatore. He'll expect you in a dress . . . with heels."

"If you think I'm wearing—"

"*I* don't care what you wear," he said, interrupting her. "But I don't think Salvatore's imagining that pretty little flower pinned to your station T-shirt."

How had she gotten herself into this? "A corsage? Really? What is this . . . a prom?" She held the corsage up again for him to see.

Jimmy examined the flower. "I hate pinning those on."

Of course. It had to be a lapel corsage. A wrist corsage would have been easy to put on and she could have hidden it by putting her hands behind her back. But no, she thought, Pinky *wants* everyone to think we're on a date. For the first time, it occurred to her that she didn't know where she was supposed to go for their meeting, date, whatever it was. She retrieved the note from her pocket, turned it over, and read "Elizabeth's at 8."

"Not there," she grumbled.

"Come on, it's not that bad," Jimmy said. She held up the note for him to read. "Okay, it's that bad."

Elizabeth's Café and Winery, acclaimed for its pairing of food and wine, was an upscale and intimate restaurant located a few miles south of Corolla in Duck's picturesque Scarborough Faire Shopping Village. It had received write-ups in magazines across the country as one of the most romantic dining establishments on the East Coast. Elizabeth's was the perfect setting for an engagement proposal, a special anniversary, or a quiet celebration . . . not for hashing out the details of a building demolition for a Burn-to-Learn exercise. Pinky had taken his flirtation with her to a whole new level.

"So, what are you going to wear?" Jimmy asked.

"I don't know." She truly hadn't given it any thought. Why would she? Pinky had seen her a million times before.

"A dress?"

She wrinkled her nose. She couldn't remember the last time she had worn a dress. Did she even own one? And what about heels? She lived in work boots and sneakers. "I'm sure I can find something in my closet," she said unconvincingly.

Jimmy folded his arms. "Really?"

"Why are you trying to get me all dolled up? It's Pinky, remember? The one you always worry about?"

"True. But last time I checked, he's the only one giving us a house to burn. And, as you've pointed out any number of times, he donates a lot to our kids program."

She hated when he was right. Like it or not, she was going to have to attempt a makeover for her dinner with Pinky. "Fine. I'll find something in my closet that can work."

Jimmy grinned.

"What is it now?" she asked, fearful that he'd advise her on her hair and makeup next.

"Reminds me of when my little sister went to a prom. The chief is all grown up," he teased.

"Well, if something goes wrong, big brother, I'm calling you," she said, poking him hard in the chest on the last word.

Jimmy rubbed where she had poked him. "Try not to act like that on your date. Remember, you're a lady," he said, and tore off inside before she really had a chance to hurt him.

"You'd better run," she called after him as he disappeared. She glanced at the corsage. A lady? How the heck was she going to pull that off?

Chapter 7

Colleen studied the brightly attired woman wearing a cowboy-themed fuchsia damask dress adorned with gold buttons and braided rope trim and bedazzled matching cowboy boots in the mirror. You look ridiculous, she thought.

After rifling through the farthest recesses of her closets, the only dresses she had found were two long-forgotten bridesmaid dresses. One was a floral tangerine polyester number with fluttery sleeves, and the other was the fuchsia cowgirl number she was wearing now. She had repeatedly tried on both and recalled with irritation how her bride friends had told her the dresses could be dyed or hemmed or in some way altered and worn again. She had never given much thought as to whether or not there was any veracity to those statements . . . until now. Not only couldn't the dresses be worn again; they shouldn't be. That little lie was something women across the globe said to their friends to make them feel better for spending a small fortune on a dress that's only purpose was to provide a beautiful setting for the gem that was the blushing bride. And Colleen had never cared. It was the bride's day, after all. Who knows, maybe I'll torture my friends someday, she thought. But there was no point in worrying about that now. She would need to leave for the restaurant soon if she was to make it down Route 12 to Duck by eight.

She caught Smokey and Sparky watching her with curiosity as she swiveled and checked herself from the side. "So what do you two think?" she asked her style advisers. Smokey stretched out on top of the tangerine dress, which she had thrown on the bed, and let out a quiet meow. Sparky lifted his head from the box that had held the boots and blinked twice, something he did when he was at his most content. "You two will never make it as fashion police," she said, and rubbed Smokey's belly. The cat purred loudly, happy to snuggle in the fabric of the tangerine dress. Sparky rolled over on the floor and she stroked his belly, too. "Be good," she said, and left her furry companions sleeping in her room.

Her boots clunked as she descended the stairs, entered the kitchen, retrieved the corsage from the refrigerator, where she had been storing it to keep it fresh, and crossed to the hall bathroom to attempt pinning it on so that Pinky wouldn't have to. She flipped on the light and, after poking herself twice, managed to get the corsage situated reasonably well on her dress.

She stared at her reflection. It had been a long time since she had worn makeup. The sight of her with pink lipstick, blush, and mascara took her back to middle school days, when her mother would come home with makeup samples from the department store. On those days, she would invite friends for a slumber party and they would attempt applying bloodred lipstick, pink rouge, blue eye shadow, and mascara. Their application had always been a little too thick, and if it hadn't been for the fact that they all had the beauty of youth, they would have looked like clowns. Maybe the lipstick is too much, she thought, and was about to wipe it off with a tissue, when the doorbell rang.

She checked the time on the clock in the living room as she crossed through the foyer to the front door. She hoped it wasn't a solicitation. She really did need to leave soon if she was going to make it to her meeting on time. She opened the door and her jaw dropped.

"Pinky," she squeaked.

"Yeehaw," Pinky said, giving her an appreciative once-over. "I see you got the corsage."

"Yes. What are you doing here?"

"Picking you up." He gestured to the limo behind him. "Your chariot awaits."

He didn't just say that, she thought. "I thought we were meeting at the restaurant."

"Won't it be nicer to take the limo? That way, you can enjoy the wine without having to worry about driving. Shall we?"

"Let me grab my wallet and phone," she said, and left him standing on the porch as she darted into the kitchen. Once out of sight, she leaned against the counter and took a deep breath. If the guys at the station got wind of this, she'd never hear the end of it. She scooped up her wallet, phone, and keys, put on a smile, and rejoined Pinky. "Ready."

He descended the steps and opened the limousine door for her. She had to admit that he was rather dashing in his perfectly tailored linen suit. And he smelled good, too. She slid into the limo, careful to keep her skirt down. He got in next to her and closed the door. *What I won't do for my job*, she thought, and inspected the limousine's interior as they began their trip.

"Champagne?" he asked, gesturing toward a bottle chilling in an ice bucket positioned on the seat opposite them.

"No, thank you," she said. "You know, this is the first time I've been in a limo."

"What do you think?"

"Not bad," she said, honestly impressed.

He beamed. They rode south on Route 12 toward Duck in silence, which both surprised and relieved her. She had been worried that Pinky might make a romantic advance in the vehicle, but, thus far, he was being a perfect gentleman.

"Thank you for the corsage," she said, deciding maybe she could handle this strange date-meeting after all.

"I thought freesia and baby's breath quite appropriate," he said, proud of his selection.

She glanced at the corsage. "So that's what the pink flower is—freesia. Smells nice."

He shifted in the seat to face her. "Freesia is known for its citrus fragrance. It's thought to symbolize friendship, trust, high-spiritedness, and perseverance. You can decide which one I was thinking of for you."

"Friendship?"

"If you say so," he said with a mischievous twinkle.

"How do you know so much about flowers?"

"Mama worked at a florist shop. She used to tell me all about flowers as a boy. The knowledge came in handy with the ladies later."

Ah, there's the Pinky I know, she thought.

"She would have approved of my choice for you."

"Since you won't tell me why you made the choice, I'll have to take your word for it."

He gave her a sly smile. "Grace under pressure."

"What?"

"Mama used to recommend freesia for someone who demonstrates grace under pressure."

"Oh," she said, uncertain how she should take the compliment. "Thanks."

"Freesia is also given for seven-year wedding anniversaries."

"Obviously, that's not us," she said with a chuckle.

"Indeed it is."

"Really?" she said, now turning in the seat to face him with raised brows. "You and I married?"

"Is that a proposal?" he asked with a wink.

"I think you know me better."

"Indeed I do." He was clearly enjoying himself. "We may not be married, but this is an anniversary of sorts for us. We met seven years ago this month . . . and it had nothing to do with my business."

She tried to recall when she had first met Pinky. As far back as she could recall, her interactions with him had always concerned his development company and his habit of burning debris. When had they met before? Could it have been at a community event? Had it been for some official opening of a local business? Nothing came to mind.

"You don't remember."

"And you're not going to tell me."

"Nope," Pinky said, pleased.

Fine. Don't tell me, she thought. But the seed had been planted, and she spent the remainder of the ride trying, unsuccessfully, to recall her first meeting with Antonio Salvatore.

They reached the restaurant and the chauffeur dropped them off near the bookstore. Shoppers stopped to stare as she and Pinky alighted from the vehicle. She had temporarily forgotten about her outrageous attire and was suddenly self-conscious again as they walked to the restaurant's front door. The sooner they got inside and out of the public eye, the better.

Colleen hadn't dined at Elizabeth's Café since attending an engagement party for a friend several years ago, but as far as she could tell, nothing had changed. An impeccably trained woman ushered them past the wine-tasting gallery to a table in the corner near the fireplace and informed them their server would be with them shortly. A votive candle burned brightly atop the lace tablecloth and the light bounced off the polished silverware and Riedel wineglasses. The owner and staff at Elizabeth's clearly took fine dining seriously. Colleen placed her phone at the corner of the table and checked the time. They were perfectly punctual for the restaurant's second seating at 8:15.

"You best hide that," Pinky said, indicating her phone.

"They have something against phones here?" she asked, thinking he was being silly.

"No, but it is frowned upon."

She scanned the tables of the other patrons. No phones in sight. She switched off the ringer, slipped the phone into her lap, and covered it with her napkin.

The server arrived and explained the unique filtration system that was used for the water as she poured them each a glass. Colleen smiled absently as the server described the evening's menu and discussed wine selections with Pinky. This isn't a bad first date, she thought, if you want to be on a date with Antonio Salvatore. From the looks Pinky had received as they had entered the restaurant, a lot of women would have traded places with her. But the heart wants what the heart wants, and right now her heart wanted Bill. Besides, she thought, it would be hard to imagine two people more different than me and Pinky.

"So," she said once the server had departed. "Should we talk about the house you're donating to the station?"

"What would you like to know?"

"Everything I've seen looks fine. My only concern is the lumber on the deck."

"You want me to have it removed?"

"For the safety of my guys . . . yes. I can't risk arsenic gas or ash exposure, not to mention the illness it could cause if anything blew down the beach."

"Consider it done," he said. "That's actually one of the reasons I'm giving it to you. Once I bought the property, I realized I wasn't going to renovate. My decks are made of recycled plastics. It may be more expensive, but it's safer and better for the environment."

"I'm impressed. Most people don't realize how dangerous it is to burn pressure-treated wood."

"It's part of my job to know."

"Yes, well, with all due respect, you and I have had conversations before about burning debris—something that isn't good for the environment."

Pinky's cheeks flushed pink. It was the first time she had seen him blush.

"In case you haven't noticed," he said, gesturing to the interior of the restaurant, "I'm trying a new approach to spending time with you."

"Also better for the environment," she said with a smile, and took a sip of her water. "So, are you going to give me a clue?"

"A clue?"

"About when we first met."

He grinned. "I'll give you this much: It was a festive occasion."

"So it was a community event," she said, trying to get him to reveal more.

"My lips are sealed," he replied, and took a sip of water.

Her phone buzzed in her lap. It was Jimmy.

"Will you excuse me? It's the station."

"Of course," he said, and rose as she left the table.

She hurried the length of the restaurant and out the front door. "Hey, Jimmy," she said, descending the steps of the restaurant's porch. "Everything okay?"

"Call came in. Possible gas leak at Rich Bailey's house."

"You're kidding," she said, instantly suspicious of the timing so soon after Rich's death.

"A neighbor noticed Rich's window was broken. Looks like a B and E."

"And the leak?"

"Sheriff's Department called it in. We're on our way."

Colleen was already heading back into the restaurant. "I'll see you in a few minutes," she said, hung up, and returned to the table.

"Bad news," Pinky said, knowing from her expression their date was over.

"A possible gas leak. I'm sorry, but—"

"I already took care of the bill," he said, interrupting. "The limo is waiting."

"Thanks," she said. The two exited the restaurant and hurried to the waiting car.

She impatiently watched the scenery roll by as the limo traveled north on Route 12. Summer evenings were always busy and the traffic rarely allowed opportunities for passing slower cars on the two-lane road. The chauffeur was trying his best, but there really wasn't anything he could do. If Pinky hadn't showed up unexpectedly at her house to take her to the restaurant, she would have had her SUV and been able to clear the road with the emergency lights and siren. In anticipation of arriving at the scene, she reached back to pull her hair up, as was her habit when out on calls. She tugged at her sleeves uncomfortably, and it was only then that she remembered what she was wearing. She exhaled loudly.

"Everything okay?" Pinky asked.

Not only would the guys at the station tease her about her attire but they'd actually see her out with Pinky. Maybe she could get him to drop her at the scene and leave . . . or, better yet, drop her down the block and she could walk. No, Pinky would never leave her on the side of the road. He enjoyed playing the role of gentleman too much. She was going to have to face her guys. There was no escaping it.

"I'm fine," she said, resigned to her fate. "I just wish I wasn't dressed like this."

"I like it. I don't think I've seen you in a dress before."

"That's because I don't wear them unless I have to—no offense."

"On the contrary, I'm flattered," he said. "You clean up rather nicely, by the way. Wait until Sheriff Dorman sees you."

She slumped in the seat and hung her head. How was she going to explain this to Bill?

Chapter 8

The second Colleen's bedazzled fuchsia cowboy boot emerged from Pinky's limo and hit the pavement, she knew she was in trouble. She had prepared for the whistles, the comments, and the looks. What she hadn't prepared for was the stunned silence. She stood and waited, still as a statue, and braced herself for . . . nothing. After a few seconds, she took a breath. Maybe my outfit isn't that outrageous, she thought, and crossed to the engine, where her men were waiting.

"What's the status?" she asked as Jimmy turned from speaking with Bobby and Chip.

Jimmy's eyes widened, seeing her for the first time in the bridesmaid's getup. He cleared his throat. "We've been inside. No gas. Ran the detector throughout. Bill swears he smelled it, though, so I don't know."

She surveyed the house. "Any possibility there are chemicals from Rich's business inside?"

"We tested. Nothing like that."

"I'll have a look around. If it checks out, you all can head back," she said, and marched toward the house.

"Everything okay?" Pinky asked from where he was standing by the limo.

She realized she'd better send Pinky on his way, especially since Bill was around. "Sorry. I need to check this out. The guys will give me a lift back to the station."

"Of course," he said, disappointed. "Perhaps another time."

"Perhaps. And thanks for making those changes to the house."

"Always happy to help the fire department," he said with a wink.

She waited for the limo to leave before heading into Rich's house to see what she could find out about the possible leak. She noted the broken foyer glass as she crossed the threshold. Whoever broke in must have reached through the window and unlocked the door. She wasn't surprised Rich didn't have an alarm. Few of the year-round residents did. Alarms were mostly installed on the vacation homes and typically succeeded only in inadvertently locking the renters out.

Her first stop was the kitchen. Most often when a gas leak was reported, a blown-out pilot light on the stove was to blame. She didn't think she'd find anything—her guys were thorough, particularly after the incident with Myrtle's house earlier in the summer—but she wanted to be sure. She surveyed the cheerful kitchen with its white cabinets and stainless-steel appliances.

The tile counter, sink, coffeemaker, toaster—all were spotless. She wondered if Rich's background and work with bodies had made him particularly conscious of cleanliness. She checked the stove burners and the oven, but there was no evidence of a leak and the room was missing the smell of natural gas.

She moved to leave and noticed a computer power cord dangling from the edge of the counter. Given the neatness of the rest of the room, it seemed odd to her that Rich would have left the cord hanging and still plugged into the outlet. Rich didn't seem like the type who would grab his laptop and not unplug the cord. She wondered if whoever had broken in had taken it.

Colleen left the kitchen, entered a combined dining and living room area, and stopped in her tracks. In complete contrast to the kitchen, this room's belongings were end over end—the obvious result of someone's frantic, angry search. Even the dining room chairs had been tossed.

"Wow," she uttered.

"You can say that again," Bill said from the other side of the room.

They locked eyes. It was the first time they had seen each other since she had told him she had plans for the evening. She'd never intended for him to see her in her current attire.

"So," she said, breaking the silence. "Someone ransacked the place pretty good."

"So it would seem," he replied, recovering from the sight of her.

She noticed that a television with its accompanying electronics and an iPod on its docking station hadn't been taken. "Any idea what they were after?"

"I checked the bedroom. Same condition. Whoever did this left jewelry and valuables behind."

Colleen stepped past an overturned chair to move closer to Bill. She didn't want to chance being overheard. "You think this had anything to do with Rich's murder?"

"The evidence doesn't indicate any connection."

"But . . ." she said, sensing he had a theory.

"But the timing so close to his death seems like more than coincidence."

That was exactly what she had been thinking. Rich was murdered because he either knew something or had something he shouldn't. Her gut told her that once she learned what it was, she'd know the identity of his killer.

"A laptop seems to be missing from the kitchen," she said. "Don't you think it's strange that all of the other electronics were left behind except for that one?"

"I noticed that, too. Since Rich lived alone, Rodney is checking with his brother about what might be missing and to be sure the laptop isn't at his office." He ran his hands through his hair. "But why ransack the entire place if you'd already found what you were looking for?" he asked, addressing the question more to himself than to Colleen.

"Because you hadn't."

Her words hung heavily in the air. No. The killer hadn't found what he was looking for. If he had, he would have stopped with the laptop in the kitchen and left. There was something else, something that a person might hide in a drawer or desk. Documents? An object? Incriminating photographs? Her mind was full of questions and not a single clue as to an answer. Better focus on questions she could get answered.

"I didn't see any evidence of a gas leak. Did you call that in?"

"Oh, yes," he said, and averted her gaze.

Her eyes narrowed. "Where, exactly, did you think you smelled the leak?" she asked, now suspicious of his motivations for the call. She found it hard to believe that he'd waste her time and the county's money by calling her crew out to break up her date, but lately a lot of things about Bill were surprising her.

"I smelled it. Couldn't tell where it was coming from, though."

Okay. I'll play along, she thought, and left the living room in search of the laundry room and furnace. She returned to the kitchen, opened a slatted panel door, and found the laundry machines. Both were electric, not gas. Only thing left to check was the furnace. She was surprised not to see it located near the kitchen. She opened another door and discovered Rich's pantry. She remembered that some homes had the hot-water heater placed in a closet off of a bedroom, so she headed in that direction.

She crept down the hall and peeked into the first room. It was a tidy space with a single bed and dresser. The fact that it didn't look lived-in made her wonder if it was Rich's guest room. She crossed to the closet, where the door hung open. Clothes lay on the floor nearby. She considered what people stored in closets besides shoes and clothing. She had seen everything from Christmas ornaments to family photographs to craft supplies. She had even found a collection of dental molds in clear plastic tubs once. She never did find out what that had been about. One thing was clear, though: The water heater wasn't in this room.

"Can I help you with anything?" Bill asked from the doorway.

"You wouldn't happen to know where the hot-water heater is?" she asked, not really wanting him tagging behind her as she did her investigation.

"Sure," he said, and disappeared down the hall.

Great, she thought. If Bill had sent her and her guys on a fool's errand, she'd want a moment to think about how to address it with him. Now he'd be right there watching her. She found him standing at the entrance to the bathroom. She eyed him as she squeezed past him and into the small room. Like the kitchen, the room was clean and tidy. She crossed to a closet next to the toilet and found the hot-water heater.

"Thanks, I'm good," she said, hoping her tone would dismiss him. It didn't.

She leaned toward the heater and used her hand to waft air toward her nose. It was something she had learned in her college chemistry lab. Never, ever put your nose straight over a substance until you know exactly what it is. After several waves, she still didn't smell gas. She felt the tank. It was cool. She shifted to lie on the ground to get a look at the pilot light and had a renewed appreciation of her usual firefighter attire of tucked-in T-shirt and pants. She smiled awkwardly at Bill, then tugged on her skirt and gingerly lay on her side with her back to him. She peered into the hole at the bottom of the heater.

"The pilot light is out," she said from her reclining position.

"Hmm," she heard him say from behind her. "That must have been it."

She examined the ignition box. "I don't know," she said, rising in as ladylike a fashion as she could. "That's why there's an emergency cutoff. From what I can tell, the hot-water heater worked as it's supposed to. I don't smell gas."

"I guess it's better to be safe than sorry. Don't need any more explosions this summer."

She could understand why he was more cautious than usual after Myrtle's house explosion, but had he really been concerned, or was the call the ruse of a jealous man? If he had called in the leak merely to interrupt her date, then she didn't know him at all. She decided to give him the benefit of the doubt.

"I'll give the guys the all clear," she said, and moved to leave.

"Before you do that, I'd like you to take a look at something."

"Okay," she said, unsure of what to make of the request. She trailed him down the hall to the back of the house.

"What do you think?" he asked, and gestured into a room.

Colleen peered in and discovered what looked to be an anatomy study of sorts. Plaster molds of hands and faces covered the desk and some of the bookcase shelves. Books about the human body sat in piles on the floor. The room had the feeling of organized chaos, and it struck her how different it was from the rest of the house. But what got her attention and gave her pause were the dozens and dozens of images of human ears that covered several bulletin boards lining the walls. She stepped tentatively into the room and squinted at the ear pictures. Some photos had lines drawn to various ear parts, with notes scratched at the end of the line indicating a "helix rim" or "lobule" or "antihelix."

"I've heard of a foot fetish but never an ear fetish," he said. "What do you make of it?"

"Reminds me of biology lab in a weird way," she said, scanning a second set of photos. "Some of these even look like pictures of the same ears."

"Guess you never can tell about a person."

Colleen stole a glance at him. "No, I guess not. Maybe this had to do with his job. I imagine you get pretty good at knowing all the details of the human body, particularly the face."

"I don't know. Seems more like a hobby to me."

"How do you mean?"

"Well, the room's nothing like the funeral home or his kitchen. It's a bit of a mess."

She had to admit that the room was not up to Rich's usual meticulousnesss. Aside from the unusual photographs and molds, the room was actually cozy, with an overstuffed chair in one corner and local artists' paintings of the beach on the walls. It reminded her of how some people had rooms in their houses that were for show but lived in other rooms, which were less formal and homier. She didn't know whether it was true, but she had a sense that this was the room where Rich had spent most of his time. She noticed the clock on Rich's desk. She had been inside the house for some time. As fascinating as the room's contents were, now that there wasn't any evidence of an emergency situation, she needed to get back to her men and the station.

"I should be getting back," she said.

They left the room and made their way to the front entrance.

"You got a ride?" he asked.

"I'll catch one with the guys."

They lingered. How could she ask Bill if he had really detected a gas smell or whether it had been a ploy to break up her meeting with Pinky? The question would undoubtedly put him on the defensive. And what about his relationship with Hayley? There was no way she could bring that up.

"Hey, Chief. We all clear?" Jimmy called from the road.

She signaled him to start up the engine.

"Sorry to haul you out here and ruin your . . ." Bill's voice trailed off and he gestured to her dress.

"It was only a meeting," she said, suddenly feeling silly for misleading him.

"Pretty fancy meeting."

"I had to wear a dress, and this is the only one I had." She glanced down at her outfit. "Pretty crazy, right?"

A grin crept over his face. "I didn't want to say anything."

"Thank you for that. Can you believe there were eight of us wearing this at a wedding?" Jimmy honked the horn. "I gotta go."

"Hey," he said as she marched away. She paused. "You look nice."

She smiled, turned, and joined her men for the ride back to the station.

As she and her crew made their way to the firehouse, Colleen gazed absently out the windshield, lost in thought about Rich Bailey's apparent ear fetish. She barely noticed that a few of the guys had started humming until, one by one, they began singing. She turned in her seat to listen, amused by their light-hearted mood. But her amusement was swiftly replaced by one of embarrassment as they joined together in singing Randy Houser's "Boots On" and finished with a rousing chorus of "Hey y'all, I'm going out with my boots on." Her face flushed as pink as her dress and the men erupted into laughter. It had been foolish of her to think that she had escaped their razzing.

"Very funny" was all she could manage, to which several of the guys added, "Yeehaw!"

Jimmy snickered from the driver's seat, and she threw him a disapproving look. "You're supposed to be supervising these hooligans," she said, feigning a reprimand.

He grinned and steered the engine into the station lot. Once they were parked, there were more chuckles and offers to help "the lady" down from the engine—something that had never happened before. She growled and shooed the guys away. She wasn't really mad. In fact, moments like this were often useful for bonding a crew together and easing tension after a call. She hopped from the vehicle, yanking on her clothes so as not to flash anyone. Boy did she hate dresses. She couldn't wait to change back into a comfortable T-shirt and slacks.

"So, that's the best you could come up with," Jimmy said, glancing at the dress. "I've got to hand it to you. . . . It's eye-catching."

"You should have seen my other choice," she said, grateful she wasn't wearing the clinging polyester tangerine number.

"The boots are kinda rockin'."

"You think?" she asked, glancing down.

He nodded. "Yeah."

"So my outfit isn't a total disaster. Now, if you'll excuse me, I'm going to get out of it pronto."

She marched up the steps, eager to slip into the clothes she had stored in her office.

"Hey," he called after her. "How'd it go with Salvatore?"

"Fine," she said as she disappeared into her office with a wave. She could tell Jimmy about all of that later.

She stripped out of the dress and boots and threw on a T-shirt with the station logo and khakis. She eyed the boots, thought, What the heck, and put them back on. Now that she was in more comfortable clothes, her mood brightened. She glanced at the dress in a pile on the floor and retrieved the corsage. The flower was pretty, after all, and she'd appreciate it sitting in a glass of water. Maybe she'd think about getting some freesia the next time she was at Island Blooms florist. She scooped the dress into a bag, put the corsage on top, switched off her light, and went in search of someone to give her a lift home. She found the guys hanging out in the rec room.

"Aw, you changed," Jimmy teased.

"I thought you looked nice," Chip said, and a few guys threw pillows at him for "sucking up."

"Thanks, Chip. I'm promoting you to first lieutenant," she said with a wink.

"Hello?" came a voice from the bay. "Chief McCabe?"

All eyes turned expectantly toward the entrance. Hayley Thorpe peered into the room. "There you are," she said, spotting Colleen.

The guys scrambled to their feet. Great. Just what I need, Colleen thought. "What can I do for you, Ms. Thorpe?" she asked, adopting a professional tone.

"Please, call me Hayley."

The guys muttered "Hi, Ms. Thorpe" and "Nice to see you, Ms. Thorpe." Colleen resisted the urge to roll her eyes.

"Nice boots," Hayley said.

"Thanks." She wished she could click the heels of the sequined footwear and instantly transport herself home.

"And you've done something different with your hair," the actress added. The guys snickered. "Did I say something funny?"

"No," Colleen said, shooting a look that instantly silenced the room. "So what brings you by?"

"I was hoping I could shadow you tomorrow. We've had a delay in filming and I figured I'd use the time to do research."

She's got to be kidding, Colleen thought.

"It wouldn't be for long. I know you're busy. I'd just like to get a sense of what you do here."

"I'm sorry," Colleen said, really not wanting to spend any time with Bill's ex. "Why, exactly, do you want to do that?"

"It's for the film."

"Yes, I got that. Are you playing a firefighter?"

Hayley giggled. The rest of the room joined the soap star. Colleen raised her brow. "What's so funny about that?"

Hayley collected herself. "I apologize. It's just that, well, nobody would ever consider me for such a role."

The guys muttered agreement. Colleen felt her ears getting hot.

"And why is that?" she asked, an edge in her tone.

"I meant no offense. I'd love to play a firefighter, but the scripts my agent gets are for divas and seductive ex-wives."

"Which one are you?"

"What?"

"Which one are you playing? Diva or ex?" She felt her pulse quicken and realized she was doing a lousy job of hiding her emotions. The air filled with tension. Her guys looked around, nervous.

"Fugitive witness," Hayley said with a smile.

"So why do you need to follow me?" Colleen asked, now more confused than angry.

"Because my character becomes involved with one of the fire-fighters and later gets pulled into an arson investigation. Oh, I know it's probably unnecessary for most actors, but I'm a little obsessive when it comes to research. I think it would help me to understand the world of my romantic interest. So . . . what time should I have Jason drop me off?"

As much as Colleen hated the idea of spending time with Bill's ex, she couldn't think of a good reason why she shouldn't help the actress, and she was too tired to think up a good excuse. "How does eight-thirty work for you?"

"Wow. You start early around here."

Take that time or leave it, she thought. She wasn't going to ad-just her schedule, no matter how famous the actress was.

"Eight-thirty it is," Hayley said with a nod. "Well, I won't take up any more of your time. Have a good evening, everyone."

And with that, Hayley was gone as quickly as she had come.

The room was instantly humming with comments about how great Hayley looked, how funny it had been that Colleen thought she'd be offered a firefighter role, and how if Colleen wanted any help showing Hayley around, they'd all be more than happy to oblige. She resisted the urge to scream and instead grabbed the keys for the official chief's vehicle from a hook on the wall and left the men talking among themselves. The station door closed behind her. A second later, the door opened again and Jimmy was at her side.

"You okay?" he asked.

"I'm fine. It's been a long day," she said, reaching the vehicle and unlocking the door. "But thanks for asking." She slid into the vehicle, slammed the door shut, and started the engine.

"See you in the morning," he said.

"Eight-thirty," she said with a little salute, and pulled from the station's lot.

Chapter 9

"*The wind of heaven* is that which blows between a horse's ears," Hayley said while gazing at a harem of wild horses from the passenger seat of Colleen's SUV.

Colleen steered the vehicle around a water-filled pool in the middle of the undeveloped road and stole a puzzled glance at her companion.

"It's an Arabian proverb," Hayley said by way of explanation.

With pretty comments like that, the actress was certainly making it hard to dislike her and making Colleen's mission more difficult. When Hayley had reported to the station, Colleen had decided to make the experience as unpleasant as possible so that today would be her first and last day of shadowing. A trip through the rough terrain of the Carova area was just the ticket. But as soon as they had entered the northernmost beach community,

Hayley had spotted a stallion with his harem, manes blowing softly in the breeze, and was charmed.

Hayley had wanted to leave the SUV to see the horses and Colleen had been forced to explain how the horses were truly wild and that it was against the law to feed or be within fifty feet of them. Their wildness captivated the actress, and the trip had only succeeded in making her want to see more. It was then that Colleen had decided to really give Hayley a ride she wouldn't forget and had headed into rougher terrain. They had been driving up, over, down, and around the Carova dunes now for almost an hour.

"So why are we up in this area again?" Hayley asked, clutching the handle above the passenger window and trying her best to keep from bouncing around the front seat as the vehicle rocked back and forth.

"I promised the Carova chief I'd do a pass through while he's gone this week."

The vehicle swayed right and left as she expertly navigated through the dunes. A four-wheel-drive vehicle was the only way to access this community situated north of Corolla and adjacent to the North Carolina–Virginia line, and that's just the way the residents liked it. The year-round inhabitants were a mix of artists, sportsmen, misfits, lifelong islanders, recluses, survivalists, and eccentrics. The residents numbered a couple hundred during the off-season, but the population swelled to well over three thousand in the summer months. The people who lived here shared the land with Corolla's wild horses, sea turtles, the endangered piping plover, duck hunters, and fisherman—at times, not so happily.

Truth be told, Colleen didn't have to make the rounds today. She had actually planned on swinging through the community later in the week, but if Hayley wanted a taste of the Outer Banks, Carova would do nicely. She slowed to allow one of the privately run oversized safari-type horse-tour vehicles to pass. Sparky pushed his head through the back window to catch a whiff of their scent. She waved at the guide and imagined Myrtle frowning with disapproval. The Lighthouse Wild Horse Preservation Society also offered tours, but with a patrol specialist or herd manager, and was the only official authority on the horses. Myrtle and Nellie sometimes took issue with what they perceived to be inaccurate information given by the private tour guides. Plus, unlike with the other tours, all money paid for the society's tours went toward the preservation of the horses and their habitat.

"So, how are you liking Corolla?" Colleen asked, and tilted the vehicle sideways around a pool of water between two dunes.

"It's nice," Hayley said, adjusting the air-conditioning so that it blew on her face.

"You ever been here before?"

"No."

"Really," Colleen said. "I heard you had friends down here."

She felt Hayley's eyes on her but kept her face blank and her eyes fixed straight ahead.

"Did Billy tell you that?" the actress asked.

"Billy?"

"Bill Dorman. The sheriff. Once upon a time, we were engaged."

Colleen steered the vehicle over a divot, and Hayley let out a small cry as she bumped against the door. Sparky thumped on the backseat. "Sorry," she said. "These roads are pretty inhospitable if you're not used to them."

"So are the people," Hayley said quietly.

There it was—out in the open—confirmation that not only had Bill been in a relationship with Hayley but at one point in time he had wanted to marry her. She felt sick to her stomach and, even though she knew it was unkind, couldn't help but take comfort in seeing that Hayley, too, seemed to be feeling queasy. The unimproved back roads of Carova were known to do that, especially to people who had a tendency to be motion-sick.

They drove in silence, and Colleen soon lost track of exactly where she was going. Her mind was too busy thinking about Bill and Hayley—engaged. How long ago was this? Did they live together? Who had ended it . . . and why?

"Chief McCabe," Hayley said in a weak tone. "I think I need to stop and get some fresh air."

The actress was pale and sweat dotted her forehead. Colleen peeked in the rearview mirror and saw Sparky let out several yawns, a telltale sign that he, too, was feeling nauseous. She felt a wave of guilt wash over her. "There's a house over this dune where one of my guys lives. We can stop there."

Hayley breathed in deeply and closed her eyes. Colleen prayed neither Sparky nor the actress would get sick in her vehicle. It would serve you right if they did, she thought. She crested the dune, steered the vehicle into the sandy driveway of a modest wooden beach house, and threw the gear into park. Hayley leaped from the vehicle and inhaled a deep breath of fresh ocean air. Sparky wiggled to the front seat and out the open passenger door. Shame on you, Colleen scolded herself, and exited the SUV.

"One of my guys lives here with his girlfriend," she said, joining Hayley and Sparky. "Let's see if we can't get you two some cold water."

"I'd be most grateful," Hayley said with sincerity.

She hadn't been to Chip's home since he had started dating Fawn, and as the three made their way to the house, she noted several new additions to his yard decor. Statues of deer, rabbits, and several chipmunks had been carefully arranged in the sand lining the drive. Each animal's head wore a wreath of brightly colored fake flowers. Sea glass wind chimes tinkled brightly in the breeze. They climbed the stairs, and Colleen detected the faint fragrance of jasmine. Sparky's nostrils flared, also picking up the scent.

The group reached the top of the stairs and approached the door. "Hello," Colleen called in through the screen, not wanting to startle Fawn.

A moment later, Fawn appeared, wearing a diaphanous yellow-and-blue maxidress. "Chief McCabe," she said, and opened the screen door. "If you're looking for Chip, he's already at the station."

"Yes, I know. I was wondering if we might trouble you for a glass of water. Ms. Thorpe and Sparky aren't feeling well."

Fawn noticed Hayley, and her eyes widened in awe. Here we go again, Colleen thought.

"Hayley Thorpe. I can't believe it's you. At my house. On my porch," Fawn bubbled.

Hayley flashed her a warm smile. "It's nice to meet you. What's your name?"

"Fawn Harkins. Oh, Ms. Thorpe, I grew up with you. You're why I'm acting."

"That's sweet of you to say," Hayley said, causing Fawn's eyes to well with tears of joy.

Colleen had to hand it to Hayley: She was amazingly gracious with her fans. The actress had a way of interacting with people that made them feel special and mutually adored. If there was a gene for that, Colleen knew she didn't have it.

"Would you mind getting Ms. Thorpe some water?" she asked. "She's not feeling well after riding through the dunes."

"I'd be honored," Fawn said, and held open the screen door.

"And a bowl for Sparky would be great, too," she added, entering behind Fawn and Hayley.

Fawn scurried to the kitchen. "I have specially filtered water, Ms. Thorpe."

"Don't trouble yourself. Tap will be fine." Colleen caught Hayley's eye and shook her head, warning her off the tap water. "On second thought, filtered water sounds delightful."

Fawn busied herself finding glasses and pouring the water. "Would you like me to add some grapefruit oil?" she asked.

"Plain water will be perfect."

Fawn handed the glass to Hayley and watched her take a nice gulp.

"Lovely," Hayley said. Fawn beamed.

"I'll take some to Sparky, if that's okay," Colleen said.

Fawn retrieved a bowl and filled it with water.

She left Hayley with her fan, exited the house, and set the bowl down for Sparky. He eagerly lapped up the cool water and blinked a kiss up at her by way of saying thank you. "You're welcome," she said, and rubbed his ears, glad that he was feeling better. She could hear Fawn happily chatting with Hayley and wondered if the young woman would end up reading the star's aura or asking her for a hug. The celebrity would undoubtedly take that, too, in stride.

The sound of angry voices in the distance caught her attention. She moved to the side of the house and strained to see who or where it was coming from. She detected two male voices and searched the nearby homes. The sound of glass breaking focused her attention and she eyed a structure tucked low in the nearby dunes. She tiptoed past the front door and down the steps. Sparky followed. "Stay," she said, and he flumped in the shade under Fawn's house.

She crept down the driveway, careful to keep her head below the top of the dune. She jogged along the sand road until she reached the entrance to the house she had spotted from Fawn's deck. The voices were louder now and it was clear to her that two men were having a heated argument. In her experience, the only things that got men this angry were women, sports, and occasionally politics. She ducked behind a pickup parked in the front of the house, checked to be sure the coast was clear, and then hurried to the side of the house.

"I don't know how many times I can say it, but I wasn't having an affair with your wife," said a man from inside the house.

That answers the question about what they're arguing about, she thought, and leaned closer.

"She wouldn't have threatened to leave me unless she'd found some other fella."

"I promise you, that fella wasn't me."

Colleen concentrated on the voices. They sounded familiar. She studied the pickup and the SUV under the house, then searched for a sign indicating the name of the owners of the house, but she couldn't find anything that revealed the identity of the men inside.

"Look, Marvin, I know it's difficult losing Doris, but she wasn't having an affair with anyone in the group. Her only love was theater . . . and you."

The fight was about Doris Jenkins and her participation in the theater production. Marvin must have thought his wife had been having an affair with a fellow member of the company. That would explain why he was so angry when Bill broke the news to him about her death.

"Sam? Is everything okay now?" It was a woman's voice.

"Everything's fine, Rita. It was just a misunderstanding."

Colleen raised her brows. She wondered what Rita thought of Sam's being accused of an affair.

"Sorry, Rita, Sam. It's . . . well . . ." Marvin said.

"We understand," Rita said. "Doris's passing was quite a shock."

Marvin was clearly having a hard time with the loss of his wife. It was difficult to get too upset with him about his behavior. Anger was, after all, one of the stages of the grieving process. She heard the door open and ducked out of sight.

"I'll pay for the glass," she heard Marvin say.

"Don't worry about it," Sam said. "Go home, have a drink, maybe go visit family."

Marvin shuffled to his pickup and drove away.

"I'll go clean up the mess," Rita said, and Colleen heard the door close.

Suddenly, Sparky appeared from the road, tail wagging. He spotted Colleen and came running.

"Hey there, Sparky," Sam said as the dog approached. "Whatcha doing here?"

Damn. There was no way of hiding now. Best to step from behind the house and make her presence known. "Hey, Sam," she said. Sparky joined her. "Bad dog," Colleen whispered, but she rubbed his chest with concern. It wasn't like him to abandon his post.

"Well, hello," Sam said with surprise.

She thought about trying to make up an excuse for why she was lurking about his property but figured the truth was actually what made the most sense. "I was at Fawn's place and heard arguing. Is everything okay?"

"How much did you hear?"

"Bits and pieces. I saw Marvin leave."

"Poor guy," Sam said. "I can't imagine what he must be going through. I'd hate to think of what life would be like without Rita."

"I heard you say Doris wasn't having an affair. Was that true?"

"Doris is gone. I really didn't see the point in hurting Marvin."

"So she *was* having an affair?"

"Just a feeling I got."

"Why'd Marvin think she was seeing you?"

"He's accusing anyone who has ever looked at Doris. Trust me; I can barely keep up with one woman"—he gestured inside—"let alone two."

She smiled. "Who else did Marvin accuse?"

"Doc Wales, Nellie's nephew. Hell, he even accused Myrtle. Can you imagine?"

Colleen's brows rose in surprise. Seems Marvin was including men and women in his search. She wondered if there was anything to it or if it was merely the irrational suspicions of a grieving husband. Suddenly, Hayley rounded the corner, barefoot, her shoes in hand.

"Oh, thank goodness I found you," she said, making her way to them. Sparky trotted to her and accompanied her the rest of the way.

"Did something happen?" Colleen asked, noting the actress's unusually frazzled appearance and flushed cheeks.

"After Fawn's reading . . . the danger warning . . . and then you weren't there, so I—" Hayley struggled to catch her breath.

"Slow down," Colleen said, interrupting her.

Sam looked on with surprised interest. Great, another fan,

she thought. Better get the introductions over with so I can find out what's going on. "Hayley Thorpe, Sam Riddle."

Hayley brushed back a loose tendril and collected herself. "Lovely to meet you."

"You, too, ma'am," he said, unfazed by Hayley's celebrity status.

Could it be? Was there actually a person who didn't know who Hayley Thorpe was? "Hayley's in town to shoot the movie," Colleen said. "You know . . . the soap actress."

"Hate to admit, but I never really watched soaps. Welcome anyway," Sam said with a slight nod. "If there's nothing further, I'll leave you two ladies to talk. I got a little mess to help Rita with. Nice to meet you, miss."

"You, too," Hayley said with a smile.

Sam disappeared inside to clean up the aftermath of his fight with Marvin. Colleen liked him better and better.

"So what happened?" she asked, and walked away toward the road. As much as she wanted to learn what Hayley had to say, she found it difficult to look her in the eye now that she knew about her relationship with Bill. It would be easier to talk to her while on the move. Sparky followed and sniffed the side of the road for the scent of a rabbit, duck, or horse.

Hayley caught up to her and Sparky. "After you left, Fawn insisted on reading my—"

"Aura?" Colleen asked.

"No. Cards."

"Cards?"

"Tarot cards."

"Of course, she reads tarot cards," Colleen muttered.

Hayley touched her arm to stop her and lowered her voice. "I hate to be disagreeable, but maybe she shouldn't . . . at least not if she's going to deliver that type of news."

"Which was?"

Suddenly, the Currituck County sheriff's pickup truck appeared from around the bend. Colleen silently groaned. Bill . . . the very person she didn't need to see right now. The vehicle rumbled down the hill and slid to a stop in front of them. She and Hayley shielded their eyes as the dust swirled around them and then cleared. Bill exited, took a step toward them, stopped abruptly, and then stole a look back. Nowhere to run now, mister, Colleen thought. After a moment, he took a deep breath and made his way slowly to them.

An awkward silence followed. Colleen studied his face to try to decipher what was on his mind, but she wasn't able to see behind his sunglasses. She was certainly glad she was wearing her shades; otherwise, her feelings toward him would have been obvious.

The tension between the fire chief and sheriff was not lost on Hayley. "I'm glad Fawn was able to reach you, Billy," she said, breaking the silence.

"Yes, well," he said, and rubbed his bicep, a nervous habit. "Fawn said something about Colleen having gone missing. Apparently, a false alarm."

"Apparently," Colleen said.

"So," he said, wiping sweat from his brow. "You two have met."

Colleen folded her arms. "We have indeed."

"On the first day I arrived, as a matter of fact. Right before I met you at your office," Hayley added. "She was allowing me to shadow her today as research for my film role."

"So you've been together all morning." He shifted his weight.

"Yep," Colleen said.

"And what brought you out to Carova?"

"I promised I'd swing through while their chief was out of town. Hayley wasn't feeling well, so we stopped at Chip's place."

"I'm afraid the terrain of these back roads through the dunes is too much for me," Hayley said. "Remember how carsick I'd get, Billy?"

"You took her through the dunes?"

"Is there another way?" Hayley asked, looking from Bill to Colleen.

Colleen averted her eyes.

"Most people drive the beach, where it's flat," he said in an accusatory tone.

Bill and Hayley eyed Colleen. The emotions swirling inside Colleen were a mix of anger, heartbreak, and now panic, but she tried to appear calm and disinterested.

"So why, exactly, did I get a call that you were missing?" he asked.

"We couldn't find her after Fawn did my reading," Hayley volunteered. "Turns out she was here," she said, and gestured to Sam's house.

He studied the house. Uh-oh.

"What were you doing at Sam and Rita's place?"

"Something I'd prefer to speak with you about in private." She turned to Hayley and added, "No offense."

"None taken. I've had my fill of research for one day."

Had the actress made a snarky remark? If so, it would be the first time Colleen had seen her be anything other than gracious. Not that she could blame her. She knew she'd been rude.

"Could you give me a ride back to my house?" Hayley asked Bill.

"Of course."

"I'll leave you to it, then. Sparky," Colleen said, and quickly walked away. The last thing she wanted to be was a third wheel. She lengthened her stride as she marched toward Fawn's house, wanting to put as much distance between them and her as fast as possible. She heard footsteps behind her and picked up her pace, but Bill finally caught up.

"Hey," he said when she kept walking.

She closed her eyes, sighed, and stopped.

He came around to face her. "You okay?" he asked with genuine concern.

She felt her eyes begin to tear. Damn it, you'd better not cry, she told herself. Not in front of him. She squared her shoulders. "I'm fine."

He took off his sunglasses and studied her face. "We need to talk."

"About what?"

"Rich's murder, or at least the circumstances surrounding it. I've learned some things. You obviously have, too."

Oh, I've learned some things, she thought, not inclined to share anything with him. Then she remembered a promise she had made to Bill after Max Cascio's arrest. She had agreed to consult with him about any investigation that was beyond the scope of her job as fire chief, and the reason she had acquiesced was because it was the safe thing to do.

"You can call me later," she said, and took off toward her SUV with Sparky at her side.

She took her time driving back to the station, preferring the back roads through the dunes to the beach highway, which Bill was taking with Hayley. She rolled down the windows. The salty sea air would help clear her head and the breeze would keep Sparky from feeling sick. She made a decision not to focus on Bill and Hayley anymore. That was a personal matter that, one way or the other, would resolve itself.

She turned her attention to the deaths of Doris Jenkins and Rich Bailey. Were they connected? She hadn't thought so. But now that she had learned of Marvin's suspicions, she wasn't so sure. It seemed likely that if Doris had been having an affair, it would have been with one of the members of the theater group. Her husband certainly believed that, and, as her father had once famously told her when asked why people always had affairs with work colleagues, it's hard to have an affair with someone you've never met. In her experience, where there was smoke, there was fire. No, if Marvin thought Doris had been seeing someone, then there had to be a reason.

This new piece of information threw suspicion on the cause of Doris's death. Had she died of natural causes, as Colleen had originally suspected, or of something more sinister? Could Marvin have killed her out of jealousy? If so, how? He hadn't been anywhere near the beach when Doris died. She had a feeling a talk with Marvin was in her future, but she wasn't looking forward to it. From everything she had seen and heard, Marvin was a man on the edge.

Then there was Rich. Was his death in some way related to Doris's? Could the same person have killed both members of the theater company? And was that the person who'd broken into and ransacked Rich's house? And what had that person been looking for? Whatever it was, she suspected that the person hadn't found it . . . or at least not all of it. Then she recalled the bizarre photographs of ears she and Bill had seen hanging on Rich's wall. What was that all about? Was Bill correct in thinking Rich had had an ear fetish? She didn't know what an ear fetishist would be like, but she didn't think Rich had seemed like one. Then again, you could never tell about a person.

Which brought her to Bill. Despite her pledge to put him out of her mind, she found her thoughts drifting to the news that he had once been engaged. She could understand why he hadn't told her about that. She hadn't told him about her breakup with her college sweetheart. But once he learned that his ex was coming to Corolla, he should have told her he knew Hayley. He had had plenty of opportunities. They had known Hayley was coming to town with the film crew for weeks. She wondered who had ended the relationship and why, but she knew there was little chance of discovering those details. They were, quite simply, none of her business. The only way she was going to learn any information about his past with Hayley was if the information was volunteered. After her behavior today, she found that extremely unlikely. It did seem, however, that he might have answers to some of the questions she had about Doris's death and Rich's and that she'd learn those later when they had a chance to talk.

Colleen drove out of the four-wheel-drive community and back onto paved road. Sparky barked with delight as they picked up speed and the wind whipped his ears back. They headed toward the station. It was time to focus on work; murder and Bill would have to wait.

Chapter 10

"Let no man's ghost ever come back and say his training failed him," Colleen said to her men, who were sweating in the sun on the back lot of the firehouse. "Those words are posted at the National Fire Academy and I've never forgotten them."

The men squinted at her through sweat as they gulped down bottles of water. She had been working them hard and now was giving them a short break to stay hydrated. Sparky was content viewing the entire scene from a pit he had dug in the sandy shade. She eyed Bobby. His cheeks were flushed red and he was holding his side.

"You okay, Bobby?" she asked.

"Just a stitch," he said.

"Or a few too many doughnuts," Chip said.

"Maybe he's training to be a cop," Kenny teased.

The men chuckled. She had to admit that Bobby still needed

to lose some weight, but he was giving it his all, and she didn't want him to get discouraged.

"Maybe Bobby could cut back on the doughnuts," she said to Chip, and raised a brow to Bobby. "But he's training like his life depends on it. Are you?"

"Aw, come on," Chip said. "You know I train hard. Look at me." He punched his rock-hard abdomen for emphasis.

"Training isn't just about what's there," she said, pointing to his toned stomach. "It's also about what's in here." She tapped a finger on his forehead.

"Chief's got you there," Jimmy said.

"Yeah, yeah," Chip said.

She assessed the group. They looked sufficiently recovered from their drills. "So," she said, stretching her quads. "Everyone ready for the run?"

The men groaned.

"Hey," she said. "You know more firefighters—"

"—die from heart attacks than from smoke inhalation," the men said in unison, finishing her sentence.

"Okay, then," she said. "Give me three miles."

The men groaned again.

"Fine. It's hot. Let's make it two." The men cheered. Given the heat, she had already decided on the lesser distance, but by initially assigning them three miles and then cutting back to two, the men felt like they were getting off easy. "All right. Let's go. And make me proud."

One by one, the men took off jogging in pairs north on Whalehead Drive. Sparky raised his head. "Stay," she said, wanting him to rest in the shade. She took off after the group and caught up to Bobby, who was chugging along at the back of the pack.

"How's it going?" she asked, slowing her pace to match his.

"Okay," he said between breaths.

They jogged in silence past Marlin and Sailfish streets.

"Chief? Can I ask you a question?"

"Sure."

"You really think I have what it takes to get certified?"

"Are you having doubts?" she asked with concern. It was one thing for him to struggle with his weight. It was another thing if he was struggling with his decision to be a firefighter. She couldn't have partially committed men on her team.

"Oh, no," he said with a passion that surprised her. "I really want this."

"So what is it, then?"

"Mother. She says I'm too chicken to be a real firefighter."

She signaled him to stop jogging. "Let me tell you something," she said. "In firefighting, there's a fine line between being courageous and being stupid. The latter has no fear. You understand?"

He paused a moment and nodded.

"You're doing fine. But Chip's right," she said. "You do have to lay off those doughnuts." He grinned sheepishly. "Come on." They resumed their run. "So tell me. How's your mother doing with the play?"

"You don't want to know," he said with a roll of the eyes.

"I sensed there was some friction between her and Lane," she said, hoping that would be enough to tempt him to gossip.

"Friction? More like hostility. Yesterday, Mother told me she could kill Lane for casting Nellie without her permission. What a thing to say after what happened to Doris and Rich."

"If I know one thing about Myrtle, it's that she doesn't take well to not being in charge. And," she said, trying to be delicate but truthful, "she can sometimes have an abrasive way about her."

"It might be hard for you to believe, but she does have a soft side."

She glanced at him with raised brows. "Really?"

"How everyone sees her is how she wants everyone to see her."

"Cranky and ornery?" she blurted out. "Sorry," she added.

"It's okay," he said with a shrug. "I know Mother can be difficult."

As they plodded down Whalehead Drive and made the turnaround at the halfway point, she considered Bobby's idea that Myrtle was choosing to play a role—that of the cantankerous schoolteacher turned horse preservationist—and that there could be a softer side to her. She recalled having observed that side for the first time several weeks ago when Myrtle had thought Bobby didn't love her after her presumed death in the explosion. But it was a side people rarely witnessed and, apparently, one Myrtle chose not to let people see. She wondered if Myrtle found acting in the play a relief from being, well, Myrtle. Maybe all actors found playing someone other than themselves liberating. It also made Colleen wonder who else in the theater company could be playing a role and if the role was that of murderer.

The men cheered Bobby as he and Colleen approached the

firehouse. Because she had been preoccupied with thinking about Myrtle and the actors, she hadn't realized that this was the first time Bobby had completed a run without walking most of the way. He picked up his pace for the last one hundred yards. She pretended to race him and allowed him to cross into the parking lot ahead of her. There were more cheers, high fives, and several compliments and shouts of "Way to go, probie!" from the guys. Bobby might drop those pounds after all, she thought, *if* he can stay away from the sweets. The men disappeared inside the station and she went out back to check on Sparky.

"Hey, fella," she said, finding him where she had left him in his sand pit.

The Border collie rose and wagged his tail. She absently rubbed his furry lopsided ears and felt a bump along one ridge. It was a bump he had had since he was a puppy. Her mind drifted to the wall of ear photographs she had seen at Rich's house. What was it about those photos? She wondered if someone in the theater company might know about his apparent obsession with ears. But who could she ask without arousing suspicion that she was investigating possible suspects? It would have to be the least likely suspect—someone who could keep her confidence . . . someone she could trust. She ran through the list of troupe members in her mind and then heaved a sigh of resignation. Of course. Who else?

"How'd you like to see Myrtle?" she asked her canine friend. Sparky wagged his tail and circled around her, ready to go. Myrtle it is, she thought, and went inside to clean up before heading out.

She pulled into the lot of the Lighthouse Wild Horse Preservation Society's office and gift shop. The building was located in old Corolla Village and not only served as headquarters for the nonprofit organization but was where people could arrange for a tour of the wild horse refuge with a patrol specialist or the herd manager. She knew that the theater troupe members would be working their day jobs, so it had seemed likely Myrtle would be occupied with her work at the Preservation Society. Since Myrtle didn't believe in leaving her cell phone on and Colleen had only been able to get through to an answering machine, the society's office was the first place she had thought to look for her. She was relieved to see Myrtle's pickup parked out front.

She and Sparky approached the front door. A sign next to the door read CAT HAS HAD SHOTS BUT IS FICKLE. TOUCH AT YOUR OWN RISK. Below the sign was a small wooden house—Inky's home when the cat wasn't wandering the Whalehead Club and Heritage Park grounds. She peered inside and was relieved to see Inky's house was empty. She didn't need Sparky terrorizing the cat again. "You leave Inky alone if he comes by, you hear?" Sparky cocked his head, the picture of innocence. She tied his leash to a shady part of the porch and went inside.

She peered into the gift shop on the left. Several people were milling about, shopping for T-shirts, mugs, and other wild horse–related souvenirs. She heard Fran, one of the patrol specialists, doing her introduction to the horse tour in a small education center room off of the gift shop. She turned right toward Myrtle's office.

"I don't see why Lane needs those lines," she heard Myrtle say. "I think they can be cut or given to someone else."

"I agree," a male voice said.

"So what's the problem?"

"I don't want it turning into a big thing. You theater folks are more vicious than vipers."

"Lane will have to accept that anything that isn't accurate or doesn't serve the horses has got to go. You're the expert, Doc. He can't argue with that."

Myrtle was really working the equine veterinarian, and Colleen doubted that it was entirely out of concern about the accuracy of the wild horses' history.

"Okay," Doc Wales said with hesitation. "But if Lane gets mad, you're dealing with him."

"Gladly," Colleen heard Myrtle say in a triumphant tone.

Chairs scraped on the wooden floors. Colleen stepped forward into the office entrance as if she had just arrived. "Well, hello," she said, feigning surprise at seeing Doc Wales with Myrtle.

"Hello," the veterinarian said. "See you later, Myrtle."

Colleen studied the doctor as he hurried from the building. "Plotting the overthrow of the theater group?" she asked.

"I don't know what you're talking about," Myrtle said. "We were discussing a new foal someone spotted this morning."

Colleen smiled.

"Don't stand there grinning at me like some psychotic clown, missy. Either come in or go out." Myrtle sat in her chair and covered some papers on her desk. Colleen was certain the papers had to do with her recent ideas for rewriting Lane's lines in the *Wild and Free* script.

"So how are things going with Lane?" she asked, taking a seat across from Myrtle.

"Were you eavesdropping?"

"Does that sound like me?" she asked, feigning innocence.

"As a matter of fact, it does."

Damn. Myrtle had known her since childhood and was well aware of every bit of trouble she had been in during elementary school and that some of that trouble had been for snooping on teachers. She leaned forward and lowered her voice. "I want to talk to you about Rich Bailey."

"What about him?"

"Did you know him well?"

"As well as anyone, I imagine."

"Did he have any unusual interests or hobbies?"

"Like what?"

"I don't know. Anything you can think of."

"For Pete's sake," Myrtle said with irritation. "Spit it out. I don't have time for twenty questions. You never could get to the point. In class you'd tell a story or do a book report and every detail had the same weight. You'd go on and on: 'She said this' and 'He said that' and—"

"Myrtle!" she said, losing her patience. The woman never failed to get under her skin.

Myrtle folded her arms. "Well, you did," she said, getting in the last word.

Maybe it was time to put Myrtle on the defensive. "Did you threaten to kill Lane for casting Nellie?"

Myrtle's cheeks flushed red. "Did Mr. Hollywood tell you that?"

Mr. Hollywood? Wow, Doc Wales was right. They were worse

than vipers. "You can't go around threatening to kill people, especially given the fact that two members of the group are dead. It's
insensitive, and you'll make yourself murder suspect number one."

Myrtle's eyes widened. "The sheriff thinks Doris was murdered, too?"

Uh-oh. She had said too much. "Well, no. I don't have a clue
what's on his mind."

"But you believe she was."

"I don't know what to think," she said truthfully, and sat back
in the chair. The visit had been a complete waste of time. She
didn't know why she had thought it would be otherwise.

Myrtle motioned for Colleen to move closer and then whispered, "I think she was murdered, too, in a manner of speaking."

She sat up. "What do you mean?"

"A feeling I have. Nellie has it, too. Doris seemed to be under
a lot of stress. I think it could have caused a heart attack. So whoever it was Doris was worrying about killed her."

"That's a bit of a stretch. You'd have to prove someone was
deliberately provoking Doris. And even then, it's not a crime. One
thing I do know is that Rich didn't end up dead in that elevator
from natural causes."

Myrtle studied her across the desk. "You think there's a murderer in the theater group."

She could almost see the wheels turning in Myrtle's head. "I
never said that."

"You didn't have to," Myrtle said, and then got an idea. "I could
help you," she added with enthusiasm. "Investigate from the inside, go undercover."

"Stay out of it," Colleen said, now panicked Myrtle would start butting her nose in and interfere with the investigation.

"Aren't you worried someone might try to kill me?"

She looked at Myrtle straight on. I could think of a few people who might want to, she thought. "No. You're too tough to kill."

"Damn straight," Myrtle said with pride.

Colleen rose. The interview with Myrtle had not been as productive as she had hoped. It was time to go, before Myrtle had them playing amateur sleuth again. "I'll leave you to your"—she glanced at the papers on Myrtle's desk—"rewrites."

She made her way from the offices, unleashed Sparky, and was about to pull out from the lot, when Myrtle burst from the building. She rolled down her window. Myrtle shaded her eyes and squinted into the SUV.

"You might try talking to Ruby. She said Rich had been spending a lot of time at the library lately. Maybe she can tell you why."

"Thanks."

Myrtle stepped away as Colleen shifted her vehicle into reverse. "Next stop, the library," she said to Sparky, and pulled onto the unpaved road leading to Ocean Trail.

She idled at the Route 12 intersection, waiting for a break in the long line of traffic. The summer activity often made it impossible to get anywhere in a hurry, especially on the weekends when some visitors were departing from rental properties and then, later, others were arriving at them. If you were a local, you knew to try to do all your chores, such as grocery shopping, during the week to avoid getting stuck in the summer congestion. She looked at the library parking lot across the street. Since the library sat adjacent to Corolla's branch of the Currituck County Offices and, hence, the Sheriff's Department, there was the strong possibility she might run into Bill. But his pickup was nowhere to be seen. She was safe from any interaction with him—at least while entering the building.

Finally, there was a break in the traffic. She hit the gas, shot across the road, coasted into the parking lot, and cut the engine. "Too short a ride?" she asked Sparky, knowing he wanted another trip with the windows down. They exited the SUV and went in search of Ruby.

Ruby Mazur was the librarian at the Corolla Public Library, a branch of the Currituck County Library System. A transplant from Philadelphia, Ruby had moved to the island ten years ago to assume the role of full-time librarian. With the recently deceased librarian, Edna Daisey, Ruby had transformed the library into a thriving community center hosting meetings, book sales, voting during elections, a summer reading club, and storytime readings for preschoolers and toddlers throughout the year. The accomplishment Ruby was the proudest of, however, was the library's partnership with the Water's Edge Village School—a kindergarten through sixth grade charter school located across the street in Old Corolla Village—which had opened its doors to its first class in the fall of 2012. Ruby was delighted to tell anyone who came through the doors that the Corolla Public Library now also served as the library for the charter school.

Colleen climbed the stairs and found a boy and girl each lying on one of the porch benches, reading. Their feet dangled off the edges, above flip-flops and Crocs that had slipped from their feet long ago. They looked up from their books.

"Can Sparky sit with you while you read?" she asked, knowing full well the answer would be a resounding "Yes!"

She tied Sparky's leash to the arm of one of the benches.

"Nice dog," said the boy, who was about ten.

"Hi, Sparky," said the girl, abandoning her book and joining the boy.

Sparky wagged his tail and licked the children's faces, sending them into a fit of giggles. Colleen wasn't sure who was going to enjoy the visit more. She crossed the porch and went inside to find out what Ruby knew about Rich's interests and why he had been frequenting the library.

She quietly closed the door and entered the brightly lit space. It was a modest place, with wooden tables and chairs, and shelves arranged in such a way as to maximize the light streaming brilliantly through the windows. The library was busy, as it always was in the summer months, with tourists seeking a good summer read while on vacation. All six of the public computers were occupied and a roomful of children listened as a volunteer read them a story. Colleen passed the book-sale room and noted yet more people perusing the shelves in search of a good deal on a romance, science fiction, or mystery novel for the beach.

She spotted Ruby behind the desk, scanning book bar codes and helping a customer check out a book.

"I think you'll enjoy that one," Ruby said to the young woman, and slid the book across the counter.

"Thanks," the woman said, and left.

"Hello there," Ruby said, spotting Colleen.

Colleen had always liked the straight-talking librarian and her no-nonsense approach to life. "Hey there, Ruby," she said. "I see it's busy."

"It's summer," she said. "Can I help you find something?"

"Not today."

"You sure? We've got some great books on our new-fiction shelf."

"Maybe I'll check them out later." Colleen lowered her voice, not wanting the customers to overhear. "I actually came by because I wanted to talk to you about Rich Bailey."

"First Edna, now Rich and Doris. I don't mind saying, I've found this to be a difficult summer."

Ruby was still a moment, briefly lost in a feeling of melancholy, and then she reached into the book-return bin to retrieve a stack of books.

"Were you and Rich close?"

"I suppose. We had a lot in common," the librarian said, scanning a book and setting it on the TO BE SHELVED cart.

"Like the play?"

Ruby shook her head. "No, mostly books and languages. He and I used to practice our Spanish together. He had an amazing ear, knew I was from Philadelphia just by my accent."

"I understand he liked to come to the library a lot," Colleen said.

"He liked doing research—especially on true-crime stories. Personally, I always find those stories a little depressing. But he did most of that online from home. It was only in the last week or two that he started coming in."

"Was he looking for anything in particular?" Colleen asked, wondering what the library had that he couldn't find on the Internet.

"A book on ears." Ruby noticed Colleen's raised brows. "Strange, right? I figured it had to do with his work, or maybe a lecture he was going to give at the Funeral Directors of America's meeting next month."

"Do you know what the book was called?" she asked. Maybe the book itself would give her a clue.

"I can do you better than that," the librarian said, and disappeared into an office. She emerged a moment later with a large brown envelope and handed it to Colleen. "I had to place an order for an interlibrary loan from the Charles Chesnutt Library at Fayetteville State."

Colleen paused before opening the envelope and sliding the book out. The cover read *Ear Identification.* The author's name was Alfred Victor Iannarelli.

Ruby read the title. "Told you it was a book on ears."

Colleen had no idea what to make of her find. Perhaps the content of the book would shed some light on why Rich had requested it, but she didn't have time to study it right now. "Would it be possible for me to check this out?" she asked.

"Sure. Just let me make the changes in the computer. You have your library card?"

Colleen fished her wallet from her back pocket, thumbed through several credit cards and receipts she had stuffed into the wallet, and found her card. "Here it is," she said, and handed it to Ruby.

"Be right back," the librarian said, and moved to the computer at the end of the checkout counter.

Colleen's heart raced with anticipation. She couldn't wait to get the book home and examine its contents. She didn't know why, but somehow she felt like the book would lead her one step closer to discovering who had killed Rich, and possibly Doris.

"All set," Ruby said, returning with the book. "You want to keep the envelope?"

"Please," she said, took the book, and slid it back into the packaging.

"You should still check out those new-fiction titles," the librarian said, nodding to the shelf before turning to help a waiting customer.

Colleen exited the library and, much to the disappointment of the children and her canine friend, retrieved Sparky. She hoped the book would hold some clues as to Rich's recent activities and perhaps lead her to his killer before he or she struck again.

Chapter 11

As the sun set over the sound outside Colleen's kitchen window, she sat at her dining room table, hunched over the words of Alfred Victor Iannarelli, the man who, she had only an hour ago discovered, was the author of the Iannarelli System of Ear Identification and a pioneer in the field of earology. She combed the pages of his book, searching for insights into what had been on Rich's mind the days before his death. One thing she had discovered by reading the text was that the human ear was as unique as fingerprints and because of its distinctive features could be used for identification purposes. She was now convinced that Rich's fascination with ears had little to do with a fetish and more to do with trying to ID someone. Whom Rich was trying to identify and why were still very much a mystery.

Smokey sprawled on the table, stretched her paws under the book's pages, blinked several blue-eyed kisses, and purred.

Colleen had been so engrossed in her reading that she hadn't paid attention to when the Siamese had jumped on the table. The cat knew that this was normally a forbidden behavior and seemed to be relishing this rare occasion when it was being allowed. "Let me see your ears," Colleen said, rubbing the cat's soft, pointy gray-tipped ears. Smokey chirped and rolled her head upside down. Colleen had never thought much about ears before, but now couldn't seem to keep from looking at them, even if they were feline.

The sound of a car engine outside drew Sparky away from where he had been lying at her feet and into the foyer. He gave a low growl and stared intently at the front door. She rose and felt the foot she had been sitting on tingle as blood rushed into it. She hobbled to the window next to the door and peeked through the curtains. Bill climbed the stairs and waved. She released the curtain. What was he doing here? She collected herself and opened the front door. Sparky rushed forward, happy to see Bill.

"Hey there, Sparks," Bill said, using his special nickname for the Border collie and rubbing the dog on the head.

Sparky raised his nose toward a bag that Bill was carrying. He lifted the bag out of the dog's reach. "I brought you dinner," he said. "Unless you've already eaten."

The smell of the food drifted past her nostrils and some of her recent unhappiness with him faded. "Thanks," she said, and her stomach growled.

"Looks like I got here in the nick of time," he said.

Her cheeks flushed pink. "Sorry," she said, and closed the door behind him as he stepped into the foyer. "Is that Chinese food?"

she asked, catching another whiff of the bag's contents as she moved past him into the kitchen.

"Your comfort food, right?"

Whenever she felt out of sorts or under the weather from a cold, Chinese food had always soothed her. She took the bag from him and crossed to the counter, Sparky on her heels.

"Please ignore the poorly behaved cat on the table," she said.

Smokey meowed from atop the open book, which was now her bed.

"I'll take care of Smokey while you take care of the food," he said, and gently lifted the cat from the table. The cat purred until she realized he was putting her on the floor, and then she let out a yowl of protest, as only a Siamese could.

He grabbed paper towels from the counter to wipe down the table. He lifted the book, noticed the subject matter, and looked at her with surprise. "Something I should know about?"

"I have a theory," she said, bringing plates and silverware to the table. "But first, food."

He put the book aside and she set the food down. She filled two glasses with water and joined him. Sparky hovered nearby, hoping to catch a scrap if it fell to the floor. Her mouth watered as she lifted cashew chicken, egg rolls, and brown rice onto her plate. She glanced at the microwave's clock and was surprised to discover how late it was. She ate in silence for several minutes. Food had never tasted so good. She swallowed a big gulp of water before finally speaking.

"I guess I was a little hungry."

"I can never get over how much you can eat."

It was true. She had inherited her father's high metabolism and had always been able to eat as much as she wanted without gaining weight. Still, it was probably not something a man should say to a woman.

"Care to tell me about your interest in"—he glanced at the book—"ear identification and how you came by this?"

"Rich requested the book from the library before he died. Ruby let me check it out," she said matter-of-factly.

"I suppose I don't need to ask if that means you've been investigating his death." He had been down this path before with her. There was no use trying to talk her out of sleuthing.

"And Doris's," she said, daring him to order her to halt her inquiry.

"Doris? I thought you suspected heat exhaustion or a heart attack."

"I'm not so sure anymore."

"You have any proof?"

"No," she said, helping herself to more food. "But you should call the ME. And let's hope the new guy is faster than the old one."

The previous medical examiner had been swiftly replaced a few weeks ago, after he had taken too long to identify Edna Daisey's body earlier this summer and failed to request backup help.

"Already called him."

"Wow," she said with surprise, her fork in midair. "I didn't know."

"I haven't had a chance to fill you in. So you talked to Ruby. How'd you know she'd be helpful?"

"Myrtle."

Bill sat back in his chair. "Maybe you should start from the top."

How could she recap everything she had discovered? It would take all night. Then she thought of what Myrtle had said about her telling stories as a child and how she could go on and on. Better focus and give him the highlights, she decided.

"Fawn told Chip there's been a lot of drama in the theater group lately, particularly between Myrtle and Lane."

"So I gathered," he said. "From what I could tell from the interviews, the only person who didn't have a problem with anyone was Rich."

"And yet he's dead," she said. "So someone had a problem with him."

He couldn't argue with that. "Anything else?"

"Sam told me Marvin is accusing everyone, and I mean *everyone*, of having an affair with Doris, and Myrtle threatened to kill Lane for casting Nellie."

"Myrtle make a specific threat?" he asked, leaning forward.

She knew what he was thinking, but there was no way Myrtle was a killer. "Trust me. The only thing Myrtle is guilty of is cutting Lane's lines, which, by the way, she has recruited Doc Wales to do."

"Wales has been sucked into their intrigue?" he asked with amazement.

She nodded.

"And the book?"

"Rich requested it before he was killed. I asked Ruby if I could check it out, and, voilà, there it is."

She was proud of herself. She had given him the highlights

and managed to leave out any mention of Hayley. He was silent for a long moment. "What is it?" she asked, concerned.

He paused and then said, "I'm fairly certain Rich was trying to identify someone using Iannarelli's earology. I thought it the moment I saw the photos in his house. I had training on the system several years back."

Her brows furrowed. "But you said Rich had an ear fetish. Why didn't you tell me?"

"I don't want you in danger."

"Now wait a minute—" she began.

"And," he said, interrupting her, "I didn't get the impression you wanted to talk to me."

An awkward silence filled the room. She spotted the fortune cookies on the table, next to the condiments. "Fortune cookie?" she asked, changing the subject.

He took one of the cookies. "You first."

She tore open the clear wrapper and cracked open the cookie. You've got to be kidding me, she thought. Printed on the tiny slip of paper above her "lucky numbers" was: *It takes courage to admit fault.*

"What does it say?"

Maybe the cookie was a sign, or maybe it was the guilt she had been feeling about her recent behavior, but she knew she needed to speak with Bill about his ex if there was any hope of feeling comfortable around him and moving forward with their relationship and the investigation.

"There's something I need to tell you," she said. "I took Hayley over the rough part of Carova this morning because, well . . ."

Why had she done that? Out of jealousy? Anger at him? How could she put into words something she wasn't entirely sure of herself?

"It doesn't matter," he said, shifting his weight in his chair.

"But it does. I've always hated women who treat other women badly. She didn't do anything to deserve it." She held up her fortune. " 'It takes courage to admit fault.' "

He smiled kindly at her and his eyes crinkled in that way that always made her heart soar. It felt good to get that off her chest. She felt more like herself again. Her worry returned, however, when his smile faded.

"I should have told you," he said quietly.

He didn't need to say *what* he should have told her. She knew he was referring to his past engagement. She wanted to ask him why he had kept it a secret, but she wasn't sure she was ready to hear the answer.

"What about you?" he asked.

She raised her brows, confused. "What about me?"

"And Salvatore."

Despite the awkwardness of the conversation, she had to smile. The thought of her and Pinky being romantically involved was preposterous. "We were just meeting about the house he donated to the station."

"You always get dressed up for meetings?" he asked with an edge to his voice.

Her eyes narrowed. At least I've never been engaged and not told you, she thought. "The place he picked . . . I couldn't wear jeans."

He nodded, but she could tell he was unhappy. "So," she said, breaking the tension, "what does your fortune say?"

He opened his cookie. "'Things are never quite the way they seem.'"

"Why don't they ever say things like 'You will be fortunate in everything'?"

Bill chuckled. "Because that's like using a wish to get more wishes."

"You know, that fortune may be onto something," she said, recalling her earlier conversation with Bobby about how Myrtle chose to be the way she was.

"How do you mean?"

"Something Bobby said to me earlier today got me thinking about the theater and acting. It's really all illusion made to look like real life. It's never the way it seems."

Bill thought about this for a moment. "I suppose we're all playing roles—sheriff, chief, friends . . ." His voice trailed off.

It was obvious it wasn't going to be easy getting things back to the way they'd been. She took a deep breath. Maybe things would be easier if they stuck to solving Rich's murder. "Okay. So we both think Rich was trying to ID someone. The question is, who?"

"And is the person living or dead?"

"Maybe we should ask Fawn about that," she joked.

"Maybe not," he said with a frown. "She read Hayley's tarot cards, said they indicated negative external forces were at work and to expect impending danger. Hayley's pretty shook up."

Despite her feelings about the actress, Colleen couldn't blame her for being disturbed by the reading. Even if it was all carnival magic, nobody liked to hear something bad was going to happen. She felt lucky she had gotten off easy with her aura reading.

"And," he said with hesitation, "Fawn saw someone in the cards that could protect her."

"Good," she said, wondering what his hesitation was about. A second later, she got it. The protector was Bill. "And who, dare I ask, is this protector Fawn sees?"

He leaned closer. "You."

"Me? That's absurd."

"Not to Fawn . . . and not to Hayley."

"How could I protect her? And from what?" She rose from the table, annoyed. "I wish Fawn would lay off that mystical stuff."

He grabbed their plates and carried them to the sink. "You and me both," he said. "But don't be surprised if Hayley says something to you."

"I seriously doubt after that ride she'll want to talk to me," she said, rinsing the plates and placing them in the dishwasher.

"I don't like the idea any more than you," he said, handing her the glasses.

She caught his eye. It struck her how awkward it must have been for him when he discovered his ex with his . . . well, whatever she was to him. No wonder he had wanted to run. Now, thanks to Fawn and her tarot cards, it looked like she was going to be spending a lot more time with the actress and that her efforts to stop the woman from shadowing her had been for naught.

"I do have one bit of interesting news," he said. "Seems the elevator at the Whalehead Club normally rests in the basement, where the museum store is. Whoever put Rich's body in there either knew the elevator had been hoisted to the first floor or had intended to shove him down the shaft. Either way, it's someone who knew the building fairly well."

"Which means whoever killed Rich is likely someone we know."

The realization hung heavy in the air. Someone they knew, played bingo with, saw at the supermarket or walking their dog . . . someone they regarded as a respected member of the community had killed one of their own. She felt a mixture of disappointment and anger and hurt, and then, rising from deep within her, she felt determination. No matter what it took, she was going to catch the person who had brought death to Corolla.

Chapter 12

The morning sun skipped brightly over the water of Currituck Sound as Colleen zipped along Route 12 on her way to the station. Like the light rain of the night before, her meal with Bill had helped wash away the dirt that had been clouding her thinking. It was hard to stay mad at a man who brought you dinner.

Sparky, too, seemed happier. They had been companions for many years and the dog knew her too well not to sense that she had been out of sorts the last few days; and when she wasn't feeling well, neither was he. She rubbed the Border collie's head as she cruised down Ocean Trail. She was determined to work with Bill to set things right in Corolla and expose the murderer in their midst.

It was good having a plan. As fire chief Jerry Smith had once famously said, "The very worst fire plan is no plan. The next worse is two plans." She knew if they had any hope of catching the murderer, she and Bill must work together—even if he didn't like the idea. His concern about the danger wasn't lost on her. The person they were seeking was someone whom, until now, they had never suspected of evildoing. The fact was Corolla hardly had any serious crime . . . until recently. No, their killer was a wolf in sheep's clothing. If she was going to stay safe, she'd need to keep her guard up, especially around anyone connected with the production. Who knew theater could be so deadly?

She didn't relish the thought of making nice with Hayley, but it was better to face the reality of the woman and her past with Bill head-on. Maybe she'd even gain a little insight into Bill—probably why he was less than thrilled at the idea of the two women being together. The last thing a man wants is his ex and current interest comparing notes—not that she had any notes to compare.

Bill had agreed to return to Rich's house and gather the ear photographs. They now suspected that one of the ear photos had its perfect match on one of the citizens of Corolla. She had learned through her recent research that the ear was the least looked at and yet the most important part of the face for identification. She and Bill would have their work cut out for them. Not only were they not in the habit of examining ears but the body part was often hidden by hair. They'd have to be sneaky; otherwise, it might be awkward and suspicious peering around someone's face to see the person's ears. Given everything she had learned so far about earology, she wondered why the Department of Motor Vehicles didn't have both front and profile pictures on driver's licenses. That would give authorities an ear database to use for comparison and supplement fingerprint information in their efforts to catch criminals.

Colleen slowed at a pedestrian crossing to allow bikers to cross Route 12. She tried to study their ears, but they were covered by helmets. This was going to be harder than she thought. The road cleared and she picked up speed. She noticed Rodney, Bill's deputy sheriff, down Schoolhouse Lane and behind him the film crew. She decided to swing by and see how he was doing before going to the station. She crept down Schoolhouse Lane into Old Corolla Village and slowed to a stop.

"Morning," she said, pulling up to the deputy. "Looks like you've got film duty."

"Sure do," he said cheerfully.

It was clear Rodney was enjoying his assignment. The crew was using the front porch of Island Bookstore for the scene they were filming. Hayley was on the porch, doing a scene with a handsome male costar, booms held above their heads, out of the frame. The sound, lighting, and makeup crews were nearby. Hayley's assistant, Jason, and the production manager, Wendy, huddled together. The director stood near the cinematographer, looking at the monitor. Beyond the perimeter stood a small crowd of curious onlookers and what Colleen imagined were Hayley Thorpe fans.

She was surprised to find Myrtle, Lane, and Nellie among the background players. She wondered if the film director was getting on any better with them than Adam had been back at play rehearsal. The extras were pretending to mill about with books and shopping bags in hand. She was about to turn away to head to work, when she noticed Marvin in the group. Her brows furrowed. Given how she knew he felt about the theater company and Doris's involvement with it, she found it strange that he'd signed on to be an extra.

"Something wrong?" Rodney asked, sensing her change in mood.

"I'm not sure," she said, and cut the engine. "Don't go anywhere." She left Sparky in the car with the windows down and strode toward the film set.

She quietly crossed the fifty or so yards toward the bookstore, never taking her eyes off of Marvin. Unlike the other extras, Marvin was not pretending to buy books or talk to fellow shoppers. Instead, he was staring intently at Lane, whose back was to him. Marvin inched closer to Lane, and she picked up her pace.

"Cut," said the director.

The extras and crew relaxed while the director hopped onto the bookstore porch to speak with Hayley and her costar. Colleen joined the perimeter, where the crew members were standing. The assistant director crossed to Myrtle, Lane, Nellie, and the other background players.

"Now, ma'am," the AD said to Myrtle.

"The name's Myrtle. I've told you before."

Uh-oh. This guy was clearly experiencing Myrtle's charm.

"Right," the young man said. "Myrtle, if you could stay on the mark that I gave you, that would be great."

"This isn't my first time at the rodeo, you know," Myrtle said with indignation.

Nellie suppressed a giggle.

"Just stay on the mark, ma'am," the AD said, trying not to lose his patience.

"But that mark is back there," she said, pointing to an area behind the extras and clearly off-camera. "Nobody will see it's me because of this one's big head." She pointed a finger at Lane.

"Exactly," the man said, and scurried away.

Myrtle scowled. Lane snickered.

Myrtle caught Nellie's eye. "Why don't you and I switch places, Nell?"

"I don't think the assistant director would like that very much," Nellie said, and turned away so that Myrtle couldn't see the grin break out over her face.

Colleen probably would have enjoyed the moment of Myrtle's comeuppance, too, had she not been concerned about Marvin's unexpected presence on the set.

"Places," the AD called at the signal of the director.

Hayley, her costar, and the extras moved to their designated locations. Myrtle shuffled unhappily to the back of the crowd.

"Roll camera," the director said.

"Speed," said the cameraman.

"Cue background," the AD added, signaling the extras to begin moving about. Seconds later, the director called, "Action," and the scene was under way, and so was Myrtle.

"The biddy's on the move again," the AD muttered under his breath.

Despite his instructions, Myrtle was pretending to read a book and nod to passerby extras while slowly inching her way toward the front of the extras and the camera.

But it wasn't Myrtle who bothered Colleen. It was Marvin, who was lurking among the background actors. Why isn't he interacting with anyone? Where's his prop? What is he up to? She wondered. She signaled Rodney to join her with a subtle wave. He left his vehicle and swiftly made his way to her.

"What's up?" he whispered, catching his breath.

She indicated Marvin. The man slipped behind an extra who was adjusting a large sun hat and, as the woman pretended to browse the books, followed closely behind her. Colleen felt her muscles twitch. Marvin trailed the woman until she passed Lane. He stopped a few feet behind Lane, stood eerily still, and stared at the actor's back. I don't like this, she thought. Marvin's hand slid up the side of his leg toward his pocket. She squinted. Was there a weapon in his pocket? Her eyes darted to the director, hoping he'd call "Cut." Marvin's chest heaved as his breathing grew heavier, and then suddenly, he reached into his pocket and lunged.

"Home wrecker!" he yelled, and jabbed at Lane with a Taser.

Lane jumped to the side, just avoiding being shocked. Colleen and Rodney rushed at Marvin. There was a scream from one of the onlookers, and the director yelled, "Cut!"

"He has a gun!" someone yelled.

"Duck!" shouted another.

Colleen grabbed one of Marvin's arms and tugged on his shoulder while Rodney grabbed the arm holding the weapon.

"You couldn't keep your hands off of her, could you?" Marvin spit at Lane, trying to zap him.

She and Rodney dragged Marvin away from the others. She

was surprised by how strong the man was. Given his age, she didn't think he would have been capable of putting up such a fight. But rage is a powerful emotion, and he was seething with it. She and Rodney forced him toward the deputy's vehicle.

Rodney wrenched the Taser from the man's grip and it dropped to the ground. "I got him," he said.

"You sure?" she asked. Rodney nodded. She released Marvin's arm, retrieved the Taser, and returned as Rodney pressed Marvin into the backseat and slammed the door.

"I've never seen Marvin like that," Rodney said. "How'd you know something was up?"

"Just a feeling."

"You think he did in Rich?"

Despite his violent outburst and his recent threats, she found it hard to believe the retiree muttering in the back of the deputy sheriff's car was their murderer. The person who had killed Rich had been sneaky, cunning, and ruthless and had committed the crime without witnesses. Marvin was obvious, naïve, and emotional and had not only attacked Lane in public but with cameras rolling. The two profiles didn't match. She wanted to question him but didn't want to jeopardize the investigation in case he was indeed their man.

"If you're okay with Marvin, I'm going to talk to folks and see what I can find out," she said.

"I'll go ahead and call it in."

Bill would certainly want to know why Marvin had shown up at the film set, what he had planned for Lane, and if he'd had anything to do with the deaths of his wife or Rich. Marvin had made himself suspect number one in their homicide investigation and his motive was as old as time—jealousy. The lesson was not lost on Colleen. She was glad she had pulled herself off that dangerous ride.

She strode toward the chaotic set. Cast, crew, extras, and onlookers were all abuzz with what had happened. "Is everything okay?" "What's going on?" "Who let that guy on the set?" "What happened to security?" These were the questions she heard as she approached the group.

"Chief McCabe, who was that man?" Wendy asked. As production manager, it was her responsibility to see that all went well on the set. Obviously, it hadn't.

Colleen didn't want to get into the details of Marvin's recent suspicious behavior, but she realized she needed to offer some explanation. She put her fingers to the edges of her mouth and whistled.

"Can I have everyone's attention, please?" The group fell quiet. "I'm afraid Mr. Jenkins has been under a lot of stress lately. He lost his wife a few days ago and that loss seems to be affecting his judgment."

"Someone should press charges," said a man from the crowd.

Several of the vacationers had their cell phones out. Really? she thought with annoyance. "Could you please put the phones away?" she asked, giving the would-be videographers a stern look of disapproval. Each sheepishly slipped a phone into a pocket.

"What's going to happen to Marvin?" Nellie asked.

"That's up to Sheriff Dorman."

"I'm not interested in pressing charges," Lane said.

"I'm not sure that will be your decision," she said, surprised by Lane's generosity.

"That's what comes from your flirting," Myrtle muttered.

"Jealous?" Lane shot back.

"These yokels are nuts," said a crew member to another, and snickered.

Colleen's pale blue eyes turned to ice. She was about to say something in response, when Myrtle crossed to the man and smacked him on the arm.

"Show some respect," she barked.

"Hey," the man said, and rubbed his bicep.

Giggles and chortles rolled over the crowd, not the least of which came from the film company. The only person who didn't seem to think anything was funny was Hayley, who was standing on the bookstore's porch, wringing her hands. Fawn's tarot reading must still be on her mind, Colleen thought. She wondered how difficult it would be for the actress to regroup and get her head back into the scene after Marvin's disruption.

"All right, everyone," Wendy yelled as the chuckling subsided. "I know we've had a bit of excitement, but let's get back to work. We don't have this location all day."

And just like that, the drama was over and everyone returned to their jobs.

"What *is* going to happen to Marvin?" Nellie asked, genuinely concerned.

"I don't know."

"Let's rock and roll!" the assistant director called. "Could we get the extras to places?"

Myrtle, Lane, and Nellie moved away to get ready for filming. Colleen had wanted to talk to Lane and ask him about Marvin's accusations, but now was clearly not the time nor the place. She spotted Jason and Wendy and quietly made her way to them.

"Hope all the disruption didn't put you too far behind," she said.

"Our director's efficient. He'll make up the time," Wendy said.

Colleen's eyes narrowed. Despite what Wendy said, there was something in the young woman's tone that indicated a concern. "Is something wrong?" Colleen asked.

Jason stole a look over his shoulder at Hayley and then signaled Colleen to move closer. "Hayley has a fan," he whispered, "who is rather enthusiastic. Sends photo collages made of Hayley's images from magazines, the Internet, wherever."

"Tell her the creepy part," Wendy said, and left to attend to her job.

Colleen joined Jason as he moved several yards away. "The pictures," he began after he was sure they were far enough away not to be overheard, "some of them are from magazines published years ago. This person has been saving them for a long time . . . until now."

"A stalker?"

"We don't know, but the person is clearly obsessed. The photo collages have been coming in the mail for a few weeks now."

"What did the police say?" she asked while peering over Jason's shoulder at the observers, now on the lookout for a potential stalker.

"Since there hasn't been a threat, there's not much they can do."

"And you're worried."

He nodded. "Hayley doesn't know, but one of the pictures arrived yesterday at the beach house. That's why we didn't get a call about today's location until this morning. We didn't want the word getting out, just in case."

"I wondered why the press wasn't here." It would be only a matter of time, however, before the news trucks arrived. She was surprised they hadn't already.

"Cut!" yelled the director.

"Take fifteen," Wendy said.

Hayley descended the stairs and headed toward them.

"Here she comes," Colleen said.

Jason adopted an expression of disinterest and pretended to read a text on his phone. She was surprised how quickly he had changed his demeanor. Maybe that was what came from working in Hollywood: a good poker face.

"What are you two huddled together for?" the celebrity asked as she reached them.

"Can I get you anything?" her assistant asked.

"An answer to my question, please."

He hesitated. Colleen observed the interaction between star and assistant with interest.

"Since my assistant is lying, perhaps you'll do me the favor of telling me what was being discussed," she said to Colleen.

Colleen wondered what she should do. She didn't want to

alarm the actress, but if the woman was in some type of danger, didn't she deserve to know?

"I understand you've received some interesting photo collages."

Hayley turned to Jason. "Are we talking about that poster I got a few weeks ago?"

"Yes," he said quietly.

Clearly, he hadn't told his boss everything.

"From what I understand," Colleen said, "there have been several such mailings."

Hayley's brow furrowed. "Jason, I'd like to speak with Chief McCabe in private."

He beat a swift retreat.

"Do you mind if we move to the shade?" Hayley asked, and before she got an answer, she crossed to a canopy with canvas folding chairs.

Colleen took her time joining the actress under the tent. *Great. Just what I don't need—private time with Hayley.* She hoped the woman wouldn't bring up Fawn's tarot reading.

As soon as they were seated in chairs alone in the shade, Hayley's demeanor changed and she began rubbing her hands. "Did you hear about my tarot reading?" she asked, her voice quivering.

Colleen silently groaned. "I did."

"Then you'll understand why I'd like to stay with you for the remainder of my time in town."

"What?" Colleen choked out.

"I know it's a great deal to ask, but I think it would be safest."

Hell no. Her home had already been used as a safe house once this summer; she had no intention of hosting another guest. Damn Fawn and her readings.

"I don't think—" she began.

"That girl said there would be danger, and look what happened today, not to mention the fan mail I received at the house, which Jason doesn't think I know about."

"Marvin's attack on Lane had nothing to do with you."

Hayley stopped wringing her hands. "Perhaps not, but the collages do."

The fan-photo mailings were of concern—she couldn't deny that—but the thought of having Hayley as a housemate was too fantastic to contemplate. She was proud of herself for slaying the green-eyed monster, but that didn't mean she was ready to become chummy with the woman.

"I know you don't like me," Hayley said softly.

"It's not that I don't—"

"Please. Let me finish. I can tell you care about people, what happens to them, and I saw by the way you handled things with that man why your community respects you. It's clear you put others before yourself."

Please, oh please, someone make her stop.

"I suppose that's one of the reasons why Billy is so fond of you."

Wait. Did she say Bill is fond of me? What else did he tell his ex about me?

"Fawn predicted you'd protect me for a reason."

Colleen's mind was spinning. Was it really possible that Bill had told Hayley about his feelings for her? And what were those feelings? And why hadn't he told her? She realized Hayley had stopped speaking, and she refocused on the houseguest matter.

"Thank you for the compliments, but I think you're safer where you are. My house is rather remote. You have others with you in the house you're staying in now."

"But not you."

She sighed. It was time to bite the bullet and confess. "I'm not as nice as you think. I'm embarrassed to admit this, but . . . I took you through the dunes on purpose. I knew, or at least I was fairly confident, that the ride would make you sick."

The actress reached into a cooler at her feet, removed two waters, and handed one to Colleen. "Apology accepted."

Colleen received the water in stunned silence.

Hayley took a sip from the bottle and puckered her lips to refresh her lipstick. "Actresses have said and done far worse. It's part of the business."

Terrific, she thought. I'm being compared to a catty actress.

"But," Hayley added, "none has ever said 'I'm sorry.' "

How could she deny a person who had so graciously accepted her apology? If the roles had been reversed, she wasn't so sure she would have been as magnanimous.

"I'm not going to let you stay at my house," Colleen said, trying to be gentle but firm. "I really do think it's safer for you where you are. But if it will make you feel any better, I could swing by and check on things, even though I'm sure Bill has already got someone assigned to do that."

Hayley visibly relaxed. She took one of Colleen's hands in hers and squeezed it tightly. "Thank you."

Jason approached the tent with caution. "Everything okay in here?"

Hayley let go of Colleen's hand and flashed a brilliant smile. "Yes, I believe it is. Are they ready for me?"

"Yep," Jason said, somewhat perplexed. He stole a look at Colleen, then accompanied Hayley to the porch.

Colleen watched them go, not quite sure what had just happened.

"Quiet on the set," the AD yelled.

She headed toward her SUV, where she had left Sparky. How was she going to explain all of this to Bill?

Chapter 13

"*You promised Hayley what?*" Bill asked as he paced his office.

Colleen winced. She'd known he wasn't going to like the idea, but she hadn't anticipated this reaction. "You have to admit it's better than having her stay with me, like she wanted."

He couldn't argue with that. The last thing he wanted was for the women to be roommates. He exhaled. "She always did take stuff like horoscopes and palm readings too seriously. Sorry she dragged you into her foolishness."

"She does have reason to be concerned," Colleen said, surprised to find herself defending his ex.

"Don't tell me you believe that tarot card nonsense."

"*No,*" she said emphatically. "I'm talking about the packages of photos someone is mailing her."

"There's been more than one?"

Had Hayley really kept the entire story from him? "There's been only one at the house here in Corolla, but apparently she's been receiving them for weeks."

He shook his head. "That's what comes from her being too friendly with people."

"I hardly think it's her fault that some psycho has fixated on her." It wasn't like Bill to be so unsympathetic and judgmental. She wondered where his attitude was coming from.

He noticed her staring at him with disapproval. "I know that sounded bad. It's just . . . we have a history."

She squirmed in the chair and pushed at the folders on the conference table. "Yes, I'm aware of that."

They fell silent. The air conditioner hummed softly. Sparky looked up from where he had been sleeping at her feet under the table, wondering if the quiet was a sign they were leaving.

"So . . . have you interviewed Marvin yet?" she asked.

He exhaled and sat on the nearby edge of the table. "He's refusing to answer questions. Sits there going on and on about how Doris changed after she joined the community theater group, started wearing more lipstick and perfume and, as he put it, 'setting her hair.'"

Doris's behavior did sound like that of a woman having an affair, and Lane did have a reputation as a ladies' man. He had even flirted with Colleen on occasion—not that she'd ever felt it had a serious intent behind it. Perhaps Doris misinterpreted a flirtation for genuine romantic interest. Maybe the affair was really an unrequited fantasy. She could understand why Marvin was suspicious, and yet it didn't give him the right to attack someone with a Taser. However unlikely it was that Marvin was the murderer, his violent outburst toward Sam and his attack on Lane made him the number one suspect on her list.

"What are you thinking?" Bill asked.

"It might help if I talked to Marvin. His anger seems to be directed mostly at men. Maybe talking to a woman will be different." She knew Bill wouldn't like the idea, but at this point, Marvin was the best lead they had. Anything they could do to get him talking might lead to a motive or more clues about other suspects. "While I'm questioning him, you can check out his ears."

"Was that a joke?" he asked, not the least bit amused.

"No . . . yes . . . I guess not a good one," she said with a shrug.

He reached across the desk and opened one of the folders. Inside were Rich's ear photos.

"Think about how hard it's going to be for me, or you, to speak with him and look at his ears without his noticing," she said.

"I don't know."

"He's been Mirandized, right?" she asked, knowing full well how by-the-book Bill and his staff were.

"Of course, but not booked."

"So if he's willing to talk to me, why not let him?"

Bill gazed at the dozens of ear photos before him. She knew he was weighing the potential benefits of having her speak with Marvin versus the desire to keep her out of the investigation.

"I'm not leaving you in the room alone," he said.

That was all she needed to hear. He was going to let her talk to Marvin.

"I'll put Rodney in there with you, just in case."

"Of course." This was highly irregular of him to allow her to speak with a suspect. She wasn't going to push anything by making further demands. "And where will you be?" she asked.

"On the other side of the glass. Of course he'll know I'm looking, but not what I'm looking at."

"Sounds good."

"All right, then," he said, grabbing the folder with the photos. "You ready?"

She stood. Sparky moved to follow her. "Not yet," she said, and the dog flumped back to the floor.

Bill led her down the hall. She had never been in the back rooms, where the interrogations were done. She had informally questioned people before in an effort to help Bill with investigations, but there was something about the official nature of her impending conversation that suddenly made her nervous. It was different from the times when she did fire investigations. What she and Marvin said would be on record. She could either help solve the case or jeopardize it.

"You sure about this?" he asked, reaching a door.

She nodded. He tapped on the door and Rodney opened it.

"He say anything else?" Bill asked.

"Nope."

Colleen peered around Rodney into a small room with a two-way mirror that looked into an even smaller room, where Marvin sat at a table.

"Colleen's gonna talk to Marvin," Bill said. "I want you in there with her."

"Oh," the deputy said, surprised.

"Move his chair near the window—profile." He turned to Colleen. "I'll be in here. The minute you feel uncomfortable or want out, let Rodney know."

She wondered if all of this seriousness was necessary. But then she remembered Marvin's threats to Sam and Lane. She gave Bill a thumbs-up. He entered the windowed room where Rodney had been observing Marvin. She followed his deputy to the next door and into the interrogation room.

"Chief McCabe's come to see you, Marvin," Rodney said. "Mind if we make some room for her?"

"I don't have anything to say to her," Marvin said, standing as Rodney took his chair and moved it so that Marvin's profile would be in front of the mirrored window.

Rodney placed a second chair several feet in front of Marvin, motioned for her to sit, and stepped a few feet back. She peered at the window, unable to see anything but her own reflection. Her face belied her nervousness. If she was going to get Marvin to open up to her, she'd need to appear at ease—like someone wanting to understand him, rather than accusing him. She forced the muscles in her cheeks and forehead to relax, took a silent deep breath, and sat before Marvin.

"You're wasting your time. Don't know why the sheriff dragged you in here," he said.

She studied the man's face. He looked more troubled than violent now. Rather than get straight to the point, perhaps she could take a more circuitous route to the truth.

"I understand this has been a rough few weeks for you," she said.

Marvin shifted in his seat, so the back of his head faced the mirror. Damn. She had to get him to turn his head in profile so that Bill could run through the pictures in the other room. She leaned forward, rested her elbows on her knees, and moved herself as close to the side of Marvin that faced the mirror as possible. If he was going to talk to her, he'd have to shift his head back to look at her, and that would give Bill another shot with the ear identification.

"I know you're upset about Doris," she said gently. "And that you blame the theater production for her death; what I don't understand is why."

Marvin snorted and leaned back in his chair. He might not be talking to her, but at least the side of his head was to the window again. Perhaps she needed to put herself in Marvin's shoes, tap into his feelings of jealousy. If he thought she knew how he was feeling, maybe she could find out why. It was a risky avenue to pursue, since it could further aggravate him, but it was the only one she could think of to take.

"It's terrible when a person you care about keeps something from you," she said. She felt the intensity of Bill's gaze on her through the glass and realized Marvin wasn't the only one she was at risk of upsetting.

She sighed, a real sigh, not just one for Marvin's benefit. He glanced at her. He's trying to ascertain if I'm speaking from a place of truth or if my emotional appeal is a ploy to get him to talk, she thought.

"You ever have someone lie to you? I mean someone you love?" he asked after a long pause.

She swallowed hard. She had broken through. How she answered his question could either lead to more information or cause him to shut down. But why had he used the word *love*? Her feelings for Bill were being forced into the open by a murder suspect. She'd have no idea how Bill would react, and that terrified her. She gave Marvin the only answer she could, the simple truth.

"Yes . . . and when I found out, it made me do things . . . things I'm not proud of."

Marvin rubbed an arthritic hand. Her eyes narrowed. She hadn't noticed how twisted the fingers on his right hand were until now. Could those hands really have enough strength to have held a rope around Rich's throat?

"Why do you think people do that? Lie?" he asked.

She had a ton of answers she could give him, ones she had learned in her psychology classes back in college, but Marvin didn't want a textbook answer. He wanted to know why Doris had lied to him. She didn't know why his wife had lied, but she thought she knew why Bill had.

"I think sometimes the people we care about lie because they are trying to protect us."

Marvin's eyes welled with tears, but a second later he bit them back. "The only person Doris was interested in protecting was that charlatan she was sleeping with."

Despite his ugly behavior, she felt sorry for the man. It was clear that he had loved his wife, whether their relationship had been a healthy one or not. She figured it was best to accept his belief that Doris had had an affair. There was no point in asking him to prove it.

"I don't mean to be insensitive," she pressed. "But how did you find out?"

Marvin stole a look at Rodney, who stood nearby, stone-faced and arms folded. Marvin wasn't going to talk about his trouble with his wife with another man in the room, but there was no way Rodney was going to leave her alone. She leaned close to Marvin, close enough that if he had wanted to cause her harm, he could have.

"I believe you when you say Doris had an affair," she said quietly, hoping Marvin would think Rodney couldn't hear. She took a breath. "Did you do anything to Doris, Marvin?"

Marvin started. "What? No! It was that phony. He's the one who got rough with her, and yet she still wanted to be in that stupid play."

Colleen felt Rodney tense behind her. "Did someone assault Doris?" he asked.

Marvin scowled.

"Tell us what happened," she said gently.

He hesitated and then it all came out in a rush. "Doris came home one night after rehearsal with her eyes all red and puffy, like she'd been crying. I noticed some welts on her arms and asked her what had happened. She said she'd bumped into set pieces or something, but those didn't look like bruises from furniture. I told her she was gonna quit the play. She told me she'd leave me if she couldn't be in the show. I'm not an idiot. Nobody acts like that over a stupid play, even if it is for our horses."

"And what about Rich?" Rodney asked, stepping forward.

"Rich? I don't know anything about that. I always liked the fella. But you wanna know who messed with Doris, you talk to that theater group. Me? I know it was Lane Walker."

"Lane's the charlatan?" she asked.

"Oh yeah. Doris was all upset. Talking about how people aren't who they say they are. That you never know how mean a person can be. You talk to Lane. You'll find out he's not who he says he is."

"Thank you," she said, rising from her chair and reaching out to shake Marvin's hand. She was genuinely thankful for his information, but the real reason for initiating the handshake was to feel the strength of his grip. He took her hand, squeezed, and she knew those were not the hands that had strangled Rich.

She and Rodney crossed to the door.

"Hey," Marvin said. "Am I being charged, or can I go home?"

"We'll let you know," Rodney said, and exited.

As soon as she stepped into the hall, she took a deep breath. She hadn't realized how tense the interview had made her. Bill joined them from the other room.

"So?" she said.

"No match. Marvin's not the person Rich was trying to ID."

"I don't think he's our guy, not with those hands," she said.

"Looks like Lane's decision not to press charges may have been for other than altruistic reasons," Rodney said.

She checked her phone for the time. "I've got to head in to work."

"You keep an eye on our friend in there," Bill said to his deputy. "I'll be right back."

She and Bill approached his office to retrieve Sparky.

"Come on," she said, and the dog sprang up, refreshed from his long nap.

"I'll run a background check on Lane, see if anything pops up," Bill said.

"It might be a good idea for us to drop in on rehearsal," she said. "There's obviously a lot more going on there, and it's time we found out what."

"I agree."

Her phone buzzed to life. "I'd better take this. See you at rehearsal?"

"Yep."

She headed down the hall toward the exit, saw the number of the incoming call, and hit the ANSWER button.

"What can I do for you, Pinky?" she said, hoping he wasn't going to ask her to another "meeting" at Elizabeth's.

"I'm at the house you're gonna burn," he said.

"Everything okay?" she asked, crossing the parking lot and letting Sparky into her vehicle.

"There's something you need to see."

"I'm due at the station. Can it wait?"

"No, I'm afraid it can't," he said, all seriousness.

Her brows furrowed. "You want to tell me what's going on?"

"I think it's better if you see it."

Something about the house clearly had him concerned. "I'll be right there," she said, and hung up. She hoped it wasn't anything too serious. It wasn't often they had a house donated for a burn exercise. She'd make the meeting quick—she still had a murderer to catch.

Chapter 14

"*I wish I were* seeing you again under more pleasant circumstances," Pinky said, and held out his hand to help Colleen from her SUV.

Say what you would about him, Pinky was certainly chivalrous. She took Pinky's hand, not wanting to make a big deal about how she could get out of the SUV on her own. She was eager to find out what was on his mind. Sparky leaped to the ground and ran to a dune to take care of doggy business.

"You said there was something I had to see," she said, scanning the house with a faded sign that read SHORE LEAVE.

"Inside," he said, and led her up the overgrown driveway.

The building was the last of the original houses that had been built over twenty years ago, before Pinky had come to town and replaced them with the mansions that dotted much of today's landscape. Most of the new homes had private pools, elevators,

Jacuzzis, home theaters, state-of-the-art kitchens, gas fireplaces, and multiple bedrooms and baths. It was no wonder the modest two- or three-bedroom, two-bath homes like the one she was standing before now were being torn down. She walked with him under the house to a carport-level door.

"I first knew someone had been here from this," he said, and pointed to a cut screen and an open window next to the door.

"A break-in?" she asked. "Why not call Bill?"

"You'll see," he said, and unlocked the door.

The door squeaked open and Sparky rushed in from out of nowhere.

"Heel," she called.

"It's okay," Pinky said. "I closed off the room that I want you to see."

Sparky scurried about the basement, tail wagging with excitement. The dusty, cobweb-covered room contained a washer, a dryer, and two rusty beach chairs. She followed Pinky and Sparky up the steps. The house hadn't been used in quite some time. She caught up with them on the first floor. The smell of the musty brown carpet filled her nose, and she pressed her finger above her upper lip to keep from sneezing.

"You can see why I'm rebuilding," Pinky said.

She had to admit the place needed work.

"The property I'm designing for this place will be a tropical oasis," he said with pride.

"I'm sure it will be," she replied with a smile. "So what is it that you want me to see?"

Pinky crossed to a door on the opposite side of the wood-paneled room, opened it, and stepped aside. She joined him and peered in. A sleeping bag lay in a corner of the room. Empty soda cans and crumpled bags of chips littered the floor near the sleeping bag. She stepped inside to get a better look and noticed a well-worn spiral notebook on top of the sleeping bag.

"A squatter?" she asked, kneeling to look at the notebook.

"Take a look inside."

She retrieved the notebook and moved to a window. Inside were pages and pages of cutout magazine pictures of Hayley. Her heart raced. Had Pinky stumbled upon the stalker's hideout? She studied the pages and discovered quotes glued between the pictures. One read "Love sought is good, but given unsought is better." Under the quote was a picture of a radiant Hayley from a red-carpet event. Hearts and stars had been drawn around the actress's image, and around the heart was scratched another quote: "Boldness be my friend." She skimmed through the book. Numerous Hayleys smiled beautifully back at her. She flipped to the last few pages and discovered they had been less carefully arranged and some of the quotes had a more ominous tone. The final two read "False face must hide what the false heart doth know" and "Fishes live in the sea, as men do a-land. The great ones eat up the little ones."

"So what do you make of it?" Pinky asked, pulling her away from the notebook.

"A lot of Shakespeare," she said, examining the rest of the belongings.

"Personally, I prefer quoting Shakespeare in pursuit of amour."

I'm sure you do, she thought. "You find anything in the rest of the house?"

"Some crumbs in the kitchen and toiletries in the bathroom."

"In here?" she asked, crossing to a room off of the bedroom.

She peeked inside and confirmed her suspicions. Hayley's stalker was a woman. She had guessed as much from the childishly drawn hearts and stars, but the lipstick and eye shadow on the sink confirmed it.

"You really should have called the sheriff's office about this," she said, returning to the bedroom.

"The girl obviously has troubles; I didn't want to add legal ones to the mix."

"That's generous of you," she said, surprised.

"Given my nephew's recent behavior this summer, I don't think I'm in any position to judge."

Max's arrest had had a lasting impact on Pinky. She empathized. Every family had a member who had difficulties; some, as with Pinky's nephew, were criminal in nature. Still, Hayley's safety was paramount.

"I'm not sure I should be telling you this, but Hayley has been receiving collages like the ones in this notebook for several weeks now. She and her staff are concerned. So am I."

"She didn't tell me."

Her eyes widened in surprise. "I didn't know you knew her."

"Ms. Thorpe is staying in one of my properties. We met when I stopped by to make sure everything was to her liking. She's quite the flirt."

Two peas in a pod, she thought. "So you see why this has to be reported," she said, returning to the issue of the squatter-stalker.

"Absolutely, I'll—"

Without warning, Sparky barked and tore through the living room and down the stairs. Colleen and Pinky looked at each other, puzzled, and then in a flash knew what—or rather, whom—Sparky was barking at.

She dashed to the basement and out the door. There was no sign of Sparky or Hayley's obsessive fan. She gave a short whistle, and seconds later the dog appeared briefly over an oceanside dune and then disappeared again. She sprinted in his direction. It was difficult going, as the property was overgrown, and she slowed in order to pick her way through the bushes. She noticed foot and dog prints and tracked them to the top of the dune. She scanned the beach in both directions. From her vantage point, she was certain she'd be able to spot them. She squinted into the sun. Where could they be?

"You see them?" Pinky asked, joining her.

"No," she said. "Cover your ears."

He did as instructed.

She placed her fingers into the corners of her mouth, took a deep breath, blew a high-pitched whistle, and waited. Seconds went by, and then Sparky appeared around a dune several houses down the beach. She waved and gave another short whistle. The dog came running at full speed, drawing the attention of amused sunbathers and two teens throwing a football on the beach. Moments later, he climbed the dune, tongue out and tail wagging.

"Where were you?" she asked. "And what's on your face?"

She rubbed a finger over his muzzle. Was that blood? No, the consistency and color weren't right. In fact, it looked more like catsup. She sniffed the substance and confirmed that it was indeed the condiment. Their stalker must have given him a treat, perhaps a hamburger or hot dog that she had intended for her own dinner. That was how the woman had thrown the canine off her trail.

"You can never resist a treat, can you?" she said, taking him by the collar and leading him back down the dunes to the house. "We need to get someone posted at the house," she called behind her to Pinky.

He slid down the dune and stopped at the bottom to empty sand from his loafers. "She knows we've found where she's been hiding. Why would she come back?"

"Because," she said, opening her SUV and motioning for Sparky to hop in, "she'll want this." She held up the notebook of pictures. "And someone should check on Hayley tonight after she gets home from her shoot. Now that her stalker knows we're onto her, who knows what she might do."

"I can check on Hayley," he said, meeting her at the SUV. "At least until the sheriff gets someone stationed there."

"I'll call Bill and let him know."

Colleen hopped in and started the engine. She was eager to talk to Bill and tell him about what they had discovered. Pinky tapped on her window and she rolled it down.

"Yes?"

"I know you're a woman who can take care of herself," he said, unusually serious. "But do me a favor and be careful."

"Of course," she said, surprised and touched by his concern.

"Because you still owe me a date," he added with a wink.

"That wasn't a date," she called out the window, then grinned as she backed out of the driveway.

Pinky waved and she pulled away. She hit Bill's number on her phone.

"Hey," he said, picking up on the second ring. "Everything okay?"

"Hayley's stalker broke into the house Pinky is donating to the station. Looks like that's where she's been hiding. Sparky chased after her, but she got away. We found a notebook with more collages. You probably wanna get one of your guys out there in case she comes back."

"Where are you now?"

"Heading to the firehouse. I have to check in with Jimmy before he calls out the National Guard. How'd you do with the background check on Lane?"

"Turns out Lane Walker isn't his real name. He changed it years ago. Marvin may have been right about the affair after all."

"It's not uncommon for actors to change their names," she said, not convinced that a name change alone was enough to point suspicion at him.

"True, but I'd still like to know why Marvin thinks Doris had the affair with him."

"You picking him up?"

"Nobody was home. His neighbor said Lane told him he had some business to take care of but that he'd be at rehearsal tonight. Oh, and the ME reports came back on Rich and Doris."

Colleen raised her brows in surprise. That was fast, she thought. Clearly, the new medical examiner ran a tighter ship than the old one and was sending a message that cases would be handled differently than in the past. "And?"

"Cause of death for Rich was strangulation. Cardiac arrest for Doris, although the ME is still awaiting toxicology. Rich's family is having his body transported to their funeral home today. Hey, I gotta go. See you at the rehearsal."

Her mind raced with the new information she had learned from Bill. Could Lane really be Rich's murderer? If Rich had found out about Lane's true identity, why would Lane kill him? What was it about his past that he didn't want discovered? And how did Doris fit in? Bill said that the medical examiner had determined her cause of death was a heart attack; nothing suspicious about that. Besides, she had been at the training exercise when Doris had died. Lane hadn't been anywhere near the woman the entire morning. Yet it seemed that, according to Marvin, there was a connection between Doris and Lane. Could that connection also concern Rich in some way? Could Myrtle have been right about Lane all along? She had attributed Myrtle's behavior to jealousy, but perhaps those negative feelings were more intuitive. But then wouldn't Fawn have picked up on that with her aura and tarot readings? And what about Nellie, Rita, Sam, Doc Wales, and Adam? Were they hiding something, too? Stop it, she told herself. The next thing you know, you'll suspect everyone in town.

She parked in the lot and was pleased to observe Bobby helping Chip wipe down the trucks and engines. Like a good rookie,

Bobby had made himself a favorite with the senior firefighters, always arriving early, making them coffee in the morning, cleaning up after meals, and helping with any additional station duties that might arise. She was confident he would pass the written tests and, with a little extra motivation and encouragement, master the physical ones, as well.

Sparky raced ahead into the bay. After everything she had witnessed in the last few days, it would be good to return to the normalcy of work. The routine would help clear her head and put everything she had learned into perspective. Jimmy emerged from the side of the building with a family of vacationers. Tours were part of the job and especially popular in the summer months.

"And this is Chief McCabe," he said as she approached.

"Did you enjoy your tour of the station?" she asked.

"We did," the mother replied. "Your captain was quite thorough."

"Glad to hear it," she said. "Enjoy your stay in Corolla."

The family thanked her, and she heard Jimmy giving out plastic junior firefighter badges to the kids as she went inside. Yes, it was nice to be back at work, where there was a sense of calm. She entered the dining room and could tell instantly it was Kenny's turn to cook lunch. The air was filled with the spicy smell of jambalaya. He had learned to make the dish while living in New Orleans, and it was one of his favorites to make for the house. Her stomach growled. Lunch was coming at a good time.

"Come and get it," Kenny called.

Seconds later, the guys were lined up in the kitchen, scooping heaps of the steaming dish onto their plates, along with corn bread and salad. As was the custom with trainees, Bobby waited at the end of the line to allow the others first dibs. She spotted Sparky in the corner, gobbling up sausage. Kenny always set some aside as a special treat for him. After all the guys were through, she grabbed a plate, helped herself, and joined her men at the head of the long table in the dining room.

"No boots today, chief?" one of the guys teased.

It would be a long time before they forgot about her silly bridesmaid's outfit. "Maybe you could work on sweeping the floors after lunch," she jokingly ordered.

"That'll teach you," someone said, and everyone laughed.

She smiled and chewed a mouthful of corn bread. She listened as the men ribbed one another, talked about how their favorite baseball teams were doing, and generally reveled in the camaraderie that was unique to firefighters and EMTs. Yes, this was what she needed to remind her of the basic goodness in people, something she had been questioning over the last forty-eight hours.

"In all seriousness," she said to the group. "I want some people on the floors and landscaping after lunch."

"That means you," Chip said, poking at Bobby.

"And you," she said to Chip, causing another round of laughter.

Unfortunately, her peaceful time with the fellas didn't last long.

"Yoohoo. Anyone here?" echoed a female voice from the bay.

"I'll get it," Chip said, hopping from his chair.

"Bring her in if she's cute," someone said as he disappeared to attend to the visitor.

A moment later, Chip entered with Myrtle, and the entire room burst out laughing.

"Hey, rookie, your mama's here," Chip kidded.

"Show some respect," Myrtle said, and popped him in the chest with her purse, causing another wave of laughter.

Bobby hung his head and pushed his chair back.

"Stay where you are, Bobby," Myrtle ordered, approaching the group. The men looked down at their food and snickered. "It's the chief I want."

Jimmy kicked Colleen under the table. She forced a smile, kicked him back, and rose. Better to speak with Myrtle in another room and allow her men to finish their meal in peace.

"What can I do for you, Myrtle?" she asked, motioning for her former schoolteacher to join her in the recreation room.

"How's Little Bobby doing?" Myrtle asked as soon as they were in the other room.

Was Myrtle really checking up on her grown son? "He's doing fine," she said. "But it might help if his mother didn't come snooping around, checking up on him."

"I'm not snooping," she said.

"Oh? Then why are you here?"

"I have a favor to ask. I'd like you to make it rain for a scene in the play."

"What?"

"I'd like you to get your team out to the park with one of the engines on the night of the play and make it rain," she said, as if that was all the explanation that was needed.

"Why would I make it rain on the show and the audience?" she asked, truly mystified.

"Not on us," the cranky thespian said. "In the background."

Colleen was losing her patience. "Perhaps you could explain exactly what you want to happen and why."

"Do I really have to spell it out?"

"Yes!"

"Okay. No need to snap at me."

Colleen folded her arms. "You've got ten seconds."

"We're depicting the horses' arrival from Spanish ships to the shore during a rainstorm. Fawn is going to do the waves, and Nellie and I are going to hoof it with the cutout boats, but I thought it would heighten the moment if we could have real rain instead of some cheesy sound effect."

Colleen had heard of firehouses making it rain for film shoots but never for a play. The idea of helping add rain to the production intrigued her. She remembered now thrilled she'd been by being sprayed on during a safari amusement park ride as a kid and knew how much fun it would add to the show.

"Does Adam know about this?" she asked, not wanting to get herself or her guys mixed up in the group's bickering and intrigue.

Myrtle bit the inside of her lip. "I wanted to get your approval first. No point in suggesting it to him if you say no. So, are you in or out?"

"If this is another attempt to undermine Lane—"

"What the heck does that man have to do with this?" she said, unable to hide her annoyance. "He's not the director."

She wondered why Myrtle took such a strong dislike to the man. "You don't like him much," she said, stating the obvious.

Myrtle shrugged. "I don't think about him one way or the other."

She found that hard to believe. In fact, she suspected Myrtle thought about her nemesis a great deal. "But if you had to, what would you think about him?"

Myrtle hesitated. "I'm only telling you this because, well, you and I . . . earlier . . ."

"I understand," she said. She and her former teacher had been through a lot this summer. Myrtle didn't need to explain.

Myrtle checked to be sure they were alone. "I don't like how he treated Doris. We could all tell she had a crush on him. He should have left her alone, instead of making her another notch on his belt."

"By notch on his belt, you mean they . . ."

"Yes."

"Oh." Colleen absorbed the news of Doris's and Lane's—what was it? "I take it from your description that it was a fling rather than ongoing," she said, somewhat uncomfortable talking about the sex lives of people she knew.

"I think the young people call it a 'hookup,'" Myrtle said, as if Colleen was more out of touch than she.

Colleen suppressed a grin. "Did anyone else know about this?"

"Doris told Nellie and Nellie told me. Marvin must have known, considering the way he's been carrying on."

The evidence was mounting against Lane. At the very least,

he had had some type of abusive incident with Doris. At the worst, he was a killer. Bill might be doing more than questioning Lane tonight; he might be arresting him.

"One more thing," she said. "Do you think Lane would ever hurt Doris?"

"Lane? Are you kidding? I may not care for that man, but, trust me, he's a pussycat. Does he break hearts? Yes. Anything else? Definitely not. So . . . are you gonna give us the rain or not?"

"Let me get back to you on that," she said, still processing everything Myrtle had told her.

"Well, I gotta go. Nell and I are grabbing a bite before rehearsal."

Colleen waved as her cranky former teacher turned ally exited the building. She was more confused than ever. If there was anyone that would be suspicious of Lane, it would be Myrtle. But, despite the knowledge of his fling with Doris, Myrtle didn't think him capable of hurting her. So where had the bruises come from? Myrtle hadn't mentioned any. Could Marvin have made them up? It was possible Doris had kept them hidden. Nobody knows what really happens behind closed doors. Perhaps things got a little rough? Myrtle's visit had only succeeded in raising more questions.

"I saw Myrtle pull out," Jimmy said, bringing her a glass of iced tea. "You survive?"

"Yeah," she said, taking the glass.

"So, what'd she want?"

"You're never going to believe it," she said. "But first tell me how this morning went."

The two retreated to Colleen's office to go over equipment-maintenance needs, station duties, rookie training, the upcoming EMT recertification tests, and, yes, Myrtle's request to make it rain.

Chapter 15

"*If you're early,* you're on time; and if you're on time, you're late." These were words firefighters and EMTs lived by, and, according to her roommate in college, theater folks, too. This was why Colleen had left the station twenty minutes before the scheduled start of rehearsal at the Whalehead Club, even though her drive time was at most five.

She felt better about having tended to her duties at the station and drove to the rehearsal feeling more grounded and with a clearer sense of purpose. Despite Jimmy's assurance that things were under control, she felt as if she had neglected the guys for the last two days. In actuality, the last week had been relatively quiet at the station . . . well, if you discounted the calls for Doris and Rich. Prior to that, there had been the usual water rescues, medical treatments, and a fender bender at the TimBuck II shopping plaza, but, thankfully, no serious fire-related calls.

After she and Jimmy had discussed station duties, she had updated him on Myrtle's request for rain. He had said yes to the idea right away—any chance to use the engine—and agreed that the guys would all be on board if it was okayed by her and Adam. She had also informed him about the squatter at the Burn-to-Learn house. She knew Bill wouldn't want the information getting out, but she trusted Jimmy beyond measure and needed him to be ready in case anything should happen.

She was hardly delighted about returning to the drama and intrigue of the community theater group. On her last encounter, she had witnessed the discovery of Rich's body in the dumbwaiter, the group's infighting, and Fawn's rather up close and personal aura reading. At least she and Bill would be there together. Maybe with the two of them working collaboratively they could keep the group in check. She pulled into the parking lot and exited the vehicle with Sparky, who immediately spotted a Canada goose waddling near the reeds along the shore and took off in pursuit of the bird.

She followed Sparky onto the lawn that had served as a landing strip for guests of the wealthy Mr. and Mrs. Knight back in the 1920s. Since then a pond had been dredged to break up the large expanse of green, but if she squinted her eyes, she could almost imagine the fashionable visitors from Washington, D. C., and New York happily alighting from propeller planes for a week of relaxation and hunting. Sparky bounded toward her, tail swirling in circles, and he barked at a blue heron that soared above them in pursuit of an evening meal.

She strolled to the front of the Whalehead Club, an area that visitors often mistakenly thought of as the back of the house because it faced away from the park and toward the sound. Rows of white plastic chairs were set up facing the house. She wondered if it was for one of the many weddings that took place on the grounds, then remembered that this was where the group was going to perform the play. Clever, she thought. They can use the veranda as the stage and the interior of the house as the backstage.

She heard the sound of tires on gravel and waved as Bill pulled next to her SUV. Rodney's car arrived next. Bill had brought backup. Was he planning to make an arrest? Would it be Lane? Myrtle's comment about the actor being a pussycat came back to her and she wondered if Bill was right to suspect him in Rich's death. What if the only thing Lane was guilty of was being a gigolo? Then again, Lane had had a fling with Doris and had been living under another name—things that, while not illegal or even unusual, drew suspicion upon him.

"Hey," she said as the men approached.

"I saw Lane's car parked at the side of the building," Bill said. He motioned with the folder that contained the ear photographs and headed toward the building with Rodney.

She jogged to catch up with them. "In case Lane isn't our guy, maybe we shouldn't go in with the entire army."

Bill stopped. The muscles in his jaw tightened. A mild tension filled the air.

"Why don't I wait for you on the porch," Rodney said, and scurried away toward the Whalehead Club.

Sparky bounced to the deputy and joined him on the walk

across the lawn, leaving her alone with Bill. She knew he was annoyed with her for telling him how to do his job, but she wanted to be certain that if anyone was going to be arrested that it be the right person.

"Myrtle stopped by the station for something unrelated to this, but we got to talking. Apparently, Lane had a one-night stand with Doris."

"So why the reservations about him?"

"When I asked her if she thought Lane might have injured Doris, she was adamant about the fact that Lane isn't violent. There's no love lost between the two. Believe me, if there was even a hint that he could hurt someone, Myrtle would have said so."

"But he did lie about having an affair with Doris."

"Which makes you wonder what other secrets he has," she said.

"And if any would be worth killing to keep."

She sighed. "I just think we should keep what Myrtle said in mind . . . that's all."

"Is this your gut speaking?" he asked, studying her.

She resisted the urge to roll her eyes. She knew how he felt about her gut instincts. But right now, her gut wasn't telling her anything except to consider all the facts. "No," she said. "This time, it's my head."

He stared intensely into her eyes, and she found herself unable to look away. She could see why suspects caved under his scrutiny. Just when she couldn't stand the awkwardness a moment longer, he said, "Okay. I'll hear him out."

They crossed the lawn to the Whalehead Club.

"Why don't you wait out here," Bill said to Rodney when they reached the porch.

"You sure?" his deputy asked, surprised.

Bill nodded. She leashed Sparky, tied the lead to one of the porch posts, and followed Bill inside. They found Kyle pacing in the hall.

"I'm glad you're here," the museum intern said, spotting them as soon as they entered the foyer. "I was about to call."

"Has something happened?" Bill asked, now on alert.

"No. But I am concerned about how *active* it is in there. Something could get broken. The Steinway is priceless, you know."

As if to punctuate what Kyle had said, a wail the likes of which Colleen had never heard before ripped through the building. She and Bill took off running, with Kyle on their heels. They came to an abrupt halt in the doorway to the library, startled by the three-ring circus they saw before them.

At first, she didn't know where to look, there was so much activity and noise. The sound of tap shoes drew her attention to the left corner, where Nellie, dressed in a costume that resembled that of a horse with a mane and tail, was practicing a tap number that mimicked the movement and sound of a horse trotting. The shifting of her weight as she danced caused her tail to bounce to the beat. Gives a whole new meaning to tap dancers being called hoofers, she thought.

"Ouch!" Myrtle exclaimed, and Colleen turned, to see Rita stitching a tail onto Myrtle's derriere. Colleen suspected the stick hadn't been accidental.

"Could we get more wind?" Adam yelled above the noise.

Sam cranked up an enormous floor fan and aimed it at Fawn, who was holding flowing yards of blue satin fabric. The fabric billowed across the room like waves and Adam gave Sam a thumbs-up. Then came the pleading wail again, louder this time, and Bill charged into the center of the room, past the sheets of fabric to the great fireplace, where Lane stood bent over Hayley, his hands wrapped around her throat.

"Release her!" Bill barked, and grabbed Lane's arm.

"Hold!" Adam yelled, and everyone in the room stopped what he or she was doing. Sam cut the fan, the fabric fell to the floor, the room fell silent, and all eyes turned to Bill, Lane, and Hayley.

"Ouch," Lane said as Bill squeezed his arm.

"Are you okay?" Bill asked Hayley.

Hayley gave him a dismissive wave. "I'm perfectly fine. Lane and I were doing a scene from *Othello*. Turns out we were both in productions."

"Yes, but obviously I wasn't Othello," Lane said to her. "Thank you for indulging me."

Bill hesitated. Despite the antics they had just witnessed from the theater group, everyone was looking at him as if he was the one acting strangely. Time to turn the tables, Colleen thought.

"Given Rich's recent tragic death," she said, stepping forward. "I'm sure everyone understands why we're on edge. Perhaps doing that particular scene, especially here, was a bit insensitive."

Colleen stared pointedly about the room. Nellie and Fawn muttered agreement. Rita and Sam hung their heads. Myrtle pursed her lips and looked out the window. Lane and Hayley squirmed uncomfortably. That's right, she thought. Never under-estimate the power of an Irish woman's guilt trip. She caught Bill's eye and gave him a reassuring smile.

"I couldn't agree with you more," Adam said. "It's time to eliminate distractions . . . or do I need to remind everyone we open in two days?"

She silently applauded Adam. He was taking the reins and put-ting his foot down. It must be a challenge for him to direct this group, given his youth, the insular nature of the theater company, and the strong personalities and egos of its members, she thought.

Jason, Hayley's assistant, entered the room from the hall, in-nocent about what had transpired. "Hayley, we should be going. You've got an early call tomorrow."

The actress threw a pale yellow silk scarf over her shoulder. "Thank you for inviting me to your marvelous little group," she said to Lane. "Have a wonderful rehearsal, all. Ta-ta."

"Ta-ta," the thespians responded in unison, and then she and Jason were gone.

Bill released his grip on Lane. "I need to have a word with Mr. Schneck," he said to Adam.

"Mr. Schneck? Who's that?" Rita whispered to Sam, who was standing next to her. Her husband shrugged.

Lane's cheeks flushed pink.

"Are you talking about Lane?" Fawn asked, noticing his embarrassment.

"Your real name is Schneck?" Myrtle asked, took it in for a second, and cackled.

"It's Floyd Schneck, if you must know," Lane said, lifting his chin and pulling himself up to his full height.

"Floyd," Myrtle said with such merriment that she snorted like a pig.

Sam and Rita raised their brows in surprise.

"Really, Myrtle," Nellie reprimanded.

Myrtle tried to speak through her laughter but only succeeded in snorting again.

"It's not that funny," Rita said. "A lot of people change their names."

Sam tapped his wife's arm. "Honey, stay out of it."

"I agree with Rita," Nellie said. "I'm sure Lane had a perfectly good reason for changing his name."

Colleen and Bill exchanged looks. Were they going to hear the truth or another lie?

Lane sighed. "I was in my twenties, going on auditions. I didn't think anyone would hire me as Floyd Schneck. A lot of actors have worked under different names."

"It's true," Sam said. "Look at Cary Grant, or Judy Garland."

"Or Natalie Wood," added his wife.

"Or Lady Gaga," Fawn added, baffling her fellow thespians.

"Lane Walker *is* a more stageworthy name," Nellie said. "Wouldn't you say so, Myrtle?"

"Yes, I suppose," her friend reluctantly agreed.

With the group's reassurance, Lane turned to Bill with renewed confidence. "So . . . why, might I ask, is this of special interest to the police? Last time I checked, changing one's name wasn't a crime."

"Not unless you have something to hide," Bill said.

Lane's eyes darted about the room. "Perhaps we could speak in private," he whispered.

Wow, that's a switch, Colleen thought. One minute the actor is reveling in having an audience and the next he wants to avoid one.

Bill motioned for Lane to step from the room. She followed them down the hall. As she stepped onto the veranda, she heard Kyle asking the group to please respect the property and be careful of the antiques. She reached to close the door and caught Kyle's eye as he was leaving the library.

"Why the Board let Rich talk them into allowing rehearsals here, I'll never know," he said in a huff, and disappeared through the foyer door on his way to his office.

She found the comment troubling, given what had happened to Rich. Kyle was right: It probably wasn't a good idea letting them use the historic property. Live performance was often unpredictable and things could get damaged. Still . . . to blame a dead person seemed rather cold and unfeeling. She had a new suspect to consider in Rich's death, one who obviously knew Rich and the building. Perhaps she had been too narrow in thinking only of members of the group. She left the door open a crack so she could hear in case any further drama occurred inside.

"What's this really about?" Lane asked, drawing her attention back to the veranda.

Bill leaned against the railing and gestured to a rocker near where Sparky was tied up. "Have a seat."

As the actor sat, Bill glanced at Rodney, and the deputy quietly moved so that he was positioned behind and to the right of Lane. Perfect, she thought. Rodney would have a clear view of Lane's profile and could compare it to the photographs while Bill questioned him. She caught Bill's eye and pointed to the rocker next to Lane. He nodded.

"You like dogs?" she asked Lane, taking the rocker next to him and petting Sparky's head. Though it may have seemed so, it wasn't a random question. She could tell a lot about a person by how he related to animals.

"Had a beagle years ago. Caesar. Boy, could he get into trouble. He used to climb the chain-link fence, prowl the neighborhood for lady friends, and then, after making his rounds, climb the fence and act like nothing had happened. It took me weeks before I caught him."

That sounded like a beagle. They were smart, crafty dogs that often got into mischief.

"Speaking of lady friends," Bill said. "Why don't you tell me about you and Doris."

Lane squirmed in his rocker. "What do you want to know?"

Bill shifted his weight. She could see he had little patience.

"We understand you and Doris spent some time together," she said, trying to put it as delicately as possible.

"Rehearsals take a lot of time."

"It's not that type of time we're talking about," Bill said. "Care to try again?"

She glanced over Lane's head at Rodney, who had been slowly flipping through the photographs. He shook his head no and kept flipping. She moved her rocker to face Lane.

"Did you and Doris ever get together outside of rehearsal?" she asked, and gazed steadily into his eyes. She saw his pupils dilate and, in that instance, knew he knew the secret was out.

"It was one time," he said. "I swear. I've regretted it ever since."

"Why only one time?" Bill asked, unfolding his arms.

Lane rubbed Sparky's head. "I don't want to speak ill of the departed," he said softly.

Colleen, Bill, and Rodney looked at one another.

"We're not asking you to speak ill of her," she said. "All Sheriff Dorman wants is the truth."

The actor exhaled deeply. "Doris . . . well . . . she told me that she was looking for something she wasn't getting at home. I thought that meant love, affection. I soon learned she and I had very different ideas of what affection meant."

"Different how?" Bill asked.

"She wanted to be more . . . adventurous. I wasn't interested in what she had in mind."

"You sure it's not the other way around?" Bill asked, unconvinced.

"I'm a romantic, Sheriff Dorman. I like seeing women in dresses, all made up and wearing jewelry. I pull out chairs, open doors, buy them roses. I don't relish the idea of hurting them."

"That's what Doris wanted?"

Lane nodded. "When I refused, she tried to provoke me and threatened to tell her husband. I felt sorry for her. She was a lovely woman. What happened to make her want a man to treat her like that?"

Nobody said anything. Nobody moved. Even Sparky stopped scratching and lay still. The revelation was stunning, but not because of its sensational nature. It was because they all sensed that it was the truth. As if to confirm Lane's innocence, Rodney closed the folder and shook his head. None of the ears depicted in the photographs was a match.

"I saw bruises, Sheriff, but they didn't come from me," Lane said. "For what it's worth, I'm deeply saddened by her passing."

That makes two of us, Colleen thought. Lane had said everything she needed to hear. As far as she was concerned, the only thing Lane was guilty of was having a fling with a troubled woman. She felt bad for him . . . and for Doris. Movement from inside the building grabbed her attention. She peered into the doorway opening and caught Rita's eye.

"What is it?" she asked.

The costumer nervously stepped forward. "I'm sorry," she said. "I didn't want to interrupt. Adam was wondering if Lane would be returning to rehearsal."

Everyone looked at Bill. "One more question," he said. "You and Rich ever have a run-in?"

"I should go," Rita said.

"It's okay, Rita," Lane said, and turned to Bill. "There wasn't a member of our group who I respected more than Rich Bailey, Sheriff. Ask anyone."

Bill studied him a moment and then said, "You can go."

Lane rose and moved toward the door with Rita.

"Oh, I almost forgot," Rita said to Colleen. "Adam says he has something for you, if you have a second."

"Me?" she asked, surprised.

Rita nodded and disappeared inside.

"Don't go anywhere," Colleen said to Bill. "I've got a theory I'd like to share with you." She entered the Whalehead Club to find out what Adam could possibly have to give her.

"Fawn, Lane, Myrtle, and Nellie, can I have you take places?" Adam said as she entered the library.

Nellie's and Myrtle's tap shoes clicked as they made their way to the front of the fireplace. Fawn positioned herself offstage. Lane took his place downstage.

"Sam, we'll hold off on all the effects for a moment. Oh, and Rita, the costumes look great."

Sam gave Adam a salute and Rita beamed. They may pull this show off yet, Colleen thought. She rapidly crossed to the director, not wanting to interrupt.

"You have something for me?"

Adam removed an envelope from his back pocket. "I've been meaning to give this to you."

"What is it?" she asked, feeling a small object inside.

"The footage from your training exercise on the beach. It's on an SD card, so you can just pop it into your computer. I skimmed through to make sure it all recorded. Hope it helps."

"Thanks. I completely forgot," she said, placing it in her back pocket. "I'm sure it will be quite instructive."

"I hope we did a good job for you," Nellie said.

"Of course we did," Myrtle said, as if they could do anything but.

"You'll let us know when you're going to show it," Rita chimed in.

"I'll see what I can do. Have a great rehearsal," she said, and left.

She returned to Bill and Sparky, who had been waiting for her on the porch.

"Where's Rodney?" she asked.

"He had to take care of a call. So, what's this theory of yours?"

She unleashed Sparky and motioned for Bill to join her on the lawn, away from the Whalehead Club. Movement in a window caught her eye. Was that Kyle spying on them out the window? Or someone from the acting troupe? She blinked, and then the person was gone.

"Something Kyle said got me thinking. . . . Maybe we need to broaden our list of suspects, consider more than the theater group members."

"What did he say?"

"He was angry that the Board let Rich talk them into allowing the group to use the Whalehead Club. I don't think he intended for me to overhear him."

"I'm not sure that makes him a suspect."

"But he has been present while they've been rehearsing, and who knows the building better than someone who works here? He would have known about the elevator."

Bill considered what she had said. "Okay. It doesn't feel right, but I'll talk to him again."

She gazed at the clouds blocking out the last hint of sunset. "I don't think Lane did it."

"He's a logical suspect," he said.

She couldn't argue with that. Still, her gut told her he was innocent—at least of murder. "What a love triangle," she said.

"Uh, yeah."

Her mind drifted to their romantic situation and how Hayley's arrival had set her relationship with Bill back. Or had it? Didn't Hayley tell her that Bill had talked about her? Would he have done that if he still had feelings for his ex? And would Hayley have told Colleen about the conversation if she still had feelings for him? She stole a look at him. Maybe it was the setting sun or the breeze or the sight of the swans swimming in the sound, but her heart beat a little faster. Perhaps she should be the brave one and make the first move.

"Listen, Bill," she began but was interrupted when her phone rang. It was the station. "Everything okay?" she asked, picking up.

"Got some calls about UFOs or floating objects coming from somewhere off of Lighthouse," Jimmy said. "Sounds like Chinese lanterns again."

Her talk with Bill would have to wait. "I'm on my way," she said, and hung up. "I gotta go. Jimmy thinks someone's releasing Chinese lanterns."

"That seems to be popular lately."

"Unfortunately," she said. "Let's talk later, okay?"

"I'll let you know if I find anything out."

She touched his arm. "Not about the case."

His eyes crinkled into the smile she loved so much. "That would be nice," he said.

She grinned, whistled for Sparky, jogged with him to her vehicle, and hopped in. She flipped on her emergency lights and left the park. It was time to stop some well-meaning vacationers from burning somebody's house down.

Chapter 16

"Paper cannot wrap up a fire" was a famous Chinese proverb and one Colleen thought must have been created by a firefighter. She found it curious that the same culture that had brought the world this saying had also given it the flickering lanterns that were now drifting heavenward over the sandy dunes of Corolla. She also considered it a sign that the truth would soon come out—like fire burning away paper—and that the identity of their killer would be revealed.

She peered out her window and traced the dotted pattern of lights that danced across the night sky. She had to admit there was something magical about the lanterns carrying people's wishes for fortune and health and romance upward on the colorful paper. But whether she liked the balloons or not, they were a fire hazard. All it would take was a strong wind to tilt the delicate structure and the paper would ignite, the lantern would fall with the flame still lit, and a roof or dune grass would catch fire.

She slowed her vehicle and crept along the rows of oceanside homes, waiting to see another balloon take flight. Then she spotted the flashing lights of one of the station's vehicles in front of a house down the road and knew her guys had found where the lanterns were being released.

She pulled behind the engine at the house and hopped from the vehicle, with Sparky right behind her. She sent him to search the grounds. The dog had a special ability to detect embers, and she wanted him on the job in case anything had already fallen back to earth.

"Don't go too far," she said, and patted him on the rump. His tail wagged and he put his nose to the ground. There was nothing a Border collie enjoyed more than having a job.

She gazed at the house as she walked up the driveway. This has to be one of Pinky's, she thought. Its scale was grand and a chandelier shined through an enormous arched window over the front door. She noted several vehicles were discreetly parked behind slatted fencing under the house, but she couldn't make out what type they were. If they were minivans, it could mean several families were vacationing together. If they were pickups, it might mean sportsmen, although she didn't imagine Chinese lanterns were their style. She climbed the stairs. She'd find out soon enough.

As she reached the top step, she heard laughter from behind the front door, which stood ajar. She pushed it open and entered the foyer.

"Here's my favorite fire chief," Pinky said, crossing to greet her with a glass of champagne in hand, as if she were late to a party.

She glanced around the great room. Kenny and Jason were sharing a laugh with Hayley, while Jimmy spoke with Wendy.

"Champagne?" Pinky asked, smiling warmly at her.

"Really," she said, suspecting he had been the lantern supplier. "You should know better."

"Are you talking about the champagne or the lanterns?" he asked with a wink.

"Both. I thought we were past smoke signals."

He grinned. "A variation on an old theme."

Pinky was nothing if not consistent and persistent. "You're supposed to be checking on Hayley," she whispered.

"This *is* how I check on people."

"Is that the fire chief?" Hayley said from across the room. "You and your men are so sweet to come out."

Colleen climbed two steps and joined everyone in the great room. "It's not about being sweet; it's about safety. But I understand you weren't the source of the sky lanterns, so I'll spare you the speech," she said, directing her comment to Pinky.

"What can I say? If I don't see your beautiful face often enough, I suffer withdrawal," he teased.

She felt her cheeks warm from blushing. Kenny and Jimmy snickered. Wendy raised her brows in amused surprise.

"Maybe you should schedule Salvatore into your rounds," Kenny joked.

Jimmy hit him on the arm. "Lay off the chief." It was one thing to tease at the station, another thing in front of citizens.

Colleen caught Hayley studying her.

"So," she said, wanting to get the focus back on the job at hand. "No more lanterns. And Pinky, if you need our help, you know the station's number."

Pinky pretended to straighten up like a scolded schoolboy. "Yes, ma'am," he said.

"All right, fellas. Party's over. Let's head back," she said, and motioned for them to exit.

"Colleen," Hayley said. "Might I have a word with you?"

"I'll meet you back at the station, guys," she called to Jimmy and Kenny as they left.

Hayley turned to Jason. "If you don't mind, I'd like to speak to Ms. McCabe in private."

"How about another drink?" Pinky said to Jason, and they joined Wendy in the kitchen.

"Thank you for stopping by," Hayley said once she and Colleen were alone.

"I'm here because the call came in about the lanterns."

Hayley put a hand on a hip and narrowed her eyes. "You and Mr. Salvatore seem to have a special bond."

"I'm not sure I'd call it a bond," Colleen said, amused.

"What would you call it?"

She wondered what business it was of Hayley's what her relationship was with Pinky. "Why are you so interested?" she asked, trying not to be annoyed.

Hayley leaned closer and lowered her voice. "If you're not interested in Billy, then I suggest you let him know. I don't want to see his heart broken."

"We don't have that type of relationship," she said, not wanting to get into the particulars of how she and Bill felt about each other with his ex-fiancée.

Hayley waved her hand dismissively. "Oh please. Everyone can see it."

"See what?"

"Antonio, can I get your opinion on something?" Hayley called to the group in the kitchen.

Oh dear, no. Please leave Pinky out of this.

Pinky left Jason and Wendy in the kitchen and joined them. "What is it?" he asked.

"Colleen says she doesn't have *that type* of relationship with the sheriff," Hayley said, and raised her brow in a skeptical expression.

Colleen wanted to hide under a rock. What had she done to deserve this? She pleaded with her eyes for him to remain silent.

"I don't know what type of relationship they have," Pinky said. "But I've heard some have placed bets. Personally, I say don't count me out as a long shot."

Hayley folded her arms in triumph. Colleen felt the blood drain from her face. Pinky chuckled.

"I'm teasing about the betting, but not about me," he said, heading back toward the kitchen. "Sure I can't get you any champagne?"

Colleen shook her head in stunned, mortified silence.

Hayley stepped closer. "You and Bill . . . you're right for each other. That's a rare thing," she said, and walked away to join the others in the kitchen.

Colleen's mind was awhirl. Had everyone in Corolla been gossiping about her and Bill? And if so, for how long? How could it have been that obvious? Nothing had actually transpired between them other than a handful of innocent dinners. How much had Bill told Hayley? She needed to get some fresh ocean air so she could think. She slipped out, closed the door quietly behind her, and descended the stairs.

"Sparky," she called as she headed toward the back of the house and the private boardwalk that led to the beach.

She rounded the side of the building and found the dog at the back by the pool and shuffleboard. "Come on," she said.

He looked at her and then back at a sliding glass door.

"Walk," she said, encouraging him to follow.

Usually the word *walk* sent Sparky running and his tail wagging. Instead, he cocked his head and stared at the door. Her eyes narrowed and she came to a stop. Was the door open a crack? Was he trying to get in? The sound of something falling to the floor inside caused Sparky to bark, and a surge of adrenaline flooded her bloodstream. An intruder was inside the house.

"Stay," she quietly commanded the dog, and took off to the front of the house. Her heart raced as she took the steps two at a time and burst through the door. She leaped up the steps into the great room and dashed to the group laughing in the kitchen.

"Jason and Wendy, take Hayley into a back room and lock the door," she said, trying to speak quietly and between breaths. "Pinky, you come with me."

"What's going on?" Hayley asked.

Colleen locked eyes with Jason and his pupils widened in understanding.

"Let's do as she says," he said, and ushered Hayley to a back room with Wendy.

"There's someone downstairs," she said, turning to Pinky. "Sparky's on the door."

"Someone broke in?" Pinky asked, heading toward the stairs that led down to the lower level.

Colleen touched his arm to stop him and hit Bill's number on her phone. He picked up after the first ring.

"Hey," she said, trying to catch her breath. "I think Hayley's stalker is in her house."

"What?"

"Hayley's locked safely in a room. Pinky and I are upstairs."

"Stay right where you are. I'm on my way."

Colleen hung up. She paced. So did Pinky. How could they just sit there while the stalker was downstairs? She looked at Pinky and knew he was thinking the same thing.

"I'm going down there," she said.

Pinky grabbed her arm, and she was surprised by the strength of his grip. "In this case," he said, "I don't think it should be ladies first."

"You got an extinguisher in the house?" she asked.

"Of course. In that closet."

She rushed to the closet and found the extinguisher hanging on the wall. If she needed to, she could take the woman out with extinguishing agent. She returned to the foyer, where Pinky was impatiently waiting at the top of the stairs, and gave him a thumbs-up.

They crept down the steps, Colleen peering over Pinky's shoulder. They reached a landing, heard movement below, and, a second later, were plunged into darkness. They heard the muffled sounds of the group speaking excitedly on the floor above.

"The breaker's been flipped," Pinky said.

Sparky barked below.

"Let's hurry," Colleen said, and nudged him forward.

They stumbled down the dark stairs and into the recreation room. The security lights outside the pool lit the room just enough that she could make out a shadow near the glass door. Sparky paced outside.

"I'll get the lights," Pinky whispered, and made his way to the breaker box.

She squinted and studied the shadow. It moved to the left toward a window. "I wouldn't if I were you," she warned, and lifted the extinguisher.

Red and blue lights flashed across the dunes. She heard the sound of Bill's vehicle sliding to a stop in front of the house and a car door opening.

"Got it," Pinky said from the dark, and the room suddenly flooded with light.

The stalker, a portly woman in her late twenties with streaked blond hair, crouched near a pool table. She wore jeans and a T-shirt with an image of Hayley ironed on the front.

Sparky ran toward the corner of the building and then reappeared with Bill behind him. Bill peered through the glass door behind the stalker with pistol drawn, slid open the door, and pushed the woman to the ground.

"I just wanted to talk to her," the woman said, her cheek to the floor.

Colleen lowered the extinguisher and exhaled. Bill handcuffed the woman and helped her to her feet. She locked eyes with Colleen.

"She'd never talk to me. I sent her e-mails, but she stopped responding. All I wanted to do was tell her how much I admire her."

"You okay?" Bill asked.

"We're fine."

He glanced at Pinky. "Thanks for your help," he said, and meant it. For the first time, she thought Bill actually respected Pinky.

"It was nothing," Pinky said.

"Come on," Bill said, and escorted the woman out the door.

"Tell Hayley how much I love her," the woman called out as she disappeared.

Colleen had never considered the dangers involved in being a celebrity. She wondered what it must be like knowing that people thought you owed them special attention. No wonder Hayley had a personal assistant and people constantly around her. Colleen had always known of the perks of celebrity, but there were clearly some definite costs. It made her grateful for her own relative anonymity. She'd hate to feel that exposed and vulnerable.

"Shall we check on Hayley?" Pinky asked.

"I'll be up in a second," she said. "Thanks . . . for everything."

"It's always an adventure with you," he said, and retreated up the stairs.

She exited onto the pool deck and rubbed Sparky's head. "You deserve a special treat when we get home." He wagged his tail and nuzzled her hand.

The dog followed her around the side of the house. Bill would have a long night taking statements from everyone and then questioning Hayley's stalker. She glanced at the unhappy fan in the backseat of Rodney's car and remembered she still had the notebook with the photos. She retrieved it from the front seat of her SUV and waited for Bill to finish talking with his deputy. When he was done, she held it in the air and he joined her as Rodney pulled away.

"I take it that's the notebook you found at the house," he said, taking it from her.

"It's interesting reading," she said.

He briefly flipped through the pages and then closed it. "I guess Fawn was right when she said you'd protect Hayley from danger," he said.

"I wouldn't put too much stock in that. She could have also predicted Pinky's help, or Sparky's, for that matter."

"Still, I'm glad you were here."

She surprised herself by saying, "Me, too. Nobody deserves to feel unsafe in their own home, or at least their home away from home."

Bill smiled kindly. She thought about what Hayley had told her earlier. Was it possible that she had been the only person in Corolla not sure about how he felt about her? Had she been that dense? Could it be that he was equally dense about how she felt about him? She chuckled at her own foolishness.

"What is it?" he asked with a puzzled grin.

If it hadn't been such a long day and Bill didn't need to interview everyone upstairs, she would have told him, but right now she needed to get home and he needed to finish up with the arrest of Hayley's stalker.

"Later. You've got people to interview."

"Chief McCabe!" called Hayley, flying down the front steps. "Where are you going?"

"Home."

"But I didn't have a chance to thank you. You don't know how relieved I am that that woman is in custody. If you hadn't been here . . ."

"Bill was the one who apprehended her, not me," she said, and let Sparky into the SUV. "And now I'm going to let him do his job."

She slid into the driver's seat and slammed the door closed.

"Good night," she said, and stole a quick look at Bill before backing onto Lighthouse Drive and heading home.

Chapter 17

As Colleen made her way home, her mind churned with the events of the day. There had been an arrest . . . but it wasn't for Rich's murder. What had she learned thus far? For starters, Marvin was out as a suspect. It didn't seem possible he could have committed murder, given his arthritic hands. Lane had indeed had a fling with Doris. Marvin had been correct about that. But if both men were to be believed, neither would hurt her. So where had her bruises come from? Their ears didn't match any of Rich's photos, so it seemed less and less likely they had anything to do with his death. But if they weren't involved, then who was, and why? Her mind drifted to what she had heard Kyle say about Rich. The intern's callous blaming of a dead man bothered her. Was he merely fed up with the thespians, or was there something more sinister behind the comment? She sighed.

Her brain hurt. It was too hard to sort through the details of the day while exhausted.

She pulled up to the front of her house and cut the engine and lights. Every muscle in her body ached. Maybe I could sleep in my vehicle tonight, she thought. She closed her eyes and allowed the insects' song to lull her to sleep. Sparky licked her hand and she stirred. He was right: They should go inside and get to bed. She forced herself out of the vehicle and up the front steps.

"Sparky?" she said, surprised he wasn't right behind her. Now he gets a burst of energy, she thought. "Come on, boy," she called. The bushes rustled. She hoped he wasn't looking for the rabbit. It would be difficult to get him in. She unlocked the front door and flipped on a light. Maybe the sound of opening his container of dog treats would get him to come in. She yanked first her left and then her right foot out of her shoes and trudged into the kitchen. Smokey meowed in the dark. "Just a minute," she said, "We've got to get your friend inside first." She retrieved the dog treats, returned to the porch, shook the container, and pulled on the lid. Sparky bounded from the bushes, tail wagging. Works every time, she thought, and led him inside and locked the door.

She clicked on the kitchen light. Smokey squinted and meowed. She poured the treats into Sparky's bowl. "You're next," she said to the cat, who was rubbing against her leg. She found Smokey's treats, dropped a half dozen or so in her dish, and joined her furry friends on the floor. She stroked the cat's back. The dog and cat finished what she had given them and looked at her expectantly.

"You two are obsessed," she said, and gave them both a second helping, too tired to tell them no.

Hayley's stalker came to mind. Talk about obsessed, she thought. Maybe it was a false sense of closeness that led people to fixate on celebrities. People see their images on the television in their living rooms, in magazines, and on billboards, so they think they know the stars, Colleen thought. She wondered if celebrities ever had a hard time living up to the personas that fans, publicists, and managers created for them. Could it change how they saw themselves, how they behaved? Even the promise of fame had made Lane change his name.

She thought about Lane's name change and Rich's ear-identification photos. What if Lane wasn't the only person with something to hide? And what if that something was more than a name change? What if it was illegal or criminal in nature? Could that be what Rich had been researching? Ruby had mentioned his love of true-crime stories. Had he stumbled upon someone's criminal past? If he had discovered someone in Corolla had a secret criminal past the person didn't want revealed, then that might be a motive for murder. And where was his missing laptop? So many questions and still no answers. It was clearly time to get some sleep. She'd think better in the morning.

She hit the lights and made her way upstairs. Smokey and Sparky raced each other up, each wanting to sleep on the prime corner of the bed—the one at the foot and closest to the window. She thought of locking them out so she could sleep uninterrupted, but something about the incident with the stalker made her not want to be alone.

She slipped out of her clothes and kicked them under the bed, too tired to bother putting them in the hamper. She threw on a T-shirt, tied her hair up in a ponytail, brushed her teeth, and crawled into bed, with Sparky at her feet in the prized corner and Smokey on the other side near the pillows. The cat rolled on her back. She caressed the cat's soft belly and Smokey squeezed her paws in appreciation. Colleen's eyes grew heavy and she was soon fast asleep.

Sunlight filtered into the room through the curtains. She glanced at the clock and turned away from the window, trying to get a few minutes more of shut-eye. A fly buzzed above her head and she sleepily swatted it away. "Smokey, get the fly," she mumbled. She opened an eye to see if the cat had seen the insect. What she saw jolted her awake like a potent shot of caffeine. Sparky and Smokey were gone and her bedroom door was closed. That could mean only one thing: Someone had been in her house.

Her heart raced as she slid out of bed, careful not to step on the floorboard that always creaked. Keeping her eye on the door, she reached under the bed, felt for her jeans, and slipped them on. She scanned the room for something she could use as a weapon. She remembered the manicure set under the sink and tiptoed to the bathroom to retrieve the metal nail file. If something has happened to Sparky or Smokey, she thought, and then stopped herself and took a deep breath. Don't jump to conclusions, she told herself. She crept to the bedroom door, twisted the knob, and opened it a crack. A gentle gust of air blew across her face. Whoever had broken in had left a window or door open.

She entered the hall and peered down the stairs. The front door was wide open. She squeezed the file and clung to the wall as she crept down the stairs. As she reached the last step, Sparky ran in through the front door, tail wagging. Her heart skipped with joy. She held up her hand, silently signaling him to sit. He cocked his head, puzzled, but did as instructed. She needed to check the rest of the house before she could be sure the intruder was gone.

She peered into the hall bathroom. Empty. She held her breath and did the same with the kitchen. Empty again. She turned to the living room. It, too, was empty, but she could see someone had been through it. The drawers on the secretary were open and the contents of some antique boxes had been dumped on the sofa. She lowered the nail file. It was time to call Bill.

She was on the porch, calling for Smokey, when she heard the sirens. She hadn't been able to find her cat, and it wasn't like the feline to wander too far. She decided she'd keep Sparky close until Bill's arrival. After that, she'd send the dog off to find her missing kitty.

Bill's pickup rounded the corner, lights flashing but sirens off. Not prone to crying, she was surprised to find her eyes well with tears. She knew it was her body's way of releasing tension, but right now she didn't have time for tears. Crying wasn't going to help figure out who had broken into her house. She hastily wiped her eyes and crossed to the top step to meet him.

He cut the engine and exited his vehicle. Sparky ran to greet him. Bill rubbed the dog's head, but his eyes were locked on her. She forced a smile, trying to reassure him she was fine, but

she could see he wasn't buying it. Sparky climbed the steps with
him.

"You okay?" he asked.

"I can't find Smokey," she said, and bit her lip.

He gazed sympathetically at her and gently touched her arm.
"We'll find her," he said. "Besides, that cat's too cranky to have
anything happen to her."

It was true. Smokey was tough, smart, and not inclined to like
strangers. She had probably run and hidden the moment she saw
the intruder. Bill knew exactly what she needed to hear.

"Besides Smokey, is anything missing?"

"I called as soon as I was sure nobody was still here. I haven't
had time to check."

"Let's do that, then."

"Sparky, get Smokey," she said, and the dog took off into the
bushes. If the cat was outside, he'd find her.

She stepped into the foyer and entered the living room. "They
were looking for something," she said, and pointed to the open
drawers and the contents of the boxes on the sofa. "But I don't
know what."

Bill surveyed the room. "You didn't hear anything?"

"Whoever was here closed my door and must have given
Sparky a treat. I can't believe I slept through it."

"It's probably better you did. Burglars want to get in and out.
They don't like confrontation. If you had seen him . . ."

She let this sink in. It hadn't occurred to her that if she had
awakened, things could have been worse.

"You notice anything gone?" he asked.

She examined the objecttrewn over the sofa. There were pieces of costume jewelry from her grandmother, extra keys that she'd been afraid to throw away because she'd forgotten what they went to, coins from her father's trips abroad, and buttons that had fallen off of clothes and which she had yet to sew back on. Nothing of great value and nothing missing. She crossed to the secretary.

"Looks like everything is here."

They entered the kitchen. A basket containing mail and bills had been overturned, but otherwise the room appeared undisturbed. Bill headed upstairs.

"I haven't been back up since I called you," she said, following him. "If he took anything, it would be from my office."

She wasn't worried about confidential information from work being seen—she always left that at the station—but if someone had stolen her computer, the person would have access to information such as her Social Security number and bank accounts.

Bill peered into the guest room. Since there was nothing of value in that room and she knew the intruder hadn't been in her bedroom, she headed straight for her office. When she reached the door, her heart sank. Every drawer, file, and storage container had been rifled through.

"They did all that and I was right next door," she said, now angry at herself for sleeping so soundly.

"You'd be surprised how quick they can be," he said. "We'll definitely dust for prints."

She stepped over papers, folders, pencils, and other office supplies. It would take forever to get reorganized and figure out what was missing. She rotated in a circle and noticed the bin where she stored memory cards for her digital pictures was missing. She scanned the floor next to the shelf where the container had been sitting.

"Something wrong?" he asked.

"I don't see my digital pictures," she said, looking behind the overturned wastebasket.

"You mean the SD cards?"

"All my family photos are on those cards. Why would someone want them?"

Before he had a chance to answer, her eyes widened in understanding. She crossed to her computer and turned it on.

"What is it?" he asked.

"I think I know what they were after," she said, reaching into the back pocket of the pants she had worn the day before and retrieving the envelope Adam had given her.

"What's that?"

"The footage of our emergency exercise on the beach. Adam gave it to me yesterday."

She anxiously waited for her computer to finish its start-up process and then pushed the SD card into the slot.

"Why would someone want that?" he asked, standing above her as she took a seat in the chair.

The footage loaded and then the player indicated it was ready to be viewed.

"Ready?" she asked.

He leaned closer. She hit the PLAY button. The handheld camera panned the scene on the beach, capturing the actors with her

EMTs. A shot of Rich waving happily at the camera made her heart sink. Little did she know then that that was the last time anyone would see him alive.

"Who knew you had this besides Adam?" he asked as they studied the footage.

"Everyone at rehearsal last night."

"So let's concentrate on those individuals."

On the monitor, the actors prepared to take their places, laughing and smiling among themselves, and her guys got ready with their equipment.

"What was that?" she asked, squinting at the screen.

"I saw it, too."

Her heart raced. She went back, clicked the PLAY arrow, and stared intently at the monitor. They watched Doris finish taking a sip from a soda can, hand the can to a woman, mouth the words *Thank you,* and disappear over a dune—the dune where she'd take her last breath. What Colleen saw next sent chills down her spine. The woman Doris had been speaking to turned around, dumped the rest of the soda onto the sand, and smirked, seemingly straight at the camera. Colleen hit PAUSE and stared, stunned, at the frozen image of the person she now suspected was Doris's killer . . . none other than Rita Riddle, the play's costumer.

She recalled how Rita had lingered at the door when Lane was being questioned on the Whalehead Club's veranda. "No wonder she was eavesdropping."

"I'm calling the ME's office," Bill said, reading her mind and dialing. "See if that toxicology report has come back."

He stepped from the room. She replayed the section of footage. Why would Rita have wanted to kill Doris? Could she also be Rich's killer? It didn't seem likely that Rita could have overpowered the younger and stronger Rich. Maybe they had been going about the investigation all wrong. What if they were dealing with two killers instead of one? The thought made the hairs on her arms stand on end, and she jumped when Bill reentered the room.

"You okay?" he asked.

She took a deep breath and ejected the card from the computer. "Just spooked, that's all. What did the medical examiner say?"

"Arsenic poisoning."

"So it wasn't narcolepsy."

"Narcolepsy?"

"According to Nellie, Doris had suffered from it. That, along with other health problems and heat exposure, may have made it hard to pinpoint poisoning without testing. The symptoms wouldn't be obvious."

"The ME said Doris's poisoning wasn't long-term. What was in that drink did the job."

"It's hard to believe Rita was here last night."

"Given that, I think it's best if you let me take care of things from here on out."

"She broke into my house."

"And she may not have done it alone."

She hadn't considered two people being in her house.

"Look," he said, his tone softer now. "I know you're used to being self-sufficient. It's one of the things I admire about you. But, please, let me do this for you."

She was moved by the caring tone of his voice. He was right. She was used to handling things on her own, but in this case it was probably better that she didn't. She gave him the SD card. "Go arrest that woman."

"Thank you. I'll send guys out to collect evidence and stay at your house until she's in custody."

She escorted him from the room, down the stairs, and out to his pickup. "Why do you think she killed Doris?" she asked, more to herself than to Bill.

"I hope I'm about to find out," he said, then got into his vehicle and rolled down the window.

She smiled and, without thinking, put her hand on his forearm, which was propped on the ledge.

He put a hand over hers. "I'm glad you're okay."

She blushed. "Me, too" was all she could think to say, and after what seemed like an eternity, she pulled her hand away.

"Go find that cat," he said with a reassuring smile.

She stepped back and gave him a final wave before he disappeared down the road.

Chapter 18

Why did Rita Riddle poison fellow theater member Doris Jenkins? Did the two women have a fight? If so, about what? Money? Men? The play? These were the questions running through Colleen's mind. Based on what she had seen in the video footage, Doris didn't seem to have had any feelings of animosity toward Rita. In fact, she'd appeared quite friendly with her killer, which would seem to indicate that Doris had been ignorant of Rita's feelings. Was Rita that calculating? Had Rich, too, been the object of Rita's ire? The more she learned about the intrigues of the theater group, the more questions she had. Right now, though, her immediate question was, Where is Smokey? Panic suddenly washed over her. Could Rita have poisoned her cat after breaking into the house? No way, she thought. The woman would have to be a cat whisperer to get the suspicious feline to take food from a stranger.

She returned to the kitchen. Perhaps she could lure the cat from her hiding place with treats. She retrieved the tuna-flavored goodies, stood in the foyer, and shook the container like a maraca. Seconds later, Sparky appeared at the door. Wrong furry family member. She shook again and heard a thump from the kitchen. Seeing a lower cabinet door open and thump closed again, she sighed with relief.

"You'd better not be in my pots and pans," she said in mock admonition, and opened the cabinet door. Smokey climbed out and stretched, as if she didn't have a care in the world. Colleen had never been so happy to see the cranky Siamese. Even the fact that the cat had been in her cookware couldn't dampen the joy she felt in finding her dear friend. She stroked the cat's head and poured treats in the bowl. Sparky looked up as if to say, What about me? and she gave him some, too.

She heard the sound of an approaching car. That must be Bill's guys, she thought, scooping up Smokey and going to meet them at the door. She was glad they'd arrived. She would have a chance to get ready for work while they gathered evidence.

"How are you?" Rodney asked after the forensics team had started their work in the living room.

"It's a little weird knowing someone was in the house while I was here. It feels like it didn't really happen."

"I had a break-in once. Felt like I was moving in slow motion when I reached for the light," he said sympathetically.

"If it's okay with you, I'm going to get ready and leave you all to it. Let me know if you need anything from me." She started up the stairs. "Oh, and don't let Sparky out. He's had enough running around for one night."

Rodney gave her a salute and joined the group in the living room. She climbed the stairs with Smokey in her arms. The cat was not used to being carried around, and she purred in appreciation for the free ride up the steps. Colleen closed the door to her bedroom and got ready for work.

She descended the stairs, having showered for the day. It would be good to get out. She was relieved that Rodney's interview was brief, and after giving him instructions about how to lock up the house, she left with Sparky. The image of Rich in the video had been playing in her mind. While showering, she had recalled that Bill had mentioned Rich's body had been picked up and taken to the family's funeral home. She wondered how his brothers were doing. She decided to purchase a card at the Food Lion and stop by the funeral home to express her condolences before heading to the station.

She pulled into Monteray Plaza. It wasn't until she and Sparky were making their way across the Food Lion's parking lot that she remembered Sam, Rita's husband, worked at the store stocking shelves. She wondered how much he knew about what his wife had done to Doris. Did he know about Rita's plans to break into her house? Could he have been with her last night? She tied Sparky up near a water bowl provided by the store and entered with a second purpose.

The Food Lion was known for its efficient air-conditioning, something Colleen usually found uncomfortable, but today it felt

good on her skin. Maybe it was her growing anger that was causing her temperature to rise. She needed to remain calm if she
was going to question Sam without arousing suspicion. She took
a breath and decided to pick out the card first. It would give her
a reason to be in the store in case he asked. She strolled to the
stationery and magazine aisle, all the while keeping an eye out
for Sam. She found the cards and took a moment to consider
them. She finally found one that conveyed her sincere sympathy,
then went in search of Sam.

She crept along the ends of the aisles, casually glancing up
each as she passed. As she was reaching the last section of the
store, she worried that perhaps Sam hadn't come to work today.
Maybe he had been home when Bill had arrived to arrest Rita.
Then again, maybe she was wrong in thinking ill of the man.
She rounded the corner and saw him stocking a shelf with Rice
Krispies. His back was to her, so she had an opportunity to observe him before he saw her. Nothing about the way he was carrying himself indicated that he had a care in the world.

She strolled up the aisle and stopped in front of the breakfast
bars a short distance away. She could see in her peripheral vision
that he had turned to grab more boxes and noticed her. She
snatched a box of breakfast bars and moved as if heading toward
the front of the store.

"Oh, hey there, Sam," she said, trying to appear surprised to
see him.

"Hello," he said, and placed more cereal boxes on the shelf.

She studied his face. Did he appear nervous? Calm? Indifferent? It was hard to tell. It certainly didn't look like he knew any-thing about Rita's arrest.

"I was picking up a sympathy card," she said. "For Rich's family. I'm going to stop by there today."

"Me, too. I heard they want a quick service."

An awkward tension passed. He had finished stacking the boxes and was ready to move on. How could she keep him there without it seeming strange? Before she had a chance to think of a topic to talk about, his phone rang. She hoped the call was short and that it wouldn't pull him away from talking to her.

"Hello?" he said into the phone. "What? When?" His eyes widened. "No, I didn't know. . . . Yes. Of course I'll come down," he said, then ended the call and stared blankly down the aisle.

"Are you okay?" she asked after a moment.

He blinked, as if seeing her there for the first time. "They've arrested Rita."

She nodded. There was no point in pretending she didn't know. If Bill hadn't already told Sam that Rita had broken into Colleen's house, he most certainly would when Sam went to the station.

"What will I do without her?" he asked, struggling to keep from crying.

Colleen felt sorry for the man and guilty about having suspected him earlier. "Why do you think she did it?" she asked gently.

His sobbing grew louder, and a vacationer moved her child away.

"Why don't we get you out of the aisle," she suggested, not wanting a scene.

She followed him as he shuffled to the back of the store and went through the swinging doors to the loading dock. He stared out the open dock door.

"I never should have told Rita," he said, less tearful now.

"Told her what?" Colleen asked, puzzled.

"About me and Doris."

Her eyes widened in surprise.

"Marvin was right," he said.

"But you said—"

"I know. I had already broken it off with Doris. I didn't see the point in telling him. She was gone. Nothing was going to bring her back."

"When did Rita find out?"

"After I told Doris we were through, I confessed the whole thing. I thought we were past it."

"You may have been, but apparently Rita wasn't."

They fell silent. A bird chirped in the bushes behind the store. There it was: the reason Doris had been murdered. Rita had made Sam pay for his indiscretion by taking Doris's life, proving the truth of the saying "Hell hath no fury like a woman scorned."

"Well," he said, breaking the silence. "I'd best be getting down to the station."

"I'll see myself out," she said, and discreetly retreated.

The cold air hit her as she pushed through the swinging doors and into the brightly lit store. She made her way through the checkout line and retrieved Sparky. She needed to tell Bill what she had discovered. They crossed the lot to the SUV and hopped in. She started the engine, dialed, and got his voice mail. He must be questioning Rita now, she thought.

"Bill, it's me," she said after his message was over. "Give me a call when you get a chance. I know why Rita killed Doris."

Chapter 19

"Like the voice of a bird singing in the rain, let grateful memory survive in the hour of darkness."—Robert Louis Stevenson, *Prayers Written at Vailima,* 1904.

Colleen signed her name beneath the sympathy card's quote and exhaled. It had always been difficult for her to keep her emotions in check when it came to death. As a child, she had found it sad when summer's flowers faded, and she had always preferred the pale green of spring buds over the final colorful curtain call of fall. She knew death was a part of life, and yet it always upset her, especially when it came unexpectedly and all too soon.

She stared at the salmon-colored facade of Bailey and Sons Funeral Home with its white columns and lace-curtained windows. Now that she had signed the card, there was nothing to delay her from leaving the security of her SUV and going inside.

She hoped some words of comfort would come to her when she met Rich's brother Michael. Although, given his family's line of work, she imagined there was nothing she could say to Michael that he hadn't said to clients many times before. Perhaps words weren't necessary. Maybe her presence would be enough.

She cut the engine, exited with Sparky, and entered a peace garden next to the funeral parlor that the Baileys had land-scaped to allow those grieving a quiet place to retreat. She wound her way along the slate path to the shaded bench surrounded by ornamental grasses. She didn't think the Bailey family would mind if she tied Sparky to the bench while she went inside.

"I'll be right back," she said, and jumped at finding Myrtle standing at the garden's entrance. "Myrtle, I didn't know you were here," she said, making her way back through the garden.

"Wish I wasn't," her former schoolteacher said with sincerity. "Thought I'd stop by and see if there was anything I could do."

"How's everyone doing with the play?" Colleen asked. She wondered if they had heard about Rita's arrest yet and what impact it, combined with Doris's and Rich's deaths, would have on the show. She wouldn't blame the group if the show ended up being postponed or canceled.

"We've got a few surprises up our sleeves," Myrtle said.

"So it's still on?"

"The show always goes on."

So nobody had heard about Rita's arrest yet. Colleen motioned to the front of the building. "Shall we?"

She opened the heavy door for Myrtle. It closed behind them with a gentle whoosh. She'd never gotten used to the eerie quiet of funeral homes. She was actually glad Myrtle was there with her. She tiptoed down the softly lit burgundy-carpeted hall and peered into the first room. Upholstered chairs lined the walls, but otherwise the room was empty.

"Maybe down here," Myrtle said, and pointed toward the back of the building.

Colleen made her way to the next room. Chairs were arranged in rows before an expensive casket. She hesitated before stepping inside. Was Rich lying in there? She inched forward, Myrtle right behind her, and was relieved to find the casket empty. Of course it's empty, she chided herself. They don't just leave bodies lying around in empty rooms unattended with the lid open.

She studied the casket. It was shiny, with a slightly arched lid, rounded edges, and what seemed like layers of billowing fabric inside—the Rolls-Royce of coffins, she imagined.

"May I help you?" came a soft male voice.

Rich's brother Michael stood in the doorway, staring at them with curiosity. He was a younger, thinner version of his brother, and the sight of him made her sad all over again.

"I'm sorry," she said stepping forward. "I was merely . . ." She gestured around the room and then held up the sympathy card.

Michael smiled with understanding and accepted the card. "It's thoughtful of you to stop by," he said.

"I'm sorry about your brother," Myrtle said. "Rich was a

good kid, never gave me any trouble in class, even brought me an apple once."

Colleen was surprised to see Myrtle retrieve a tissue from her purse and dab her eyes.

"I didn't mean to come by before Rich's viewing," Colleen said, giving Myrtle a moment to collect herself. "It's just that, well, I was thinking of him this morning." She left out the information about viewing the footage of Rich's final moments alive at the training exercise.

"You chose the correct casket," Michael said, gesturing to the one in front of them. "Rich picked this one out himself."

"He had already picked out his own casket?" Colleen asked, surprised.

"Planning for such events *is* our business."

"Right. Of course."

"It's quite nice," Myrtle said, shoving the tissue back into her purse. "Is there anything I can do for you? Perhaps call people about the viewing?"

For the first time, they saw a chink in Michael's calm, professional demeanor, and his cheeks and nose flushed the way they do when someone is on the verge of tears. "What a kind offer," he said. "We've notified family, but perhaps you might inform the rest of the theater company. I'm sure Rich would have wanted them here."

Colleen bit her tongue. There might be one member he wouldn't have wanted at his funeral—his killer.

"I'd be happy to tell them," Myrtle said.

"I'll be right back with the information," he said, and left them alone in the viewing room.

"Poor man," Myrtle said.

Colleen examined the empty casket. "Looks oddly . . . comfortable," she said.

"I told Bobby not to bother with the fancy stuff."

Colleen looked at her with raised brows.

"What?" Myrtle said. "If all goes well at the pearly gates, I'll be floating around on a heavenly cloud, reading a good book. What happens with this old body won't make a hill of beans' difference."

"What does Bobby have to say about that?"

"He *says* he agrees, but I'm afraid he might make a fuss. He's not as strong as I am."

"He's stronger than you think," Colleen said.

Maybe it was being in the quiet room with her old teacher, contemplating life and death, maybe it was her gratitude for not having had to face Michael alone, or maybe it was their affection toward Rich, but Colleen felt closer to Myrtle than she ever had. It almost made her forget how aggravating the woman could be.

"I heard your body doesn't really stay all that preserved," Myrtle said matter-of-factly.

"Myrtle," she scolded in a hushed tone, and stole a glance back at the door to be sure Michael hadn't overheard the remark.

Myrtle shrugged. "That's what I heard."

She had heard the same thing. Bill had once told her about an exhumation he had witnessed early on in his career and how the body had deteriorated despite embalming. The idea of decay didn't bother her. In fact, it seemed perfectly natural and had made her conclude that, at least at this point in time, she'd prefer cremation over burial. Why bother trying to preserve the body when a person's soul, the intangible thing that makes a person who she or he is, is gone?

She scrutinized the split-lid casket with its plush pillow and matching lining. It made sense that Rich would pick out such a lovely one—if that was even the right word to use for a casket. He had spent his life providing a final dignified repose for others. If anyone deserved the best, it was Rich. While marveling at the workmanship of the container, a groove on the side of the split lid caught her eye. She studied the semioval crown over where the lower half of the body would lie and then ran a finger along the edge of the lid.

"What is it?" Myrtle asked, noticing her furrowed brows.

"I don't know. Feels almost like another part of the cap."

"Maybe it has to do with how they open and close it," Myrtle offered, also squinting at the section in question.

Colleen leaned closer and edged her fingernails along the groove. "Keep an eye on the door," she whispered.

"What are you going to do?" Myrtle asked.

"The door, Myrtle," she said, trying not to raise her voice.

Myrtle hurried to the doorway and peered into the hall. "Coast is clear," she said loudly, then caught herself and covered her mouth.

"If Michael returns, try to distract him."

"How?"

Colleen was losing her patience. "I don't know. You're an actor. Think of something," she said, trying to keep her voice down, and turned her attention back to the lid.

She pulled at the lid's edge, and a drawer slid out about a half an inch toward her. Did the coffin have a secret compartment? She tugged again, but something inside prevented her from opening the drawer all the way. She wiggled her pinkie finger into the opening and felt something hard and smooth. Whatever it was, one edge was slightly raised and was stopping her from opening the compartment completely. She needed something flat to wedge into the opening and force the object down while she opened the drawer. She pulled her keys from her pocket, but all were too thick to wedge into the opening.

"Myrtle," she whispered. "Do you have anything thin and flat, like a paper clip or a nail file?"

"Would a ruler work?" Myrtle asked, removing a thin, clear, hard plastic ruler from her purse.

She couldn't believe her luck. A ruler? Really? What else did Myrtle have in that purse? On another occasion, I'd like to find out, she thought. Right now, though, she needed to see what was inside the drawer before Michael came back and caught her monkeying with Rich's coffin. She took the ruler from Myrtle, returned to the casket, and squeezed it into the slot. Here goes nothing, she thought. She pushed the ruler down hard while gently pulling on the lid. She got as far as she had before and then again the drawer stopped. Any minute now, Michael would come through that door. Maybe if she shook the drawer a little while she pulled, it might help.

"Oh, there you are," Myrtle said, stealing a glance back at Colleen before stepping into the hallway.

"I'm sorry to keep you waiting, Mrs. Crepe. I got held up with a call."

Colleen's heart raced. It was now or never. She slid the ruler in the slot, tucked her finger under the drawer, and jimmied it as much as the well-constructed compartment would allow. Come on, she prayed.

"Thank you so much," Myrtle said, and looked back at Colleen.

Colleen shook her head. She didn't quite have it. Myrtle needed to distract Michael a few seconds more. Now's the time to put those acting skills to use, she thought.

As if Myrtle had read her mind, she clutched Michael's arm and swayed rather dramatically.

"Are you okay, Mrs. Crepe?" he asked, concern in his voice.

"Oh, I don't know what's come over me. I'm feeling a little light-headed."

Thatta girl, Colleen thought.

"Why don't you take a seat inside?" Michael said from the hall.

"No," Myrtle blurted out, and grabbed Michael's shirt, but then a second later, she was back in character and said, "Perhaps you wouldn't mind getting me a glass of water."

"Are you sure you don't want to sit?" he asked, trying to move

Myrtle toward the doorway. "I've seen this happen many times before. It would be safer."

"Oh! Did you see that!" Myrtle exclaimed.

Even Colleen looked.

"See what?" he asked.

Myrtle pointed a shaky finger in front of her, drawing his attention away from the door. "I . . . I think I saw a spirit down the hall," she said, a quiver in her voice.

Colleen marveled at Myrtle's creativity. Sweat beaded on her forehead.

"You really should have a seat in—" Michael began.

"Oh! There it is again!" Myrtle cried out.

Colleen bit her lip, tugged on the drawer, and then with a gentle thump it slid open. She paused a moment, stunned. Lying inside the coffin drawer was Rich's missing laptop. For a brief second, she couldn't help but marvel at how small and light laptops had become.

"Please, Mrs. Crepe. Have a seat in here and I'll be right back with some water."

"Oh, well, I don't know." Myrtle faltered, losing her battle of distraction.

Colleen grabbed the netbook, slid it under her shirt, and wedged it between the waist band of her pants and the small of her back. She quickly closed the drawer and swung around just as Michael helped Myrtle into the room. She nodded slightly to Myrtle, indicating she had succeeded.

"You know," Myrtle said. "I'm actually feeling much better

now. I don't know what came over me. I think I'll be fine without that water."

"Are you sure?" he asked.

"We really should be going," Colleen said, keeping her back as straight as possible as she crossed to the door. "We've already taken up too much of your time."

"Here's the information about the viewing," he said, handing Myrtle a slip of paper.

"I'll let everyone know," she replied.

"Shall we?" Colleen said to Myrtle, eager to exit before the netbook slipped from the waist of her pants and went crashing to the floor.

"Yes, of course."

She hastily exited the room. Myrtle walked behind Colleen, blocking Michael's view of her back. The hall now seemed a football field long, but Colleen resisted the urge to run. She pushed open the door and exhaled with relief. She held the netbook against her back and hurried to the peace garden to retrieve Sparky, Myrtle right on her heels.

"Really?" she said to Myrtle. "That's what you came up with? A ghost?"

"It worked, didn't it?"

Colleen rolled her eyes and untied Sparky.

"What did you find?" Myrtle asked as she followed Colleen back through the garden.

Colleen crossed to her SUV, ignoring Myrtle's question. She didn't want Myrtle any more involved that she already was.

"Colleen Elizabeth McCabe," Myrtle said in a stern, loud voice. "I deserve to know why I deceived Rich's grieving brother and assisted in stealing a personal possession from his casket."

Damn. Myrtle was good. Nothing like an old-fashioned guilt trip. She stopped and pulled the small laptop from under her shirt.

"I think this," she said, holding the laptop low, "is what the person who broke into Rich's house was searching for. Whatever is on here may reveal his murderer's identity."

Myrtle's eyes widened. "But how?"

"I can't go into all the details, but until we know for sure, don't tell anyone. If I'm right, it could put you in danger as well."

"You know who killed Rich?"

"No," she said. "But until we do and that person is arrested, please don't let on that you know about this."

She let Sparky into the SUV. A vehicle pulled into the lot. She saw who it was and her heart sank.

"Morning, Sam," Myrtle said, waving to him as he pulled in.

Colleen and Sam locked eyes. She wondered how it had gone at the Sheriff's Department. Clearly, Bill hadn't released Rita, or she would have been with her husband. Colleen placed the laptop on the seat with Sparky and hopped in. She'd let Sam tell Myrtle about what had happened with his wife and Doris . . . if he so chose. Not that it would matter even if he didn't. Soon everyone in Corolla would know about what had happened between Sam and Doris.

She rolled down her window as she passed Myrtle. "I'll talk to you later," she said.

Colleen watched in her rearview mirror as Myrtle approached Sam's vehicle and leaned on the door to talk. Hopeful that Myrtle would keep the discovery of the laptop confidential, she left and headed toward the Sheriff's Department.

Chapter 20

"*I found Rich's missing laptop* in his casket," Colleen said into the phone as she sped up Ocean Trail toward the Sheriff's Department.

"You were in his *casket*?" Bill almost yelled on the other end.

She winced. She knew it sounded bad—stealing possessions from a dead man's coffin—but something made her think Rich would have approved. In fact, she felt he had put it there for safe keeping, although she had no idea why he'd felt he had to do that. Michael had told her that his brother had picked the casket out for himself. Not many people could afford that level of expense. Rich must have been confident that nobody would disturb it until he needed it again. He probably never figured it might go to the grave with him.

A teen boy zipped across the road on a bike. She hit the brakes and threw her arm across Sparky's chest to brace him. The SUV skidded to a halt. I'd better slow down, she thought. No need to add another death to an already death-filled summer.

"Where are you?" Bill asked.

"On my way to your office."

"You'd better not. It's a zoo here."

It wasn't like Bill to put off taking custody of evidence. "What's going on?" she asked.

"Rita admitted to poisoning Doris and breaking into your house. She's confessing to Rich's death, as well."

She got why Rita might be angry at Doris, but Rich? "Why'd she say she killed Rich?"

"Something about him knowing about the affair and not telling her, but I'm not buying it. Rodney's with her now. There's more than what she's telling us."

"What did Sam say when he got there?"

"He was upset, got pretty disruptive. I told him to go home or else I'd arrest him, too. Hold on a minute," he said. She heard muffled talking and then Bill got back on the line. "I gotta go. Hang on to the laptop. I'll be over to retrieve it or send a car as soon as someone is free. And don't mess with it. It could be evidence."

"Right," she said, trying not to be annoyed by his last remark, and ended the call.

She steered into the Whalehead community and lowered her speed. None of what Bill had told her made any sense. How could Rita have overpowered Rich, a man much younger and stronger than she? Could she have poisoned him, too? The ME's report indicated strangulation as the cause of death, and nothing suspicious had shown up in the toxicology report. Perhaps adrenaline had been at work. There had been plenty of reports of people performing seemingly impossible physical feats in a crisis situation. Could that have given Rita the strength to subdue him? It didn't seem likely, but it was possible. Still, even if she were to entertain the idea that Rita had somehow been physically capable of strangling Rich, the question remained: Why? She didn't buy the explanation Rita had given Bill and his men any more than Bill did. She agreed with him; something more was going on.

She came to a stop sign on Whalehead Drive and watched as a family crossed on their way to the beach. The mother protectively hurried her young children, a boy and a girl, to the side of the road. That's what women do, she thought. They protect the things and people they love—children, students, animals, lovers . . . spouses.

A car honked behind her. She jumped and then continued toward the fire station. There was only one person who mattered enough to Rita that she would kill someone in order to keep him: Sam. Doris's death was proof of that. Perhaps Rita had thought that by getting rid of Doris, she was protecting her marriage. But whom was she protecting by lying about killing Rich? Sam seemed the most likely candidate. If she was protecting Sam, what was she protecting him from? Could he also be involved in Rich's murder? Had they killed him together? And if so, why? By all accounts, Rich was a man everyone in the theater group had respected and admired.

She arrived at the station and parked. So much had happened in the last twenty-four hours that it was almost too much to fathom. She had a growing sense that Sam was somehow involved in what had happened with Rich, but there was nothing other than her gut to go on. She felt like she was looking at a puzzle that was missing the last crucial piece. Sparky pawed at her thigh and whimpered to get out.

"Sorry," she said.

She grabbed the laptop and released Sparky from the SUV. Jimmy emerged from the garage to meet her, anxiety on his face.

"How you holding up?" he asked.

"Fine."

"The guys and I agree we'll each take a shift at your house, starting tonight."

"Why would you do that?" she asked, and then realized he was referring to the break-in at her house. "That's really not necessary."

"This isn't a discussion."

She was surprised by his stern manner. It wasn't like him to use that tone with her, but she knew it was coming from a place of concern. "Rita Riddle has confessed to the break-in at my house and the murder of Doris Jenkins. Bill arrested her a little while ago."

He stared at her, wide-eyed. "Apparently, you and I have a lot of catching up to do."

"We do indeed," she said, and patted his back.

"I thought we'd surprise the guys with an impromptu drill test," he said, his concern about her safety now significantly diminished. "You think you're ready to see how they've been doing?"

"Absolutely," she said. "Give me a couple minutes and I'll be right out."

Jimmy hesitated before leaving. "We're really glad you're okay," he said.

"Sweet talk like that won't make me go easy on everyone," she teased, but she knew that his comment was sincere.

"I'll be sure to warn them," he said with a wink, and left to give the men a heads-up about the impending drill.

She filled a water bowl for Sparky from the outside faucet and left him eagerly lapping up the fresh, cool liquid. She decided to drop the laptop off in her office and then head outside.

She climbed the stairs. Her whole body felt tired, and she knew it was from emotional rather than physical stress. She turned on the light and was surprised to find a flower arrangement on her desk. Even before she opened the card, she knew it was from Pinky. The arrangement contained freesias and the note read simply "Glad you're safe. Yours, A.S." First Bill, then Jimmy, and now Pinky. She was lucky to have so many people in her life looking out for her—most especially Bill.

She set the netbook on her desk and plopped into her chair. Bill had warned her about tampering with the computer, but what if it contained evidence that would allow him to make an arrest now? Wouldn't he want to know that? Her fingers hovered over the laptop and then she opened it, hit the power button, and waited for the start-up menu. Seconds later, a password prompt window popped up. Darn. She should have known that if Rich would hide his laptop in his casket, he would also have it password-protected.

The cursor blinked, tempting her to type in a guess. What would Rich have used as a password? Something to do with his job? The play production? Or would it be more obvious, like a pet's name? She heard footsteps on the corrugated-metal stairs. They sounded like those of a woman. Seconds later, Hayley appeared at her door.

"Hayley," she said, closing the laptop slightly and standing. "What brings you by?"

The actress set down her purse and silk scarf on the desk and took Colleen by the hands. "I heard about what happened at your house."

"News travels fast," Colleen said, surprised by the depth of the woman's worry. "But really, I'm fine."

Hayley stared at her a moment longer, then released her hands. "Good," she said, satisfied. "What pretty flowers."

"Yes," Colleen said. "From a good friend." She didn't want to get into another discussion of her romantic life with Hayley. Once was humiliating enough. She sat and leaned back in her chair. "I appreciate your concern," she said with sincerity. "But what really brings you by?"

An impish smile formed on Hayley's lips. Uh-oh, Colleen thought. What's this going to be about?

"I've been recruited by your illustrious theater company to find out if you've made up your mind about providing rain for their production."

Had the group really burdened the star with their little show?

"I'm sorry about that," she said. "They really shouldn't have troubled you."

"No trouble at all. They've asked me to serve as the play's mistress of ceremonies for opening night."

"They didn't."

"And I've accepted."

She raised her brows. "You did?"

"Why not? My roots are in theater, and if it helps raise money for those beautiful horses, I'm all for it."

"Thank you," Colleen said. "That's most generous of you."

"Oh, it's nothing," Hayley said with a wave of the hand. "So, as mistress of ceremonies, I ask you . . . will we have rain?"

Colleen had to hand it to the theater group. They had been quite clever in sending Hayley to make the request. How could she say no now? "If it's rain you want, it's rain you shall have."

"Wonderful."

Colleen looked at the laptop. "Maybe you can do me a favor," she said. "If you were going to create a password and you were a person involved in theater, what words might you use?"

Hayley's brows rose in surprise.

"I know it's a strange question," Colleen said.

Hayley studied her a moment. "Does this have something to do with what happened to that poor man who did makeup for the theater group?"

"Maybe."

Hayley nodded and thought a moment. "Well, I don't know. There are so many possibilities."

"Is there anything that jumps out at you that might be a common theater term or saying?"

"Everyone knows the expression 'Break a leg,'" Hayley offered.

"No, that doesn't seem right."

"Someone might use words that refer to parts of the stage or maybe to a play, or perhaps even a famous actor's or playwright's name. I'm afraid I'd need a little more information."

"It was just a hunch," Colleen said. "Thanks anyway."

"I'm sorry I couldn't be of more help," she said, picking up her purse. "I'll let the group know you've agreed to have it rain."

"Yes," Colleen said, walking with Hayley to the entrance. "You can report that your mission was accomplished."

She watched the actress descend the stairs before returning to her desk. She could see why Bill had once thought of marrying Hayley, although she was, for her own selfish reasons, glad he hadn't. She checked the time. The guys would be waiting for her outside. She shut the computer down, closed her office door, and trekked downstairs to see how ready they were for their tests.

They were only a few minutes into the first drill of lugging hoses when they heard a woman scream from inside the station. Colleen and the men froze for a moment, confused, but when the second scream came a moment later, they all sprang into action.

"Kenny, you and Bobby head around the left side," she ordered. "Chip, take the other side. The rest of you spread out until we know what's going on. Jimmy and I will take the back."

Before she had finished uttering her last words, her men were on the move. She motioned to Jimmy. He opened the back door and they slipped inside. She made her way cautiously through the kitchen, the dining room, and the recreation area, peering around corners as she went. She heard Sparky bark from the garage and hurried to the door leading into the engine bay. On a silent count of three, she and Jimmy went in.

Sparky's barking echoed in the cavernous space.

"Get away. Scram," a man said from inside.

She peeked around the engine and her eyes widened. Standing at the bottom of the stairs was Sam, one hand grabbing a scarf wrapped around Hayley's throat. He kicked at Sparky, but the Border collie was not so easily deterred—he had been struck by a horse's hoof before, so one human foot was nothing.

"Tell me what you want," Hayley said, pulling to loosen her scarf. "Money, a picture . . ."

Colleen signaled Jimmy and he began inching down the side of the engine. She darted to the ambulance and did the same.

"I don't want anything from you," he said, and yanked her back.

Hayley winced. Colleen worked her way to the end of the ambulance. With one hand, Sam was now pulling Hayley backward by the scarf; in the other hand, he held what he had clearly come to the station for: Rich's laptop. Her gut had been correct. Sam was somehow involved with Rich's death. He must have seen her with the laptop in the funeral parlor's parking lot. She now suspected that it was Sam who had broken into Rich's house and that is was he, more likely than Rita, who had murdered Rich. But why? Her conversation with Ruby at the library flashed through her mind. Hadn't she said Rich was into true-crime stories? Could Rich have discovered Sam had a criminal past? And what could it be to cause Sam to murder him? There would be time to figure all of that out later. Right now, she needed to get Hayley away from him without getting the woman hurt in the process. She took a breath and stepped from her hiding place behind the ambulance.

"Why don't you let Ms. Thorpe go, Sam?" she said in a calm voice.

Sparky barked and nipped at Sam's ankles.

"Call Sparky off," he said, and yanked on Hayley for emphasis.

Colleen locked eyes with the actress. She expected to see fear in her eyes; instead, she saw angry defiance. Good, she thought. Hayley's a fighter. When the opportunity came, she'd make a run for it.

"Sparky, heel," she said, and slapped her thigh. He cocked his head toward her but remained at Sam's back. "Heel," she said with more force, and he reluctantly obeyed and came to her side.

Sam inched toward the opening of the garage. Kenny peered around one side, Chip the other. Her guys were in place to take him down. Now all she had to do was convince him to release Hayley.

"Why not let her go? No need to make things worse for yourself."

Sam snorted. "You have no idea who you're dealing with," he said with a sneer.

Her eyes narrowed. For the first time, she saw something sinister in his pale blue eyes. No, she thought, I clearly don't know you at all.

"You're right," she said. "But Doris found out your true character when you gave her those bruises."

"She had some crazy notion I'd leave Rita for her," he said, as if the idea was preposterous.

She studied his face. There was a coolness about him that surprised her, especially after the waterworks she had witnessed from him in the Food Lion.

"You and Rita . . . you two are a regular Bonnie and Clyde," she said.

Sam smiled with smug satisfaction. "Rita's the best. Corolla was, too, until . . ."

"Until Rich started figuring out who you really are," she said, comprehending that the person Rich had been trying to identify through Iannarelli's system, the person's whose ears they had seen on Rich's bulletin board, was none other than grocery clerk turned thespian Sam Riddle . . . if that was even his real name.

"Rich and his damn accents. Kept asking me where I was from. He just couldn't leave it alone," Sam said, backing toward the open garage door.

"Leave what alone?" she asked, trying to keep him inside.

"I'd love to stay and chat, but I got what I came for. Call off your guys waiting around the corner." He pulled on the scarf to motivate her.

"Kenny, Chip, stand down," she called.

"No way, Chief," Chip yelled from outside.

"Do as the chief says," Jimmy shouted back.

She needed to think fast. Sam was inching toward his car in the parking lot. If he made it there, who knew what he might do. Then she caught sight of Bill and Rodney creeping toward them across the lot. She gently touched the top of Sparky's head to signal her companion to remain still and quiet. She didn't want him giving away Bill's presence. Sparky lay on the ground without so much as a whimper. Good. Now if she could distract Sam a few moments more, it would all be over and Hayley would be safe.

"You're just going to let Rita take the fall?" she asked, moving forward slightly to draw his attention away from Bill and Rodney outside. "Sounds like a coward to me."

Rage flashed behind Sam's eyes. She had struck a nerve. He released his grip slightly on the scarf and gestured with the laptop.

"See, that's what's wrong with you people. You think in black-and-white. That woman loves me."

"The prospect of a life in prison might change that love," she said.

Bill reached the vehicle parked closest to the building, where he had a clear view of Sam. He nodded to Colleen and aimed his revolver at Sam's back.

Sam grinned. "Nice try, Chief McCabe. But I know that woman. She'd do anything for me. Now, if you'll excuse me."

"Hands in the air!" Bill shouted as Sam moved to leave.

Sam froze. His eyes darted about the garage, looking for someplace to run. Colleen nodded at Hayley. The celebrity yanked hard on her scarf, broke free, and ran to Colleen at full speed. Bill inched forward, his weapon before him. Rodney flanked him on the left. Colleen's guys rounded the corner. Her heart raced as Bill and Rodney inched toward Sam, and then it was over. Rodney grabbed the laptop as Bill forced Sam to the ground and cuffed him.

"Sam Riddle, you're under arrest for the murder of Rich Bailey."

Hayley sighed with relief behind her. Colleen met Bill's eyes and forced a smile to let him know she was okay.

"You have the right to remain silent," he said as he lifted Sam to his feet. "Anything you say can and will be used against you in a court of law," he continued, and walked Sam to his vehicle.

"You two okay?" Jimmy asked Colleen and Hayley.

"Yeah, I think we are," Colleen said, smiling at the actress. "What were you still doing here?"

Hayley yanked the scarf from around her neck and threw it to the ground. "I forgot my scarf," she said. "I guess Fawn was right; you did keep me safe from danger."

Jimmy grinned.

"So," Colleen teased Hayley, "how do you like shadowing me?"

"I think I'll stick to acting. I prefer keeping the drama in my work and out of my life," she said with a wink.

Colleen smiled. Who would have thought when the woman first appeared at the station that they'd end up here?

Chapter 21

Colleen surveyed the growing audience gathered on the front lawn of the Whalehead Club with wonder. Every white plastic folding chair was taken and the grass was covered from one end of the club to the other with locals and vacationers sitting on a sea of colorful towels and blankets. Excited children ran in front of the platforms that the theater company had erected for additional performance space on the outside of the veranda railing. A blond boy of about nine climbed onto the makeshift stage, turned to the audience, and said, "Ta-da!" with such flair that everyone clapped and laughed in delight. People were clearly looking forward to the theater company's production. Colleen already sensed that the show was going to be a smash hit.

She checked her watch. The start of the play had been delayed by ten minutes to give latecomers a chance to find seats before the production began, but nobody seemed to mind. It was a comfortable evening with low humidity, and the play was an event, the first of its kind, and one to be savored.

Bill emerged from around the back side of the building and made his way through the crowd toward her. He hadn't slept much since Rita's and Sam's arrests. It turned out that the man they had known for years as Sam Riddle was in truth Mickey Parker, a callous low-level gangster from Youngstown, Ohio, who had dabbled in extortion, money laundering, and bookkeeping before murdering his business partner over a deal gone bad and then going on the run. Once in Corolla, Sam, aka Mickey, had claimed he was from Kansas. Despite his attempt to rid himself of his Youngstown accent, Rich had picked up on it and had begun asking him more and more questions and poking into his background.

To Colleen, one of the most despicable parts of the story was the discovery that Mickey had been using the name and Social Security number of a deceased child, a common practice in the world of identity theft and one harder to detect twenty years ago, when Sam had arrived and established himself in Corolla. Rita, whose real name was Mary Frank, and Mickey had been sweethearts since their teens. One thing Sam had told her had been true: Rita would do anything for him—even take the fall for murder. Fortunately, thanks to the evidence in Rich's laptop, he wasn't going to get off that easily.

"This is quite a turnout," Bill said, joining her at the back edge of the crowd and rubbing Sparky behind the ears. "We had to direct people to park across the street."

"It is something," she said, still amazed by the hundreds of people milling about.

The preshow music faded and Hayley emerged from inside the Whalehead Club and strode to center stage.

"Good evening, ladies and gentleman, boys and girls," she said into a microphone. The crowd quieted. "As many of you know, my name is Hayley Thorpe, and I am proud to be serving as your mistress of ceremonies for the world premiere opening-night performance of *Wild and Free.*"

Cheers erupted from the audience, along with a few whistles. Colleen stole a look at Bill and grinned.

"This performance will not only reveal the incredible story of how the beautiful Spanish mustangs came to make the Outer Banks their home, but it will also help to ensure their continued survival. Every dollar raised tonight will go toward helping the Lighthouse Wild Horse Preservation Society save these magnificent creatures."

More cheers.

"She really knows how to work a crowd," Colleen said in admiration.

"She always has," Bill replied.

Colleen cocked her head toward him. His comment hadn't been a criticism. More like a statement of fact. She wondered if that had been part of why their relationship hadn't lasted. Had Hayley's need for and enjoyment of the spotlight been in conflict with his desire for a more low-profile life? He caught her studying him, smiled tenderly at her, and in that moment everything seemed a little brighter.

"Volunteers with buckets will take your donations at intermission, so, please, give whatever you can. And to kick off the donations, I'm proud to announce that Zeon Pictures, the company making my latest film, *Remembering Always*, has agreed to donate twenty-five thousand dollars."

Cheers and applause exploded from the audience, with many jumping to their feet. Even Sparky howled approval.

"We love you, Hayley Thorpe," one person yelled.

"I love you all, too," she responded, and blew everyone a kiss.

No wonder fans worldwide love this woman, Colleen thought.

Hayley glanced behind her at the club's door and then back to the audience. "Now, ladies and gentlemen, without further ado, I'm proud to present on behalf of the Lighthouse Wild Horse Preservation Society, the Whalehead Club, and the citizens of Corolla . . . *Wild and Free!*"

The lights dimmed, the audience quieted, and Lane took the stage.

"The story of Corolla's wild Spanish mustangs begins in sixteenth-century Spain," he said in a booming voice as he began his opening narrative.

Fawn entered with the blue satin fabric. Bobby, substituting for the arrested Sam, aimed a fan at the fabric, and it billowed like the waves of the Atlantic. Nellie and Myrtle entered behind the fabric waves and manipulated the wooden sailing ships. Lights flickered and Bobby shook a metal sheet, creating the sound of thunder rumbling in the distance. Colleen surveyed the faces of the audience. All were transfixed. Yes, she thought, a smash hit.

"I had my doubts," Bill whispered, "but they pulled it off."

"That's theater," she whispered back. "Somehow, it always comes together."

"Yes, but not every production has to contend with two deaths and two arrests."

She couldn't argue with that. It was short of a miracle, what they had managed to accomplish, and a testament to Adam's leadership as the show's director. She had been touched that Adam had credited Doris's and Rich's contributions to the production in the program notes, dedicated the play to both, and was setting up a theater camp scholarship fund in their memory. Nellie's nephew was a good guy. She'd be sorry to see him leave for Hollywood at the end of the summer.

Her mind drifted to Adam's footage of the emergency training on the beach. If it hadn't been for him, they might never have known who had poisoned Doris. And then she might never have discovered the laptop in the casket's memory drawer and the identity of Rich's killer. It had taken a bit of work from Bill's IT expert, but he had eventually cracked the password on Rich's laptop: Shakespeare. Of course, she had thought when Bill had told her.

Once the laptop had been unlocked, they had discovered dozens of documents about the murder of Mickey Parker's business partner, wanted notices, decades-old pictures of Mickey, and, yes, images of his ears. Armed with Rich's research, it hadn't taken Bill long to get Sam to admit that Rich had confronted him with what he had found and demanded that if he didn't turn himself in, Rich would go to the authorities with what he knew. Rich had naïvely believed, despite his research, that a man like

Mickey Parker would act honorably. Perhaps it was having known Mickey as Sam Riddle, an affable guy with a clean record, that had made the funeral director let down his guard. The mistake, sadly, had cost him his life.

Colleen's phone buzzed in her pocket. She retrieved it, read the text, and returned the phone to her pocket.

"What was that?" Bill asked, noticing the smile on her face.

"You'll see," she said, and nodded toward the stage.

A moment later, water sprayed up from behind the back of the Whalehead Club and gently rained down on the roof. Light from the now-setting sun bounced in the droplets and a magnificent rainbow formed above the Whalehead Club and the production. The audience gasped and clapped in awe.

"The station's contribution to the play," she said with pride.

Bill shook his head in wonder. "How'd you know you'd get a rainbow?"

"I didn't," she said. "We were just asked to provide the rain. I guess that's Mother Nature's contribution."

Bill affectionately bumped her with his side and inadvertently squeezed Sparky between them. The dog wagged his tail, hitting each in the thigh, and pushed them apart with the force.

"Our chaperone," he said, indicating Sparky.

She met his gaze, and it became clear that they didn't need words. What had apparently been obvious to everyone in Corolla but the two of them was that they weren't just friends—they were best friends—and that perhaps now it was time to be more. She resisted the urge to leap with joy and instead broke his gaze with a smile and turned her attention to the audience.

She spotted Pinky sitting several seats over. As if he could sense her looking at him, he turned, caught her eye, and bowed to her like a boy at a dance. Her eyes widened. That's where she had first met Pinky . . . at the Italian Festival seven years ago. Everyone had done a handkerchief folk dance and she and Pinky had briefly ended up partners. She motioned as if waving a handkerchief at him, and he grinned broadly. Yes, Pinky, I remember.

"What was that about?" Bill asked about her pantomime.

"Nothing you need to worry about," she said to him, and squeezed his arm.

The play couldn't have been more successful. At intermission, people lined up to fill the volunteer buckets, and in the second act it became clear that Lane had a right to his acting swagger, bringing several ladies in the audience to tears. Fawn was sweet and pretty and had no doubt attracted a few more admirers, and Nellie and Myrtle hoofed it across the stage in a delightful horsey tap number that had the audience demanding an encore, which, of course, they were happy to oblige. But what came next was a surprise to everyone and, Colleen thought, the most perfect ending to the play.

Hayley joined Lane onstage as he finished his closing narration and then the two announced in unison, "Ladies and gentleman, please put your hands together for the true star of the show," and motioned toward the side of the building.

All eyes focused on the spot, and then from around the corner emerged Doc Wales with Rodrigo—a handsome chestnut-colored wild horse that had been rescued from the herd after being injured and was now healthy and serving as an ambassador to the public. As the horse made its way toward the front of the stage, one by one the actors took a curtain call. The audience leaped to its feet in applause and cheered "Bravo! Bravo!" Sparky barked and wagged his tail at the excitement. Colleen's eyes welled with tears as Doc Wales led the horse to center stage.

"Are you crying?" Bill asked, surprised.

"No," she said, and laughed as a tear made its way down her check and she wiped it away.

"I had no idea you were a softy," he teased, and put his arm around her shoulders.

There's a lot you don't know about me, she thought, and leaned into him.

"Ladies and gentlemen," Hayley said, trying to get the audience's attention.

"Please," Lane said in his deepest voice. "Ms. Thorpe would like to announce how much money was raised."

That got the audience to quiet. Everyone remained standing and held their breath. It reminded Colleen of when lottery numbers are called on a big drawing, only now everyone was waiting to see how much they had given, rather than received.

Hayley read what was written on the slip of paper, then looked out over the audience. "I don't think I've seen a more beautiful group of people in my life," she said. "I'm pleased to announce that tonight, at this very performance, all of you have raised one hundred thirty-six thousand twenty-two dollars and seventeen cents."

The audience was silent a moment, stunned by the amount,

and then applauded anew. Myrtle and Nellie hugged. Doc Wales rubbed the horse on its nose and it nuzzled his chest. Colleen and Bill simply stared at each other. It was an unbelievable amount of money.

"And I would be remiss if I didn't mention," Hayley added, "that one hundred thousand dollars of the total was given by one donor, who wishes to remain anonymous."

"I wonder who it was," a woman in front of Colleen said to her husband.

Colleen knew. She spotted Pinky and nudged Bill. Pinky was grinning, enjoying the audience's speculation, and then he caught Colleen's eye. She mouthed *Thank you*, and Bill motioned as if tipping his hat. Pinky raised his arms in feigned ignorance, then smiled and gave them a subtle salute. Colleen looked at Bill and then out over the crowd to the Whalehead Club and the lighthouse beyond. This was a night she wouldn't soon forget.